Drug Synthesis

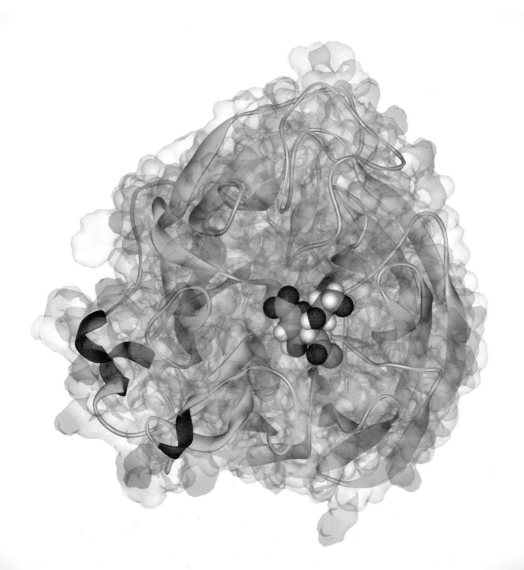

This publication forms part of an Open University module S346 *Drug design and synthesis*. Details of this and other Open University modules can be obtained from the Student Registration and Enquiry Service, The Open University, PO Box 197, Milton Keynes MK7 6BJ, United Kingdom: tel. +44 (0)845 300 60 90, email general-enquiries@open.ac.uk

Alternatively, you may visit the Open University website at http://www.open.ac.uk where you can learn more about the wide range of modules and packs offered at all levels by The Open University.

To purchase a selection of Open University materials visit http://www.ouw.co.uk, or contact Open University Worldwide, Michael Young Building, Walton Hall, Milton Keynes MK7 6AA, United Kingdom for a brochure. tel. +44 (0)1908 858793; fax +44 (0)1908 858787; email ouw-customer-services@open.ac.uk

The Open University
Walton Hall, Milton Keynes
MK7 6AA

First published 2009. Second edition 2010. Third edition 2011.

Edited and designed by The Open University.

Typeset by The Open University.

Printed and bound in the United Kingdom by Latimer Trend & Company Ltd, Plymouth.

ISBN 978 1 8487 3689 4

3.1

Contents

1 Oxidation and reduction

The first five units in this module had an emphasis on the design of drug molecules and looked at their size, shape and reactivity and how they interact with protein drug targets. The remainder of the module, Units 6–9, look at one of the core skills of the organic chemist, namely how drug molecules can be synthesised in the laboratory.

1.1 Introduction

Oxidation and reductions are synthetically powerful reactions. They enable molecular frameworks to be manipulated almost at will. One reason for the dominance of such reactions in synthesis is the high degree of selectivity that can be achieved. Many oxidation and reduction reagents have been developed that allow the interconversion of one functional group into another with high levels of chemo-, regio- and stereoselectivity in complex molecular frameworks.

Before we start looking at the chemistry and mechanisms of oxidation/ reduction reactions, we should first recap on the definitions of reduction and oxidation.

■ In inorganic chemistry what is meant by an oxidation or a reduction?

☐ A compound is oxidised if it loses electrons to another compound. The compound which gains these electrons has been reduced.

This concept is clearly demonstrated in inorganic chemistry by the ease by which oxidation states can be assigned. For example, CrO_3 is in the +6 oxidation state (+1 for each bond to an electronegative element) and turns to Cr^{3+}, chromium in the +3 oxidation state after reaction with a primary alcohol. The chromium has therefore gained three electrons in going from +6 to +3 and has been reduced. The alcohol has been oxidised to an aldehyde.

However, this concept is not so easily applied to reactions of organic compounds such as the oxidation of primary alcohols and a more useful definition in terms of loss or gain of hydrogen or oxygen, rather than electrons, is more widely applied:

oxidation is the loss of electrons, gain of oxygen or loss of hydrogen

reduction is the gain of electrons, loss of oxygen or gain of hydrogen

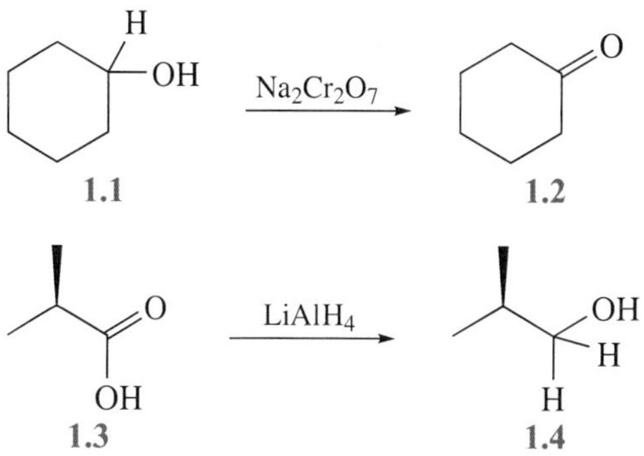

Consider the examples in Scheme 1.1 – the conversion of cyclohexanol (**1.1**) into cyclohexanone (**1.2**). Inspection of the alcohol carbon shows it has lost hydrogen during the transformation and thus has been oxidised. Conversely, exposure of 2-methylpropanoic acid (**1.3**) to lithium aluminium hydride shows the carbonyl carbon atom has gained two hydrogens and has therefore been reduced to 2-methylpropan-1-ol (**1.4**).

Scheme 1.1

With this observation in mind, organic chemists have arranged functional groups in order of increasing oxidation level (Figure 1.1) where a change in functional group to a higher oxidation state is classified as an oxidation.

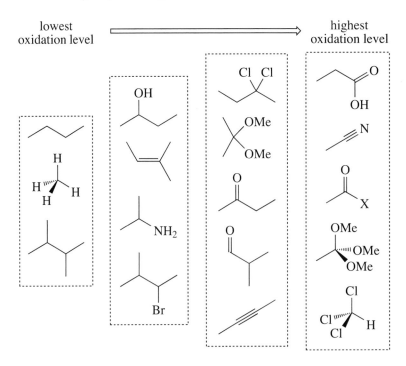

Figure 1.1 Functional groups in order of increasing oxidation level.

The classification is based simply on the structures of the starting material and product; it is independent of the process by which the two are interconverted. It should also be apparent at this point that the interconversion of functional groups within the same oxidation level is not reduction or oxidation but instead some other process, such as a hydrolysis. Moreover, the classification considers only functional groups at a single carbon atom or at two adjacent carbon atoms (the latter is done to allow for alkane to alkene to alkyne interconversions). Functional groups which are more remote than adjacent carbon atoms can generally be considered as separate functional groups and therefore should be examined independently. Such a classification does not in itself allow a chemist to determine which reagent is needed or best suited to increase or decrease an oxidation state of a functional group.

There are many reagents in use and we could not possibly cover them all, indeed, devising new reagents to carry out functional group interconversion through oxidation or reduction or increase the selectivity of a known oxidation or reduction procedure is a popular field of research.

Activity 1.1

In this activity, which runs throughout this unit, you will begin to fill in tables that show various oxidising reagents and reducing agents, and the functional groups with which they will react. Create one table for oxidising agents and another for reducing agents. A template for each table is available from the Unit 6 resources page on the S346 website. Across the top of each template table are the reagents you will encounter in this section and down the left-hand side are the functional groups and their transformations. When cross referencing a functional group transformation with a reagent, you will need to mark with a tick or a cross whether it is possible or not. In reality this distinction is not clear-cut or well defined and you may need to make extensive notes of exceptions and leave gaps in the tables.

As you work through this unit you can add more entries to the tables. At the end of this section you will compare your tables with Data Tables 8.1 and 8.2.

Later on, in the case studies covered in Unit 10, you will encounter a different set of conditions for particular transformations. Also, a more comprehensive look at the organic chemistry literature will reveal a whole host of reagents capable of conducting the same transformation. The skill that a synthetic chemist needs to develop is the ability to select the best available reagent based on its selectivity and cost.

The tables you have started in Activity 1.1 will illustrate the two key points of **reactivity** and **selectivity** that underpin this section. In choosing a reagent we need to consider all the functional groups in a molecule that it may react with, that is, how selective it will be, in oxidising or reducing functional groups.

The following sections are arranged in such a manner that they cover the oxidising and reducing agents used in the relevant template tables. We will survey in turn the functional groups listed down the left-hand side of each table and then consider the selectivity and reactivity of each reagent.

1.2 Oxidation

This section will deal with oxidation and will survey the interconversions of various functional groups by common oxidising agents.

1.2.1 Oxidation of saturated C–H bonds

The oxidation of C–H bonds that are remote from functional groups is usually difficult to carry out selectively and is therefore not a synthetically useful reaction. For example, one such method, that you may recall if you have studied the Level 2 module, is the free radical substitution of alkanes to halogenoalkanes, Equation 1.1 (which would be classified as an oxidation using Figure 1.1). However, this reaction lacks selectivity and produces a complex mixture of products limiting its synthetic utility.

$$CH_3CH_2CH_3 \xrightarrow{Cl_2} CH_3CH_2CH_2Cl + CH_3CHClCH_3 + \underset{\text{compounds}}{\text{dichloro}} + \underset{\text{complounds}}{\text{trichloro}} + \dots \quad (1.1)$$

However, C–H bonds in proximity to functional groups are usually more labile, or unstable, than other 'alkane' type bonds. This is due to the fact that the hydrogen is lost as either H^-, $H^•$ or H^+ and the nearby functional group is able to stabilise the carbon, C^+, $C^•$ or C^-, left behind following the loss of hydrogen (in whichever form). Thus, these C–H bonds are susceptible to various modes of oxidation, as discussed below.

1.2.2 Oxidation of benzylic and allylic carbon centres

Benzene is an exceptionally stable compound and is not usually modified by standard oxidising agents. However, the carbon centre adjacent to benzene rings (e.g. toluene, **1.5**) are known as benzylic carbon centres and have more activated C–H bonds. These can be readily oxidised to the corresponding carbonyl and carboxylic acid. A useful example of this is shown by the conversion of toluene (**1.5**) into benzoic acid (**1.7**) using permanganate, MnO_4^-.

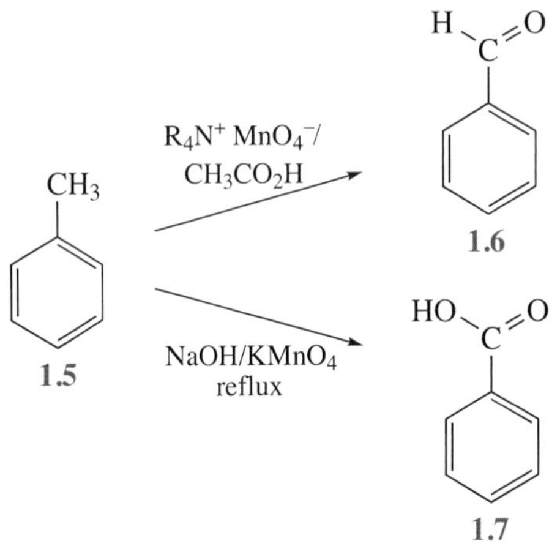

The reaction can be controlled to give the aldehyde (benzaldehyde, **1.6**) if tetraalkylammonium permanganate in acetic acid ($R_4N^+ MnO_4^-/CH_3CO_2H$) is used in preference to potassium permanganate, which gives the carboxylic acid (benzoic acid, **1.7**). This transformation can also be carried out with chromium trioxide, CrO_3, in acetic acid at room temperature. The use of CrO_3 shows no chemoselectivity if other oxidisable functional groups, such as alcohols, are present in the molecule.

■ Which of 4-chlorotoluene (**1.8**) and 4-hydroxymethyltoluene (**1.9**) will be selectively oxidised by potassium permanganate to the corresponding benzoic acid?

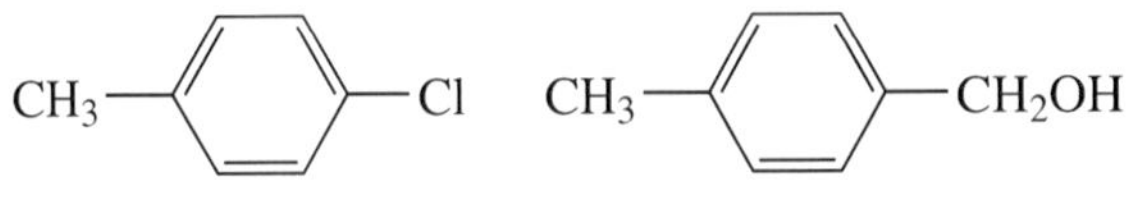

□ Only 4-chlorotoluene can be selectively oxidised to 4-chlorobenzoic acid. Use of permanganate to oxidise 4-hydroxymethyltoluene to 4-hydroxymethylbenzoic acid will oxidise the alcohol group to the corresponding carboxylic acid group as well. In other words, the oxidation of **1.9** is not selective.

A carbon centre next to an alkene is known as an allylic carbon centre and, similar to benzylic carbon centres, the C–H bonds are more activated towards oxidation. Unlike benzene, however, the alkene is more reactive towards oxidation. The reagent *N*-bromosuccinimide (NBS, **1.10**) has been developed to chemoselectively oxidise allylic positions in preference to the alkene.

allylic carbon centre

1.10

The reagent is also able to carry out the same transformation at benzylic positions. The reaction is carried out in carbon tetrachloride, CCl_4, as shown in Equation 1.2.

$$\xrightarrow{\text{NBS/CCl}_4} \quad \text{—Br} \qquad\qquad (1.2)$$

■ Do you think the regioselectivity of the bromination would be difficult to control in unsymmetrical alkenes such as hept-3-ene, $CH_3-CH_2-CH_2-CH=CH-CH_2-CH_3$?

□ Reaction of the unsymmetrical alkene hept-3-ene could result in attachment of a bromine on either side of the double bond and is thus not selective

$$CH_3-CH_2-CH_2-CH=CH-CH_2-CH_3$$

$$\Big\downarrow \text{NBS/CCl}_4$$

$$\overset{\overset{\displaystyle Br}{|}}{CH_3-CH_2-CH_2-CH=CH-CH-CH_3} \quad + \quad \overset{\overset{\displaystyle Br}{|}}{CH_3-CH_2-CH-CH=CH-CH_2-CH_3}$$

The displacement of the allylic bromide by alkali allows access to allylic alcohols, which themselves are useful intermediates (as we shall see later). The formation of allylic alcohols from alkenes can be carried out directly using selenium dioxide (SeO_2), which is an extremely selective oxidising agent for oxidising allylic carbon centres to alcohols.

The reaction proceeds via an initial reaction between the allylic C–H and SeO_2, as shown in Scheme 1.2, with the electrophilic attack of the selenium on the C=C double bond to form the seleninic acid (**1.11**); rearrangement of the seleninic acid and cleavage of the O–Se bond affording the desired allylic alcohol.

allylic alcohol

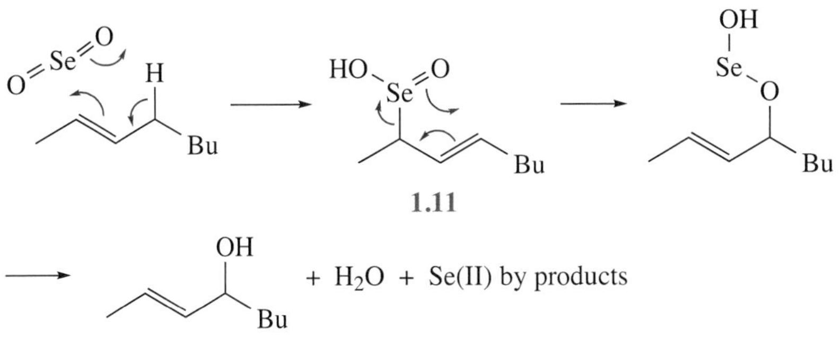

Scheme 1.2

Remember to update the table of reagents that you started in Activity 1.1.

In the presence of *tert*-butyl hydroperoxide, only a catalytic amount of selenium dioxide is required, as the peroxide re-oxidises the product selenium (II) back to selenium dioxide after each cycle of the reaction. This offers the advantage of avoiding large amounts of selenium-containing compounds which are toxic. An example of this is shown by the oxidation of β-pinene (**1.12**) to *trans*-pinocarveol (**1.13**). The selenium dioxide approaches from the least sterically hindered side of the C=C double bond in β-pinene and thus only the –CH$_2$– is oxidised to the alcohol.

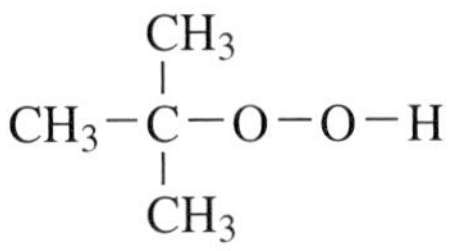

tert-butyl hydroperoxide

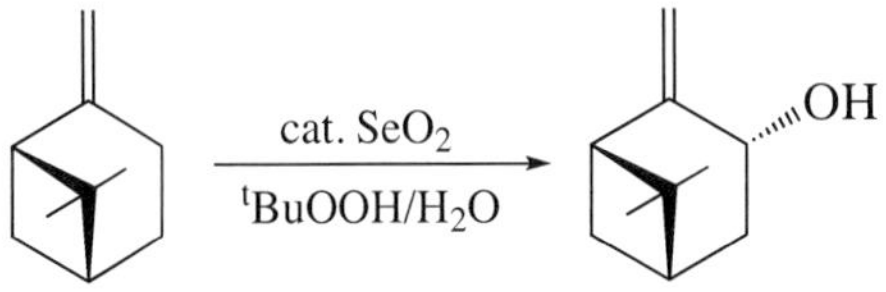

1.2.3 Oxidation of alcohol groups

The oxidation of an alcohol to an aldehyde/ketone or to a carboxylic acid (Equation 1.3) is probably the most common functional group interconversion (FGI) with an array of reagents and conditions capable of carrying out this transformation.

$$RCH_2OH \longrightarrow RCH{=}O \longrightarrow RCOOH \tag{1.3}$$

■ What would you predict are the products of the oxidation of primary, secondary and tertiary alcohol, with dichromate in dilute sulfuric acid?

☐ Primary alcohols are oxidised to the corresponding aldehyde. However the reaction does not stop at this stage. The aldehyde is oxidised further to the carboxylic acid. Secondary alcohols are oxidised to ketones which do not undergo further oxidation under these conditions. Tertiary alcohols cannot be oxidised under these conditions.

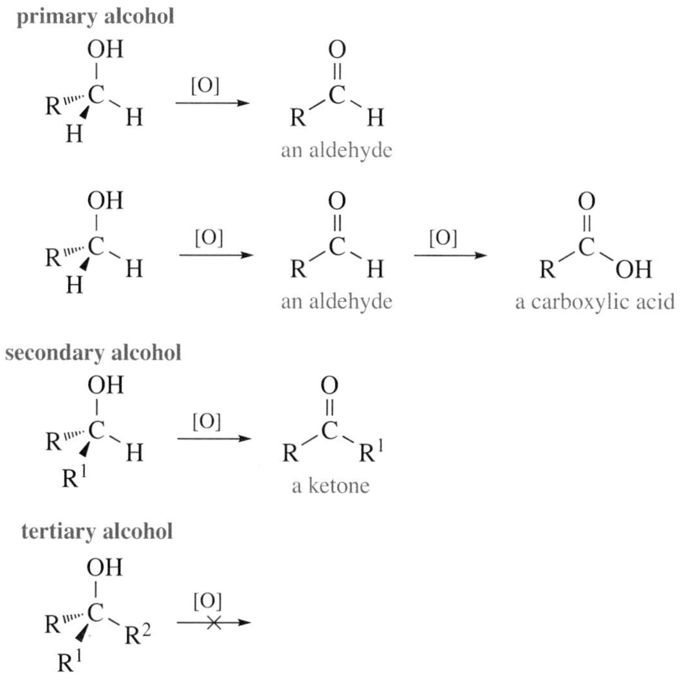

primary alcohol

secondary alcohol

tertiary alcohol

The formation of an aldehyde by oxidation is problematic since it is so readily oxidised to the carboxylic acid. The formation of the carboxylic acid, and other by-products, from primary alcohols can be avoided and a satisfactory yield of aldehyde can be obtained if the aldehyde is continuously distilled off from the reaction mixture, as shown in Scheme 1.3. However, this is only partially soluble and chromium trioxide in sulfuric acid, known as Jones reagent, is more generally used to transform primary alcohols directly into carboxylic acids. Consequently, a range of more selective reagents have been developed to stop the oxidation at the aldehyde stage and these are discussed below.

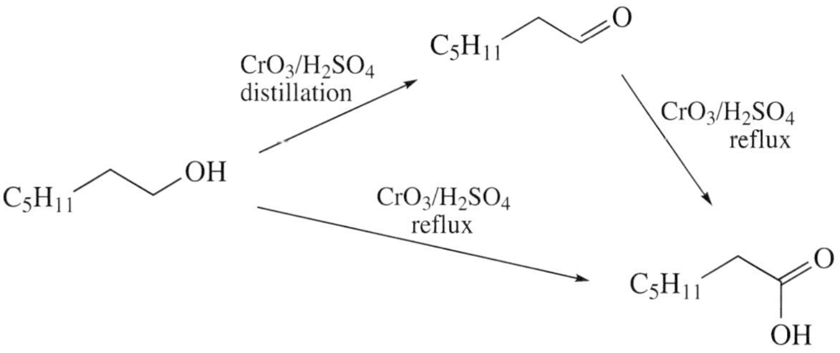

Scheme 1.3

Oxidation of primary alcohols to aldehydes

The need here is to control the extent of the oxidation. The use of pyridinium chlorochromate (PCC) and pyridinium dichromate (PDC) in anhydrous dichloromethane gives excellent yields of aldehydes with no further oxidation to the carboxylic acid. The complexation of the chromate to pyridine enables Cr(VI) to be used in non-aqueous conditions and the lack of water stops the formation of the hydrate from the aldehyde preventing its overoxidation to the carboxylic acid.

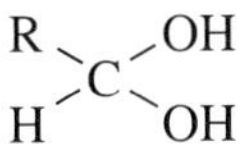

R   OH
  \C/
  / \
H   OH

hydrate

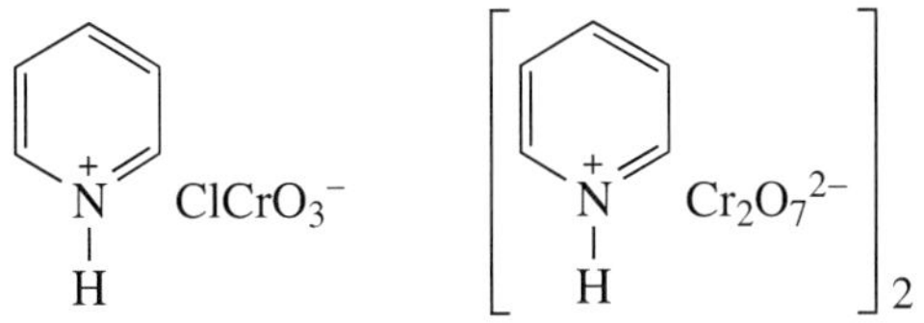

PCC   **PDC**

These methods are particularly useful for compounds which contain acid-sensitive groups (e.g. acetals, silyl ethers) or other oxidisable groups like alkenes that can be oxidised by CrO_3.

A more modern approach to controlling the extent of oxidation is the Swern oxidation. This involves reaction of a primary alcohol with dimethyl sulfoxide (DMSO), oxalyl chloride ($(COCl)_2$), and triethylamine (Et_3N). These conditions avoid the use of toxic chromium salts, work under mild conditions, have volatile by-products (although the stench of dimethyl sulfide, DMS, is unpleasant) and are highly chemoselective, showing exquisite selectivity for alcohols to form aldehydes (in the case of primary alcohols) and ketones (in the case of secondary alcohols), to the exclusion of other functional groups.

The mechanism of the Swern oxidation involves activation of DMSO by an electrophile, usually oxalyl chloride, as shown in Scheme 1.4. Other electrophiles, such as acid chlorides and acid anhydrides can also be used. The electrophile oxalyl chloride (**1.14**), in Scheme 1.4, reacts with the nucleophilic oxygen centre of the dimethyl sulfoxide to form the intermediate **1.15**. This is then reacted with the alcohol to form a second intermediate **1.16** that is reacted with base, commonly Et_3N. The base removes the acidic proton from the methyl group attached to the positively charged sulfur atom, thus producing the ylide **1.17**, which rearranges to form the desired carbonyl compound **1.18**.

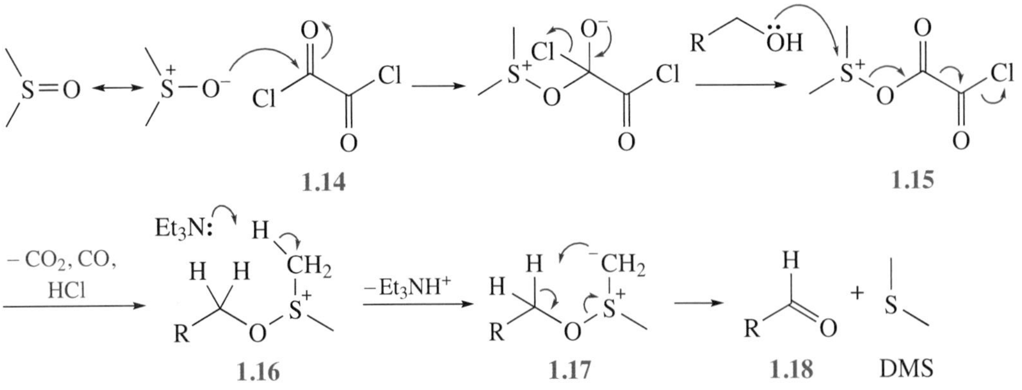

Scheme 1.4

Another non-transition metal oxidising agent capable of forming aldehydes from primary alcohols is the periodinane (**1.19**) which contains a hypervalent iodine, I(V). This reagent is highly selective for alcohols and the reagent is easily prepared from potassium bromate, acetic anhydride and *ortho*-iodobenzoic acid.

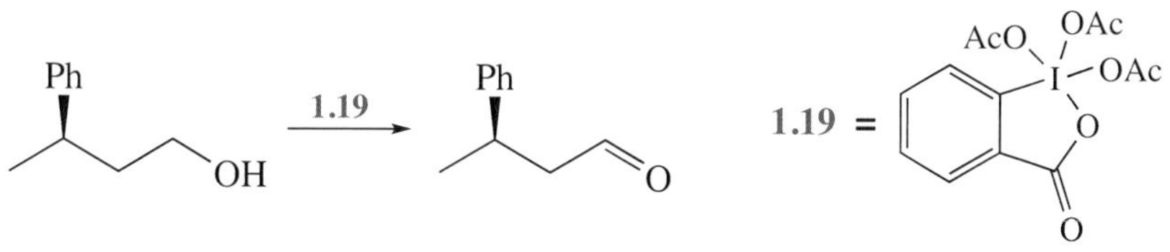

1.2.4 Overview of oxidation of carbon–carbon double bonds

We will first begin with the oxidation of alkenes. Alkenes are highly versatile starting materials in organic chemistry and can produce a vast array of functional groups and many oxidising agents have been developed for this purpose. Alkenes can essentially be oxidised in any one of four ways which are shown in Scheme 1.5.

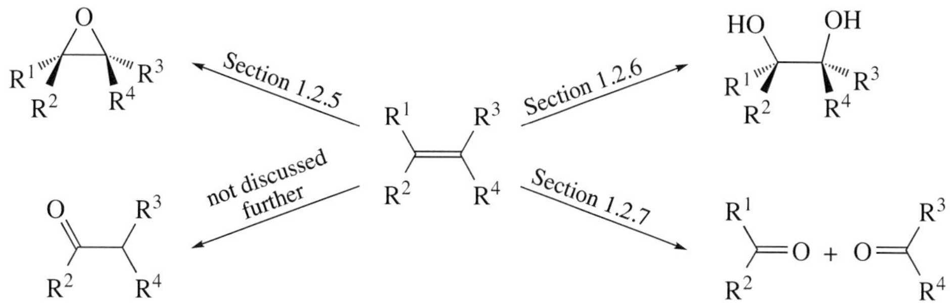

Scheme 1.5

1.2.5 Epoxidation

The principal method by which alkenes can be converted into epoxides is through the use of acyl peroxides; the most commonly used reagent is a peroxycarboxylic acid (RCO_3H). The mechanism of epoxidation resembles in many ways the bromination of alkenes (which you may be familiar with if you have studied the Level 2 module). The peroxycarboxylic acid acts as an electrophile in which the terminal oxygen atom is the electrophilic centre. Electrophilic attack on the alkene by the peroxycarboxylic acid proceeds in a one-step mechanism where the terminal oxygen is transferred to the alkene to form the epoxide, as highlighted below. This mechanism is supported by the stereospecific nature of the reaction as both R groups retain the same stereochemical relationship in the products as in the original alkene.

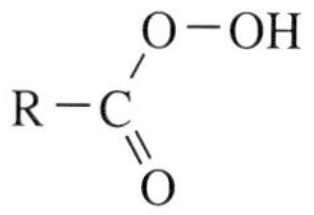

peroxycarboxylic acid

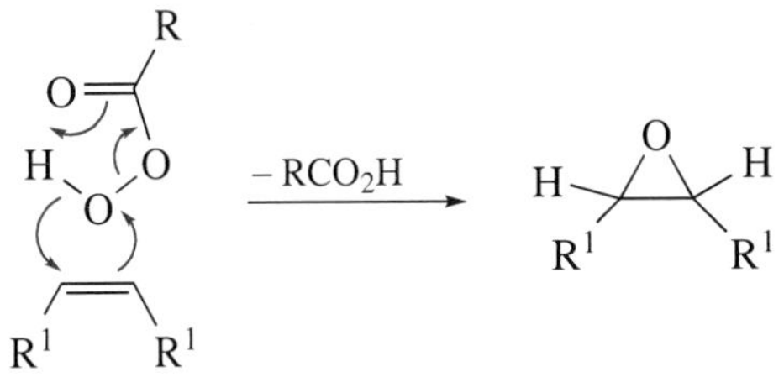

- ■ The rate of this epoxidation increases with the nucleophilicity of the double bond. How will alkyl substitutions on the double bond affect the rate of reaction?

- ☐ Alkyl groups are electron donating and so the rate of epoxidation of alkenes is increased through substitution of the alkene. Thus, more heavily substituted double bonds will undergo epoxidation in preference to less electron-rich double bonds.

For example, the cyclohexadiene **1.20** undergoes epoxidation at the more substituted double bond, as this double bond is more electron rich owing to the electron-donating effects of the alkyl substituents.

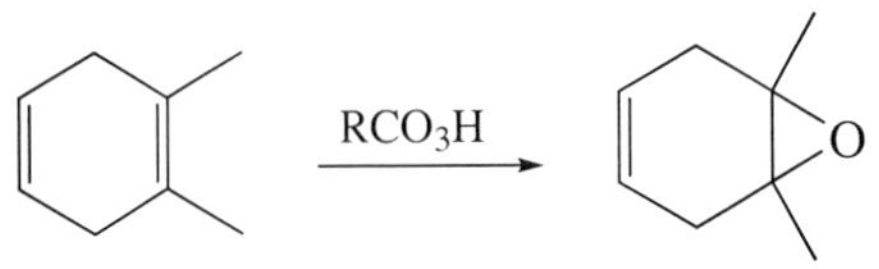

1.20

This preference is accordingly reversed for alkenes conjugated to electron-withdrawing groups, which show limited reactivity to peroxycarboxylic acids and will only epoxidise under elevated temperatures.

The stereoselectivity of epoxidation with peroxycarboxylic acids has been well studied and shows that addition of the oxygen occurs preferentially to the least hindered face of cyclic alkenes. Consider the epoxidation of **1.21**, in which the double bond is diastereotopic (as discussed in Unit 4, the two faces of the double bond are non-equivalent) leading to two diastereoisomeric epoxides **1.22** and **1.23**. For R = H, epoxide **1.22** predominates due to the two axial hydrogens blocking the lower face as shown on the structure on the bottom left in Scheme 1.6, but when R = CH$_3$, the upper face becomes more sterically hindered and epoxidation occurs from the bottom as shown on the lower right-hand structure in Scheme 1.6 (see also Unit 6 iFigure 1.1).

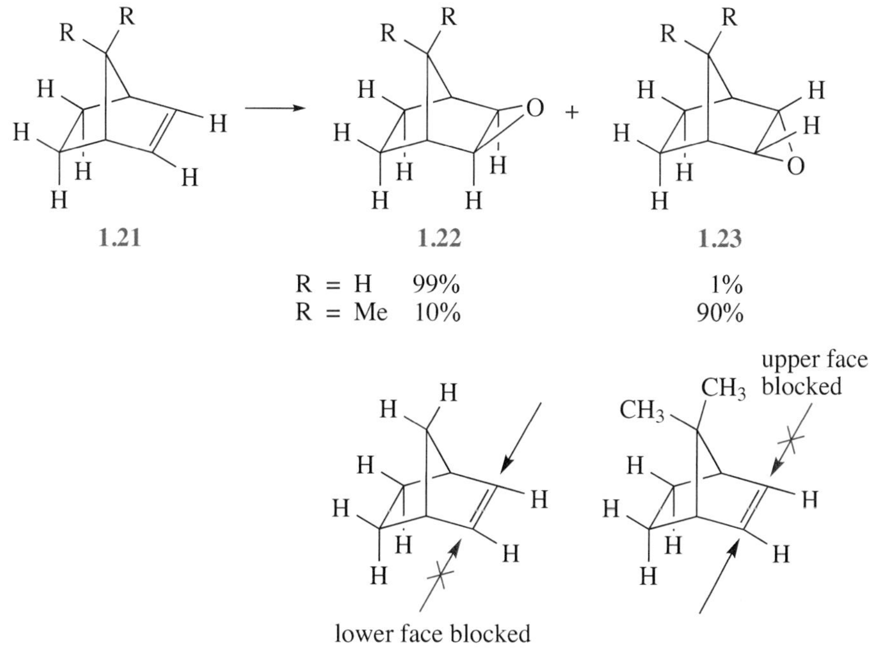

Scheme 1.6

This stereoselectivity is also observed in the epoxidation of **1.24** with a peroxycarboxylic acid. This results in the preferential formation of the epoxide **1.25** as a consequence of the increased steric bulk caused by the axial methyl substituent being positioned on the top face of the molecule. This prevents formation of the isomer **1.26** with the epoxide on the top face. Structure **1.26** can be prepared via its corresponding bromohydrin, which is covered in the Level 2 module.

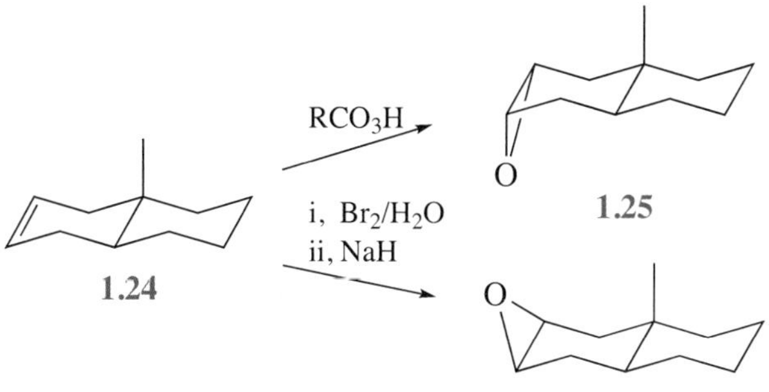

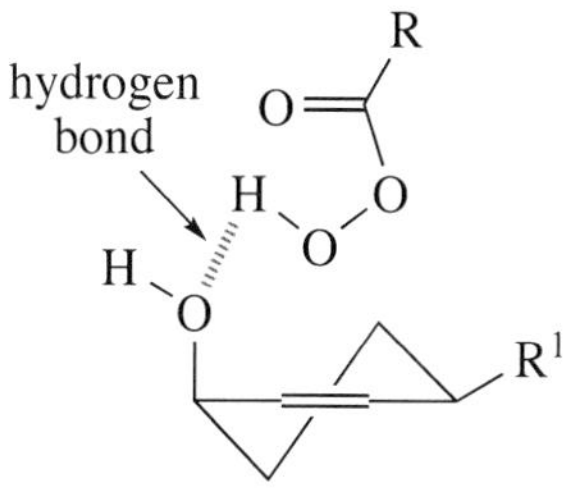

Interestingly, this stereoselectivity, caused by steric hindrance to the attack by the electrophile, can be overcome if the double bond contains a hydroxy or ether group adjacent to the double bond, as in an allylic alcohol. In these cases the more sterically hindered epoxide is formed where the hydroxyl group exerts a directing effect on the peroxide through the formation of a hydrogen-bonded complex. (See also Unit 6 iFigure 1.2.)

This complex delivers the electrophilic epoxide oxygen onto the same face of the alkene as the hydroxyl group.

■   What would be the product of the reaction between *cis*-4-*tert*-butyl cyclohex-2-enol (**1.27**) and a peroxycarboxylic acid RCO$_3$H?

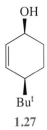

1.27

□ Although the upper face in **1.27** is more sterically hindered, reaction with a peroxycarboxylic acid RCO₃H produces the epoxide **1.28** rather than the epoxide **1.29**. This may be rationalised on the basis of the formation of the hydrogen-bonded complex delivering the electrophilic oxygen from the same face as the hydroxyl group.

1.27   **1.28**   **1.29**

It should also be noted that the presence of the hydroxyl group not only overcomes stereoselectivity but also overcomes double bond regioselectivity; because of hydrogen bond formation, a double bond adjacent to a hydroxyl or ether group is epoxidised in preference to an isolated double bond, even if it is more substituted. Allylic alcohols, such as **1.30**, can also be oxidised by other peroxides, such as *tert*-butyl hydroperoxide (TBHP, **1.31**) in conjunction with transition metal catalysts such as V^{5+}, Mo^{6+} or Ti^{4+}.

1.31

$Ti(OPr^i)_4$
(+)-DET
1.31

1.30   **1.32**   **1.33**

These conditions show exquisite selectivity for the epoxidation of the alkene with the allylic alcohol even in the presence of other more electron-rich double bonds. This level of selectivity is due to the formation of a complex between the hydroxyl group, the transition metal and the peroxycarboxylic acid, and thus the oxidising agent is found in close proximity to the alkene.

So far we have only considered diastereofacial selectivity, that is, the original compounds have structural elements in the molecule which make the two faces (upper and lower) of the alkene different.

■ The epoxidation of allylic alcohol **1.30** yields two enantiomeric epoxides, **1.32** and **1.33**. What would you expect the relative yield of the two epoxides to be?

□ They will be produced in equal amounts because both faces of the alkene are equally likely to be attacked.

In the early 1980s, Sharpless and co-workers found that by using titanium tetra-isopropoxide, $Ti(OPr^i)_4$, as the catalyst for the *tert*-butyl hydroperoxide epoxidation in the presence of a single enantiomer of diethyl tartrate (DET), an allylic alcohol such as **1.30** can be epoxidised with a high degree of enantiotopic selectivity. That is, the chiral DET ligand is able to effectively determine the formation of a single enantiomer and thus this reaction is a powerful way of controlling absolute stereochemistry in a synthetic route.

Sharpless chose the enantiomers of the ethyl esters of tartaric acid (DET), **1.34** (2R,3R-(+)-diethyl tartrate) and **1.35** (2S,3S-(−)-diethyl tartrate), as both compounds are commercially available at relatively low cost.

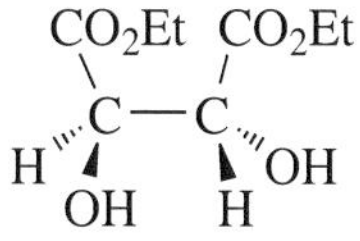

2R,3R-(+)-diethyl tartrate   2S,3S-(−)-diethyl tartrate
1.34   **1.35**

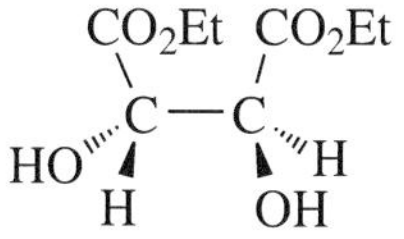

When the 2R,3R compound **1.34** is used as the enantiomeric ligand, alkenes can be epoxidised to give one enantiomer almost exclusively, whereas the use of the other 2S,3S ligand, **1.35**, gives the other enantioner of the epoxide.

These observations are summarised in Table 1.1.

Table 1.1 Asymmetric epoxidation of allylic alcohols.

Allylic alcohol	Auxiliary	Major product	Minor product	Yield/ %	e.e./ %
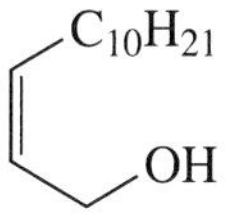	1.35	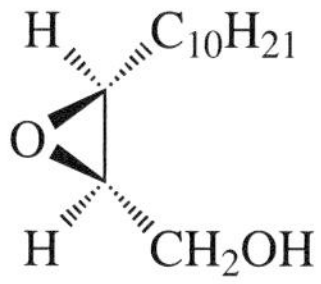	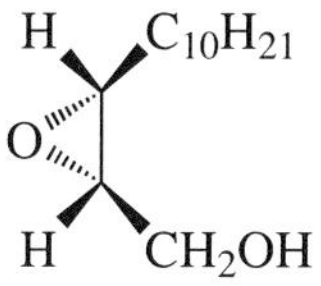	80	90
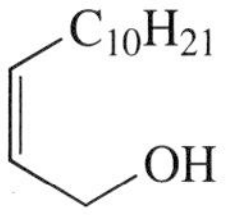	1.34	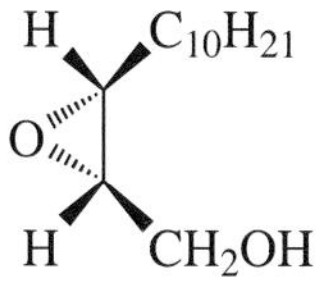	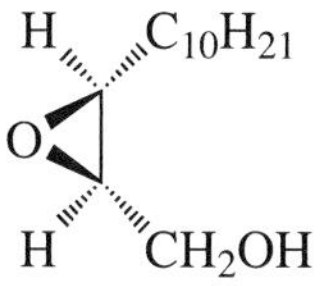	82	90
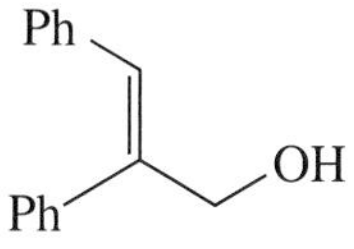	1.34	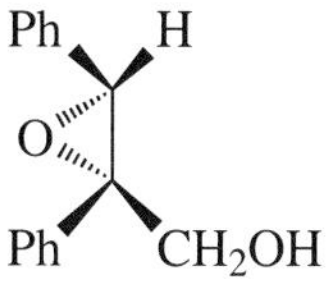	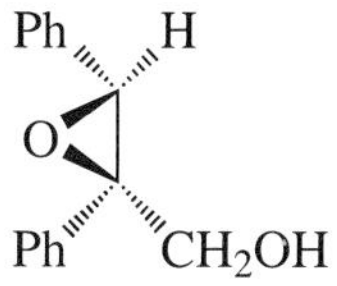	87	> 95

e.e. = enantiomeric excess.

The yields for this reaction are very high but the enantiomeric excess (e.e.) values, which are a measure of the enantiofacial selectivity, are excellent, with most cases showing an e.e. of greater than 90%.

■   If the enantiomeric excess (e.e.) is 90% what percentage of the product is the major enantiomer? (You might like to refer back to Unit 4 for the definition of enantiomeric excess.)

□   Enantiomeric excess is defined as the percentage of the major isomer minus the percentage of the minor isomer, 90% e.e. = 95% − 5%, and therefore the major isomer is 95% of the product.

The discovery of this reaction led to Professor Barry Sharpless sharing the Nobel Prize for Chemistry in 2001 'for his work on chirally catalysed oxidation reactions'. This reaction, known as the Sharpless asymmetric epoxidation, is of particular importance as it creates chirality at two centres. Although this reaction is only applicable to allylic alcohols, you will see later that epoxides can be opened with a great deal of stereoselectivity, and therefore this epoxidation method is a powerful tool for enantioselective synthesis.

1.2.6 Formation of 1,2-diols from alkenes

The modern method for reliable preparation of 1,2-diols is via direct dihydroxylation through the use of osmium tetroxide (OsO_4). Reaction of an alkene with OsO_4, Scheme 1.7, produces a cyclic osmate ester (**1.36**) in which the osmium has effectively gained two electrons and has hence been reduced. Hydrolysis of the ester, commonly with aqueous sodium sulfite, yields a 1,2-diol and osmium trioxide.

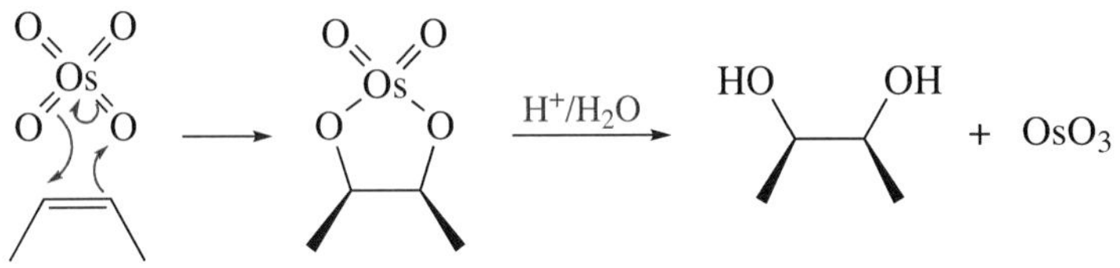

Scheme 1.7

The reaction is another stereospecific oxidation: the stereochemistry of the double bond (E or Z) is transferred to the stereochemical relationship in the product, this being a consequence of the concerted *syn* addition in the first step of the mechanism. Furthermore, reaction with alkenes exhibits the same preferences for hydroxidation as those observed in epoxidation. Thus:

- OsO_4 reacts with the most electron-rich double bond, that is, the most substituted double bond, thus it can be used regioselectively when more than one double bond is present.

- Owing to the bulky nature of OsO_4, the osmate ester, **1.36**, forms on the least hindered side of alkene and brings about an element of stereoselectivity, but only if the two faces of the double bond are diastereotopic.

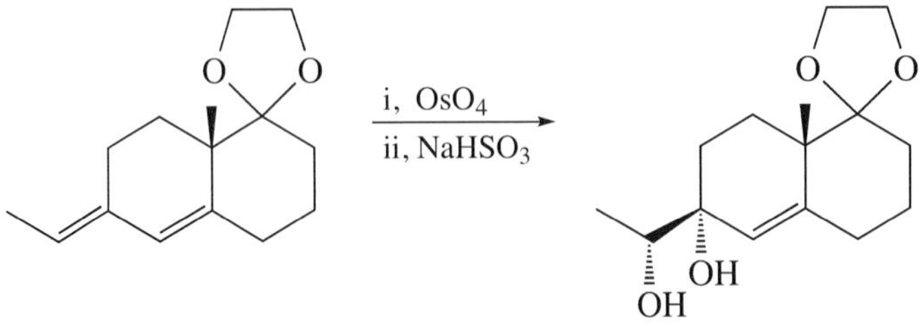

- It is worth noting that the dihydroxylation of allylic alcohols does not lead to the hydroxylation of the same face of the alkene as the alcohol group.

The OsO$_4$ does not normally hydrogen bond to the alcohol group, and thus steric factors need only to be considered.

Potassium permanganate (KMnO$_4$) can also be used in a similar fashion to OsO$_4$. The reaction of KMnO$_4$ is usually carried out under alkaline conditions to prevent the *cis*-diol formed from being oxidised further by KMnO$_4$ to an α-hydroxy ketone or undergoes oxidative cleavage (see Section 1.2.7) of the C–C bond. In general, this reaction is less useful than that of OsO$_4$ due to reduced yields and poor selectivity; however it does have the advantage of lower toxicity and cost.

Scheme 1.8 further highlights the stereospecific nature of direct dihydroxylation and epoxidation. Both reagents effect *cis* oxidation of an alkene, but the epoxide ring opening occurs with inversion of configuration to afford the 1,2-*trans*-diol, therefore, both routes offer opposite diastereoisomers from the same starting alkene geometry.

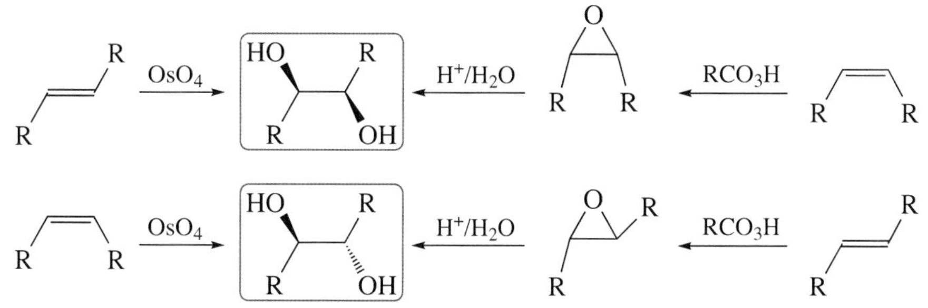

Scheme 1.8

1.2.7 Oxidative cleavage of carbon–carbon bonds

In this next section we will consider reactions which act like 'molecular scissors' and dissect C=C bonds to introduce new functionality to the carbon backbone. The most common oxidative cleavage of an alkene is carried out with ozone (O$_3$) (Equation 1.4).

$$C_2H_5CH{=}CHC_2H_5 \xrightarrow{\;O_3\;} C_2H_5CH{=}O \; + \; C_2H_5CH{=}O \qquad (1.4)$$

The reaction demonstrates a high level of chemoselectivity for the alkene as ozone will not oxidise other functional groups like alcohols, esters or amides. Owing to ozone's electrophilic character, it will react in preference to electron-rich double bonds.

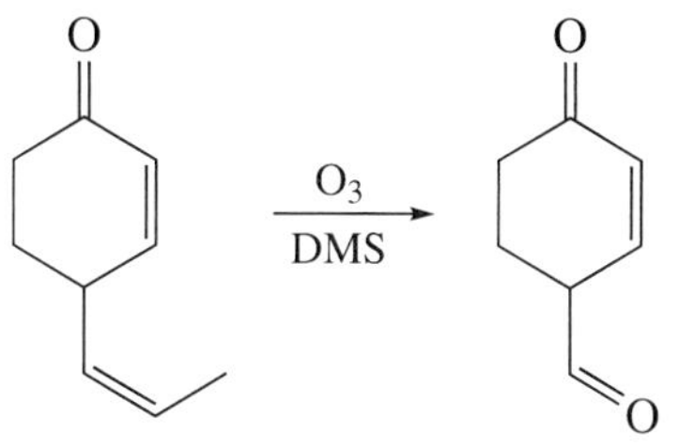

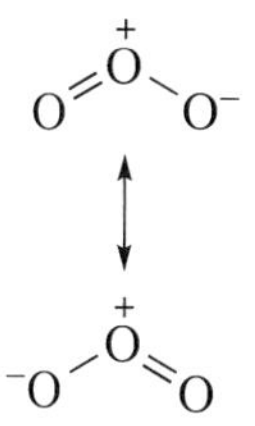

Here the presence of the electron-withdrawing carbonyl group makes the ring alkene less reactive. Another common method used for the oxidative cleavage of the carbon–carbon backbone is the treatment of 1,2-diols with sodium periodate ($NaIO_4$). The use of periodate cleavage has been successfully employed in the industrial preparation of lamivudine (**1.37**) which is used in combination with AZT (azidothymidine) to manage AIDS (Scheme 1.9). The 1,2-diol, **1.38**, is a key intermediate in this synthesis. The reaction with IO_4^- cleaves the C–C bond between the two hydroxyl groups to produce two carbonyl-containing compounds, formaldehyde and the aldehyde **1.39** for the next step in the synthesis.

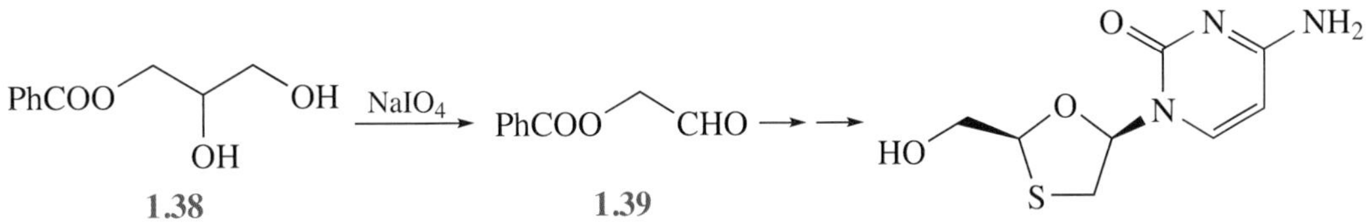

Scheme 1.9

1.2.8 Oxidation of ketones

We have seen that alcohol groups CH–OH can be oxidised to carbonyl groups C=O and that several reagents can further oxidise C=O to CO_2H. There are a few reagents that are capable of oxidising a carbonyl C=O while leaving a CH–OH group untouched. One of the best known examples has already been used in this unit for the oxidation of an alkene.

■ What reagent have you met that can oxidise an alkene but does not react with an alcohol group?

☐ Peroxycarboxylic acids will oxidise alkenes to form an epoxide, but as shown in the peroxycarboxylic Sharpless epoxidation, the −OH group is untouched.

Peroxycarboxylic acids will readily react with ketones to form esters, and with aldehydes to form carboxylic acids via insertion of an oxygen atom.

$$RCHO \xrightarrow{R^3CO_3H} RCOOH$$

$$R^1COR^2 \xrightarrow{R^3CO_3H} R^1COOR^2$$

The first step in Scheme 1.10 involves a nucleophilic attack by the peroxide oxygen at the protonated carbonyl compound to form the usual tetrahedral intermediate **1.40**. This intermediate collapses and cleaves a carbon–carbon single bond; the driving force for this step being the good leaving group ability of the carboxylic acid, R^2CO_2H. Thus, one of the R groups originally bonded to the carbonyl carbon migrates to the peroxy oxygen atom and the overall result is the insertion of an oxygen atom into a carbon–carbon bond. This reaction is known as the Baeyer–Villiger oxidation.

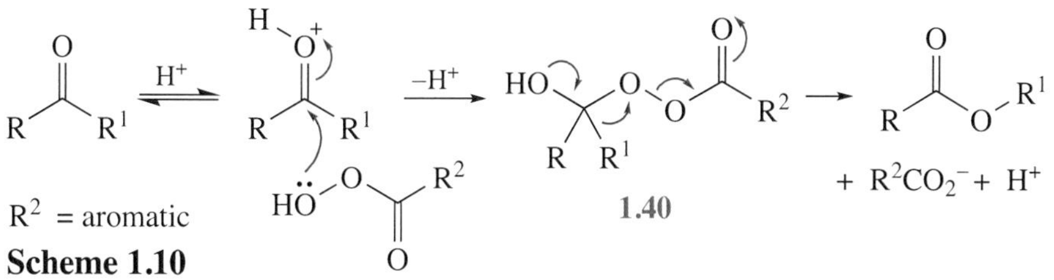

R^2 = aromatic

Scheme 1.10

- For an aldehyde, R = alkyl and R^1 = H. How do we know which group migrates if a carboxylic acid is formed from an aldehyde?

□ Since the hydrogen is now bound to the oxygen, it must have migrated.

This observation is generally true; aldehydes are oxidised to carboxylic acids following exposure to peroxy acids. However, the problem becomes a little more complex with unsymmetrical ketones.

- What is the potential problem for unsymmetrical ketones $R–CO–R^1$ in this reaction?

□ In principle, either the R or the R^1 group is able to migrate. Thus, if R migrates, R^1COOR would be formed, or conversely, if R^1 migrates, $RCOOR^1$ is produced. Fortunately, the migration process is highly predictable and an order of migration preference has been devised.

Migration preference:
tert-alkyl (3°) > *sec*-alkyl (2°) > benzyl > aryl (sp²) > *n*-alkyl (1°) > methyl

- Predict the product of the following reaction.

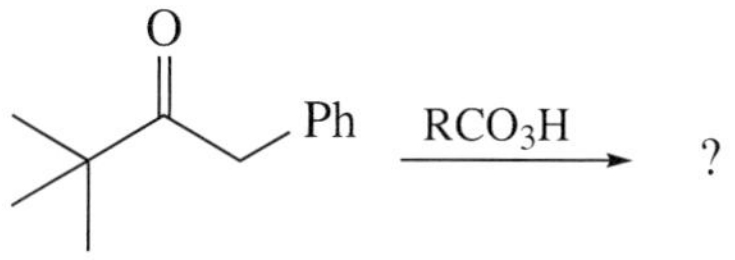

□ This reaction would have the tertiary centre migrating in preference to the benzylic centre. This reaction adds another method for the preparation of esters.

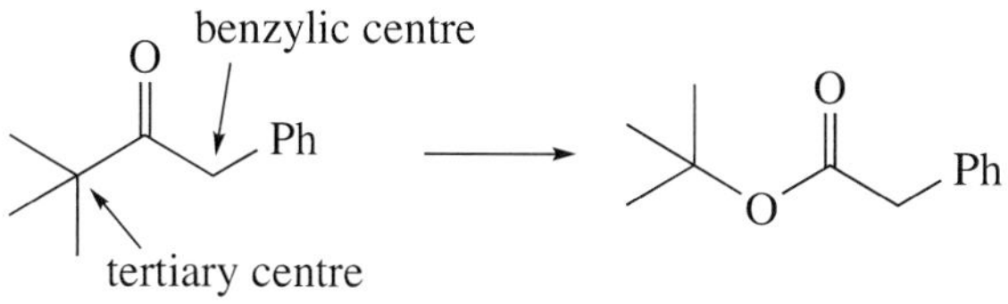

The Baeyer–Villiger oxidation has been used, in two steps, in the synthesis of the lactone (**1.41**) as shown in Scheme 1.11. (*Note*: TBDMSO is a protecting group for alcohols and you do not need to consider its structure here.) In each step, the preference for the tertiary alkyl carbon (the most substituted carbon centre) to migrate to the peroxy oxygen atom is used to achieve the regioselectivity required. In the first step in Scheme 1.11, the oxygen is inserted between the carbon centre A and the carbonyl group. In the second

You should now have completed the table for oxidising agents that you started as part of Activity 1.1.

Baeyer–Villiger oxidation step, the oxygen is inserted between the carbon centre B and the carbonyl group. You might notice that the configuration of the migrating group remains intact; the migration is said to have occurred with retention of configuration.

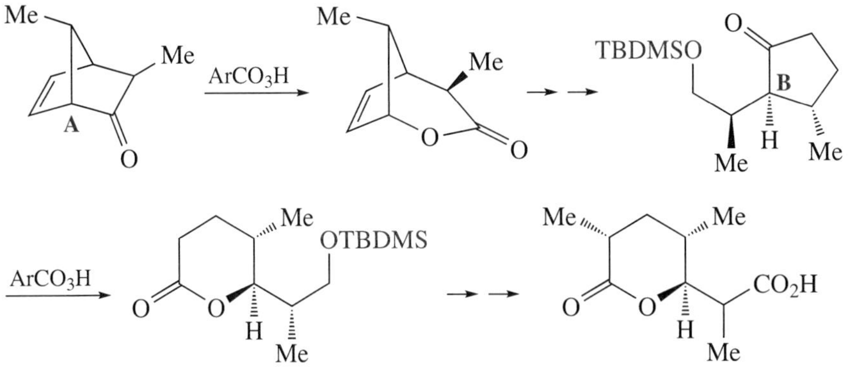

Scheme 1.11

1.3 Reduction

This section describes some of the reagents used in the reduction of organic compounds. The chemical literature contains many examples of reducing agents that show chemo-, regio-, diastereo- and enantioselective properties and the following sections will survey the selectivities demonstrated by the most commonly used reducing reagents. As this section deals with an array of reagents capable of reducing a variety of functional groups, it is possible you might lose sight of which reagent can be employed to carry out a particular reduction. To help you identify the reagents, continue with Activity 1.1 and use the table template to summarise the reactivity of functional groups with selected reducing agents. As with the preceding section covering oxidation, the reagents should be listed across the top of the table and the functional group transformations should be listed on the left-hand side. At the end of the section you should compare your table with Data Table 8.2. Many of the reductions carried out by chemists involve the carbonyl group and so these will be considered first.

1.3.1 Reduction of carboxylic acid derivatives

The best reagents for reducing carboxylic acid derivatives are the **hydride-transfer agents** such as lithium aluminium hydride (LiAlH$_4$).

■ Look back at the definition of reduction at the start of this unit. Reduction could be defined as the gain of hydrogen. What type of hydrogen reagent is needed to attack the electrophilic carbon centre of a carbonyl group?

☐ A nucleophilic hydride, H$^-$, is required. This is a hydrogen atom to which one electron has been added. Having only one proton but two electrons results in the negatively charged H$^-$ hydride ion.

LiAlH$_4$ is capable of reducing all carbonyl-containing compounds. This occurs due to the electrophilic nature of the carbonyl carbon and its ability to accept the nucleophilic H$^-$ from the tetrahydroaluminate anion, AlH$_4^-$. The reaction does not involve a free hydride ion as such, but ALH$_4^-$ behaves as a source of hydride ion. While the mechanism is complex, it can be considered as a hydride transfer, as shown in Scheme 1.12. It would therefore seem that the reduction is straightforward – always use LiAlH$_4$. However, what about chemoselectivity? How can a carboxylic acid be reduced in the presence of an ester? Lithium aluminium hydride is not a selective reducing reagent; it will reduce all carbonyl functional groups to their corresponding alcohols, amines or even alkanes.

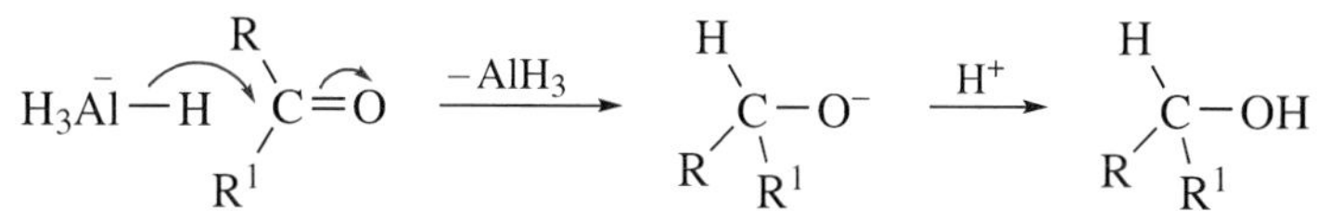

$$H_3\bar{Al}-H \quad \overset{R}{\underset{R^1}{C}}{=}O \xrightarrow{-AlH_3} \underset{R \quad R^1}{\overset{H}{C}}-O^- \xrightarrow{H^+} \underset{R \quad R^1}{\overset{H}{C}}-OH$$

Scheme 1.12

Furthermore, you should always aim to reduce a functional group under the mildest of conditions as this will minimise potential side reactions and make it easier to carry out practically, as there is less need to rigorously exclude air and water from the reaction.

Look at Extract 1 from Data Table 8.2, which lists the anionic hydride transfer agents. They are arranged in order of reactivity starting with LiAlH$_4$ as the most reactive and sodium cyanoborohydride (NaBH$_3$CN) as the least reactive. Examining the functional group transformations down the left-hand side reveals that carboxylic acids are only reduced by the most reactive reducing agents, LiAlH$_4$ and LiAlH$_2$(OCH$_2$OMe)$_2$.

Carboxylic acids are the most difficult group to reduce as they form a carboxylate anion under the reaction conditions.

$$RCOOH \xrightarrow{-H^+} RCOO^- \xrightarrow{LiAlH_4} RCHOH$$

- What effect does the formation of a carboxylate anion have on the ease of reduction of the carbonyl group?

□ It makes the carbonyl group harder to reduce. Formation of the anion makes the carbonyl carbon less electrophilic than other carbonyl groups and thus less reactive to the hydride nucleophile.

This problem can be easily avoided by first converting the carboxylic acid into an ester and then carrying out the reduction. The reduction of acid derivatives to their corresponding alcohols proceeds through the formation of an aldehyde intermediate. Stopping the reaction at this stage is often highly desirable but is quite difficult to achieve in practice and requires careful experimental control.

- Why is it difficult to stop the reaction at the aldehyde stage?

□ Aldehydes are generally more easily reduced to alcohols than carboxylic acid derivatives are to aldehydes. In other words, aldehydes are more

Extract 1 from Data Table 8.2

Process		$LiAlH_4$	$LiAlH_2(OCH_2CH_2OMe)_2$	$LiAlH(OBu^t)_3$	$NaBH_4$	$NaBH_3CN$
RCOCl →	RCHO			✓[6]		
RCOCl →	RCH_2OH	✓	✓		✓	
R^1COOR^2 →	RCHO		✓[6]	✓[6,7]	×	×
R^1COOR^2 →	RCH_2OH	✓	✓	✓	✓[7]	×
$R^1CONR^2R^3$ →	R^1CHO			✓	×	×
$R^1CONR^2R^3$ →	$R^1CH_2NR^2R^3$	✓	✓	×	×	×
RCN →	RCHO		×	×	×	×
RCN →	RCH_2NH_2	✓	×	×	×	×
RCO_2H →	RCHO			×	×	×
RCO_2H →	RCH_2OH	✓	✓	×	×	×
RCHO →	RCH_2OH	✓	✓	✓	✓	✓
R^1R^2CO →	R^1R^2CHOH	✓	✓	✓	✓	×

reactive towards $LiAlH_4$ than carboxylic acid derivatives. The order of reactivity is shown in Figure 1.2.

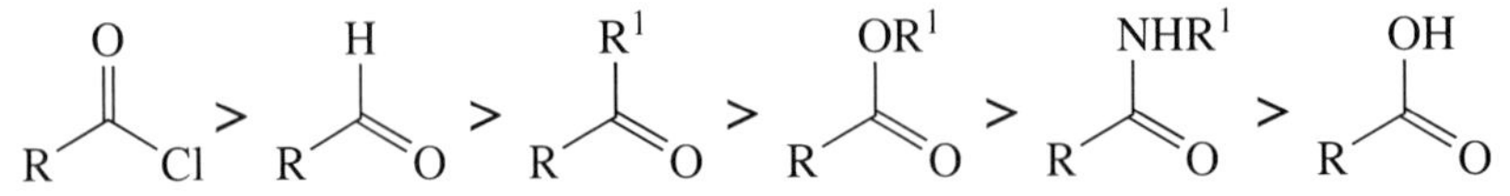

acyl chloride > aldehyde > ketone > ester > amide > acid

Figure 1.2 Reactivity of carbonyl compounds to anionic hydride transfer agents.

This reactivity sequence can therefore be exploited as we can tune the hydride source, through a combination of electronic or steric factors, to react with a specific derivative only. Thus, exchanging $LiAlH_4$ for sodium borohydride, $NaBH_4$, a less reactive source of hydride, enables only the reduction of the more reactive carbonyls, aldehydes and ketones (and acyl chlorides) to alcohols (Figure 1.3). The less reactive carbonyl esters, amides and carboxylic acids react only slowly and therefore are left untouched.

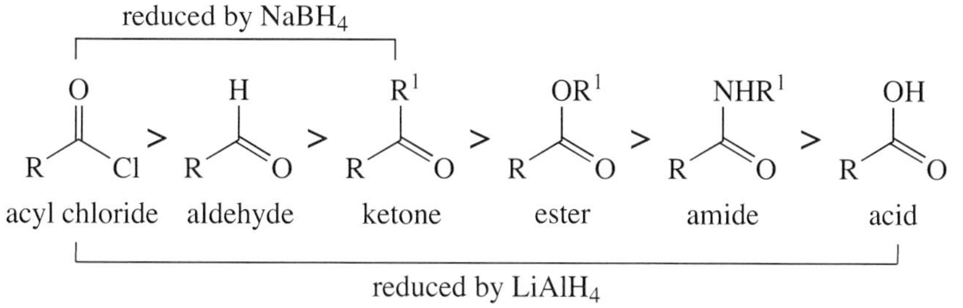

Figure 1.3 Reactivity of LiAlH$_4$ versus NaBH$_4$ towards carbonyl compounds.

Furthermore, NaBH$_4$ is easy to handle in the laboratory and so NaBH$_4$ has become the reagent of choice for reducing aldehydes and ketones.
Scheme 1.13 shows the chemoselective use of NaBH$_4$ in the reduction of a ketone, **1.42**, to a secondary alcohol, **1.43**.

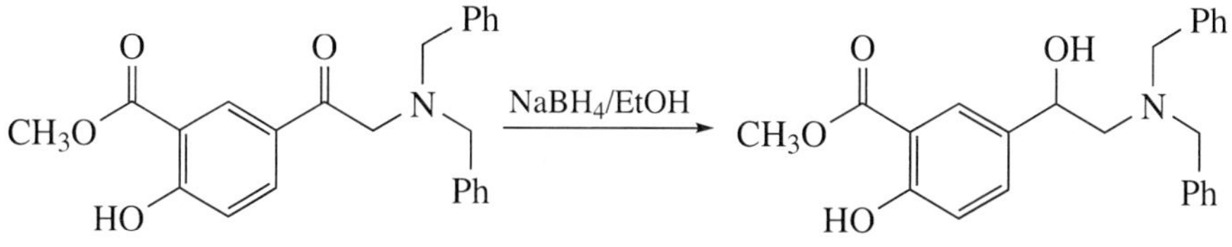

Scheme 1.13

■ Why could LiAlH$_4$ not be used in this reaction?

☐ LiAlH$_4$ would also have reduced the ester group to a primary alcohol.

Sodium borohydride is not the only solution to achieving a chemoselective reduction of one functional group in the presence of another when LiAlH$_4$ cannot be used. Indeed, Data Table 8.2 shows sodium borohydride is unable to carry out some reductions. For example it cannot be used to reduce a carboxylic acid to an aldehyde.

$$RCOOH \xrightarrow[\times]{NaBH_4} RCHO$$

This is because as we saw in Figure 1.3, the carboxylic acid group is among the least reactive carbonyl compound towards anionic hydride transfer agents such as sodium borohydride. Here again, a chemoselective reagent is required rather than using LiAlH$_4$.

So far we have focused on the anionic hydride transfer agents, however, reagents like borane (BH$_3$) and diisobutylaluminium hydride (AlH(CH$_2$CHMe$_2$)$_2$, DIBAH) are also widely used chemoselective-reducing agents. These reagents are neutral compounds of boron and aluminium respectively and are known as neutral hydride transfer agents. The boron atom and aluminium atom in these reagents are both six-electron species and therefore electron deficient. They are electrophiles and rely on the nucleophilicity of the carbonyl oxygen for their reactivity. The reactivity of neutral hydride transfer agents can be ordered in a similar manner to that of the anionic transfer agents; from most reactive to least reactive as shown in Extract 2 from Data Table 8.2.

Extract 2 from Data Table 8.2

Process		AlH_3	$AlH(CH_2CHMe_2)_2$	BH_3	$BH(CHMeCHMe_2)_2$
$RCOCl$ →	$RCHO$			×	×
	RCH_2OH	✓		×	×
R^1COOR^2 →	$RCHO$		✓	×	×
	RCH_2OH	✓		×	×
$R^1CONR^2R^3$ →	R^1CHO		✓		✓
	$R^1CH_2NR^2R^3$	✓		✓	
RCN →	$RCHO$		✓		×
	RCH_2NH_2			✓	×
RCO_2H →	$RCHO$				×
	RCH_2OH	✓	✓	✓	×
$RCHO$ ⟶ RCH_2OH		✓	✓	✓	✓
R^1R^2CO ⟶ R^1R^2CHOH		✓	✓	✓	✓

DIBAH is more reactive than borane and so will react faster with less nucleophilic substrates such as esters and acid chlorides and can reduce these groups, whereas borane cannot.

In order to understand the chemoselectivity of neutral hydride transfer agents, we need to consider the order of nucleophilicity of the carbonyl oxygen of the carboxylic acid derivatives. As shown in Figure 1.4, this is the reverse of the electrophilicity series previously discussed, when considering the reactions of anionic hydride transfer agents.

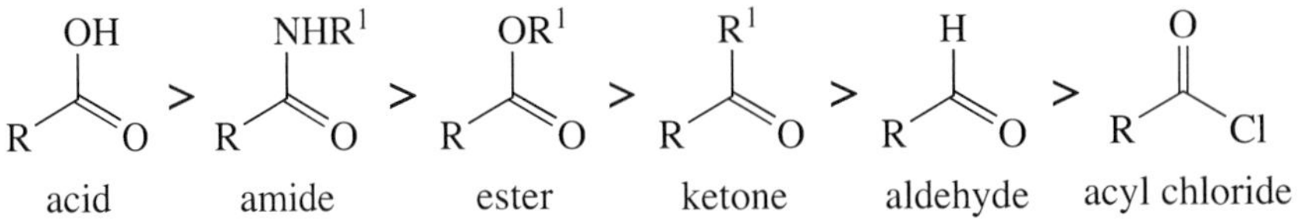

Figure 1.4 Reactivity of carbonyl compound towards neutral hydride transfer agents.

■ Examine the reduction of the amide in **1.44**.

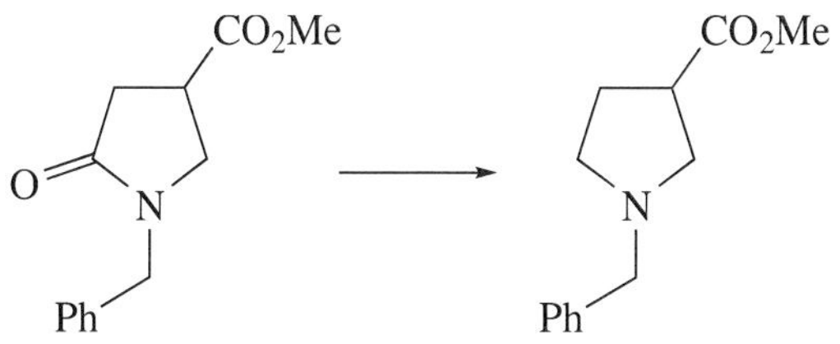

1.44

Would you use borane (BH$_3$) or DIBAH to carry out the chemoselective reduction required?

☐   Borane would achieve the required chemoselectivity – it will reduce the amide while leaving the ester unchanged. DIBAH would reduce both the amide and the ester (see Extract 2 from Data Table 8.2).

The mechanism of reduction with neutral aluminium hydrides (R$_2$ALH) is shown in Scheme 1.14. The mechanism for boranes (R$_2$BH) is similar and the first step involves the formation of a complex between the electrophilic aluminium and the nucleophilic carbonyl oxygen **1.45**, which then delivers a hydride ion to the carbonyl carbon. The resulting intermediate **1.46** is unstable at room temperature. It will rapidly decompose to give the aldehyde which can be reduced by a second molecule of hydride to give the corresponding alcohol after work up.

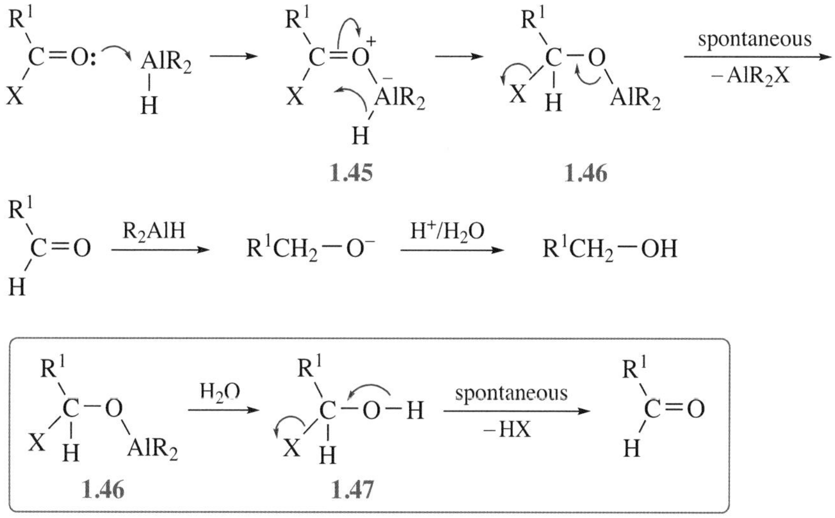

Scheme 1.14

Use of DIBAH enables the isolation of the aldehyde since the intermediate **1.46** is stable at low temperatures (−78 °C) and can therefore be intercepted usually by the addition of water. Water reacts with **1.46** to form a second intermediate, **1.47**, which decomposes to the aldehyde as shown in Scheme 1.14 (blue box). The addition of water also destroys any residual reducing agent, AlR$_2$H, preventing reduction of the aldehyde.

DIBAH is the only neutral hydride transfer reagent that has an intermediate which is stable at low temperatures. As a result, DIBAH provides a way of reducing esters, nitriles and amides to their corresponding aldehydes as shown in Extract 2 from Data Table 8.2. DIBAH has been used in the reduction of lactones (cyclic esters) and has been employed in a key step in the synthesis of the reverse transcriptase inhibitor AZT, **1.48**, which is part of the triple therapy management of AIDS.

1.48

It should however be noted that if the reaction is carried out at room temperature then complete reduction to the alcohol **1.49** does occur.

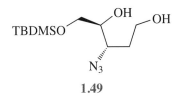

1.49

Reduction to the alcohol always occurs for carboxylic acids, even at low temperature, as the entry in Data Table 8.2 shows. This arises from the high nucleophilicity of the carboxylate. It was the most reactive group in the nucleophilicity series (Figure 1.4).

We have just seen how the chemoselectivity of anionic (LiAlH$_4$, NaBH$_4$) and neutral (BH$_3$, DIBAH) hydride transfer reagents run in opposite directions. The acid chlorides react most readily with anionic reagents, and carboxylic acid salts react the least. In contrast, for electrophilic reducing agents like borane and DIBAH, it is the carboxylate salts that are the most reactive and the acid chlorides the least. This gives the organic chemist the flexibility to choose a particular synthetic transformation that will change only one carboxylic acid derivative.

1.3.2 Chemoselectivity of the reduction of aldehydes and ketones

The following sections are concerned with both the chemo- and stereoselectivity of reductions of aldehydes and ketones.

First, let us consider chemoselectivity; aldehydes and ketones are more reactive than most carboxylic acid derivatives to hydride transfer reagents, and conveniently lend themselves to reduction with NaBH$_4$ rather than the more reactive LiAlH$_4$. However, it is possible to discriminate between two functional groups on the basis of the increased electrophilic nature of the aldehyde with respect to the ketone.

■ We can discriminate between the aldehyde and ketone functional groups by increasing the selectivity of the reducing agent. How could this be achieved?

- We can increase the selectivity by decreasing the reactivity of the hydride either by electronic effects or by increasing its steric bulk. Such a decrease in reactivity results in the reaction of the hydride reagent with the less reactive functional group being so slow it is essentially not observed, whereas the reaction with the more reactive functional group still occurs.

A less reactive reducing agent than sodium borohydride, $NaBH_4$, is sodium cyanoborohydride, $NaBH_3CN$. The electron-withdrawing cyano group decreases the electron density on the boron and therefore reduces its ability to donate a hydride ion, so it reacts with aldehydes, but not with ketones.

$$R-\overset{\overset{O}{\|}}{C}-(CH_2)_n-CHO \xrightarrow{^-BH_3CN} R-\overset{\overset{O}{\|}}{C}-(CH_2)_n-CH_2OH$$

Thus, a less reactive reducing agent, for example sodium cyanoborohydride, has led to greater selectivity in reactions involving the reduction of aldehydes in the presence of ketones. Such behaviour is not a hard and fast rule but it does illustrate the effect of the reactivity of both the reducing agent and the functional group on the selectivity of the transformation.

1.3.3 Stereoselectivity of the reduction of aldehydes and ketones

Now let us consider stereoselectivity of aldehydes and ketones.

- Do we need to consider the stereoselectivity of reduction for aldehydes?

- For aldehydes, stereoselectivity does not need to be considered as the aldehyde will produce a primary alcohol that does not have a chiral centre.

- Think back to the stereoselective syntheses discussed in Unit 4. What can you say about the stereochemistry of the product of the reduction of a ketone by $LiAlH_4$ if the R^1 and R^2 groups are different?

$$RR^1C=O \xrightarrow{LiAlH_4} RR^1CHOH$$

- The product will be chiral and was formed from a prochiral carbonyl group.

You should be able to see in Figure 1.5 that the hydride can attack from either above or below the plane of the ketone, **1.50** (or more specifically, the *Si* or *Re* faces, see Unit 4).

If both these faces were enantiotopic, then there would be no preference as to which was attacked and therefore equal amounts of the *R* and *S* enantiomers would be formed (i.e. there would be no enantiomeric excess). However, if the two faces are diastereotopic, for example if R or R^1 contains a chiral centre, then one face, generally the least sterically hindered face, is more likely to

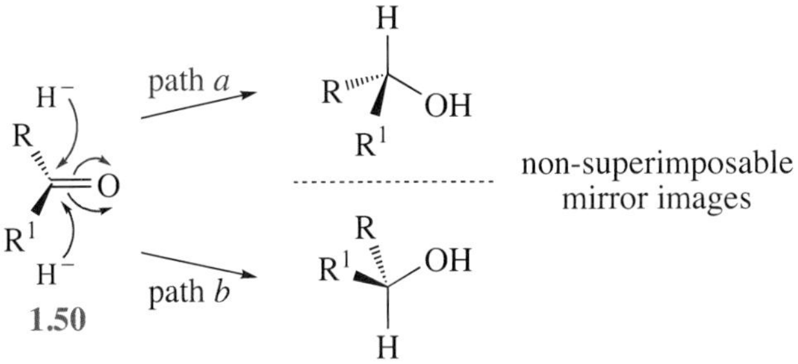

Figure 1.5 The two possible paths, *a* and *b*, by which hydride, H⁻, attacks the carbonyl carbon.

undergo hydride delivery. For example, in Unit 4 we saw how the diastereoface selectivity of acyclic ketones can be predicted by Cram's rule.

Enantiofacial selectivity: asymmetric reduction of ketones

When the two faces of the ketone are equivalent, that is, they are enantiotopic, a standard achiral reducing agent will show no selectivity, resulting in a racemic mixture. However, if the reducing agent is chiral then hydride delivery might well occur from a preferred direction, leading to the production of a secondary alcohol as a single enantiomer. One of the earliest chiral reducing agents developed was *R*-Alpine-Borane® (**1.51**), which employs (+)-α-pinene (**1.52**) as its **chiral auxiliary**. This reagent has the advantage that the chiral auxiliary is readily available in both enantiomeric forms, + and −, and thus *S*-Alpine-Borane® is also commercially available and will produce the opposite enantiomer when used in the reduction.

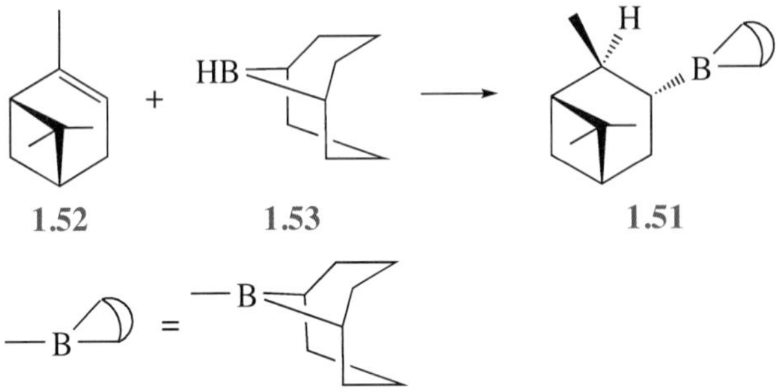

The reaction of 9-borabicyclononane (9-BBN, **1.53**), with α-pinene (**1.52**) leads to *R*-Alpine-Borane® where the bicyclic group attached to the boron has been abbreviated in the representation of the product. Depending upon the substrate, these reagents are capable of producing enantiomeric excesses of close to 100%, that is, effectively the exclusive production of a single enantiomer. Some examples are highlighted in Scheme 1.15.

This observed selectivity can be explained through inspection of the mechanism that is proposed to occur via a six-membered boat transition state **1.52** (Scheme 1.16; Structure **1.52** is shown in Unit 6 iFigure 1.3). The substituents on the ketone are arranged with the largest R group, R_L, in a pseudo-equatorial position and the sterically smaller group, R_S, in an axial position, thereby eclipsing the axial methyl group on the adjacent carbon. This

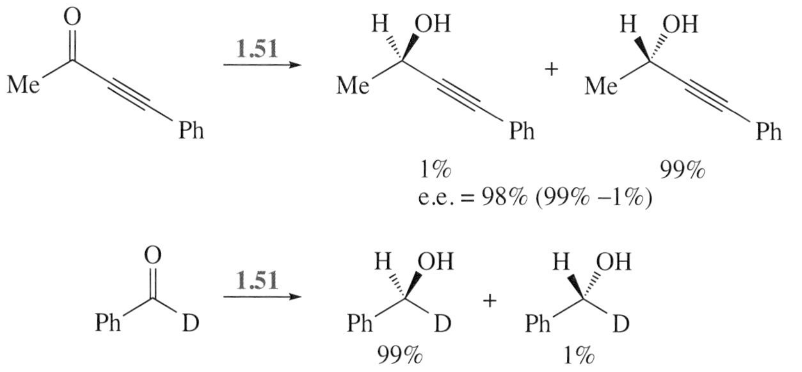

Scheme 1.15

arrangement thus minimises the unfavourable steric interactions that could occur if the larger group were axial.

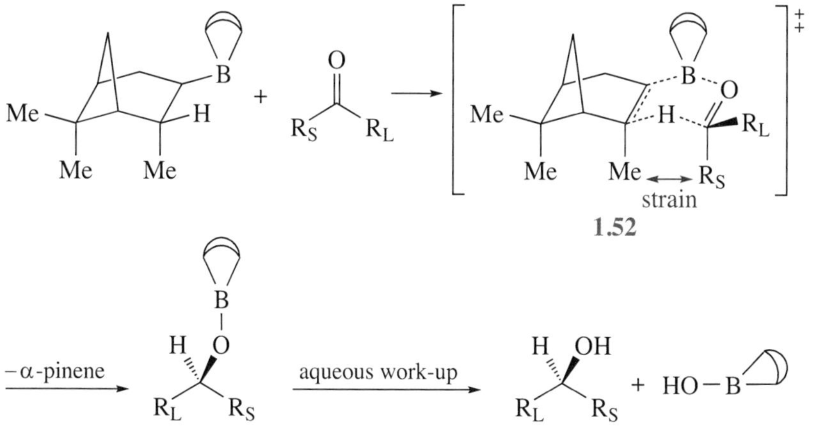

For example,

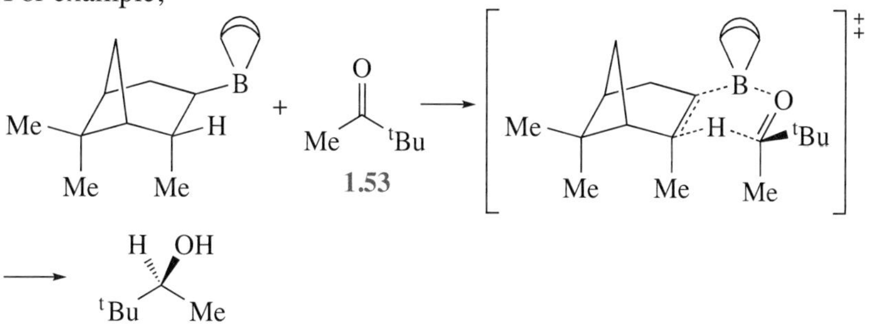

Scheme 1.16

Notice that with 3,3-dimethylbut-2-one (**1.53**), the smaller group, in this case the methyl, adopts the axial position with the larger *tert*-butyl group in the pseudo-equatorial site.

1.3.4   Reduction of carbon–carbon multiple bonds

Reduction of alkenes

The reduction of carbon–carbon double bonds proceeds most easily by catalytic hydrogenation. Almost all alkenes can be reduced in very high yield by treatment with hydrogen in the presence of a metal catalyst (Pd or Pt). The catalytic hydrogenation of alkenes is a chemoselective process; alkenes are reduced more readily than other unsaturated functional groups with the exception of alkynes (see subsection below), nitro groups and acyl chlorides. Therefore, catalytic hydrogenation can be used for the selective reduction of alkenes in the presence of carbonyls and aromatic systems.

Furthermore, less substituted carbon–carbon double bonds undergo reduction more easily than more substituted alkenes. An example that illustrates this can be seen in the hydrogenation of *S*-limonene (**1.54**).

It is generally true that such catalytic reduction is stereoselective with the addition of hydrogen to the double bond occurring in a *cis* fashion to the least hindered face of the double bond. For example, 2*R*-2-methyl-1-methylidenecyclohexane (**1.55**) yields *cis*-1,2-dimethylcyclohexane as the major product since the methyl substituent hinders the approach of the H$_2$ catalyst such that it attacks preferentially from the opposite face of the double bond.

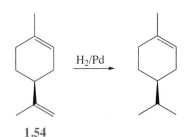

1.54

Alkenes can also be reduced to alkanes using dissolving metal reductions although those methods are in general less valuable than catalytic hydrogenation. The reaction conditions are often too harsh for complex molecules. Nevertheless, they do offer the chemist an alternative method when catalytic methods fail. For example, consider the reduction of the sterically hindered, tetrasubstituted double bond in steroid systems (**1.56**).

1.56

Alkyne reduction – formation of E versus Z alkenes

Alkynes can be fully reduced to alkanes by the addition of two moles of hydrogen using either heterogeneous catalysis, for example palladium metal, or homogeneous catalysis, for example Wilkinson's catalyst, which is a rhodium-based catalyst ((Ph$_3$P)$_3$RhCl). Of more significance is the fact that catalytic reduction of alkynes to alkenes (C=C) occurs faster than the reduction of alkenes to alkanes (C–C). Thus it is possible to partially reduce alkynes to alkenes and stop the reaction at this stage. Moreover, we can control the resulting double bond geometry.

(i)   *Formation of Z-alkenes from alkynes*

Alkynes can be converted into the corresponding Z-double bond through direct hydrogenation using Lindlar's catalyst, which is a palladium-based catalyst. In this approach the palladium catalyst is deactivated (poisoned) through the addition of lead acetate and quinoline and is thus not able to reduce alkenes to alkanes effectively. The reduction mechanism is virtually identical to that of the heterogeneous reduction of alkenes and the two hydrogen atoms add in a *cis* manner to produce the corresponding Z-alkene.

(ii)   *Formation of E-alkenes from alkynes*

The best method for converting alkynes into *E*-alkenes is through the use of sodium in liquid ammonia. Reaction is thought to proceed by alternating electron and proton transfer. The first step involves the transfer of a single electron from the sodium to the alkyne to create a radical anion **1.57**. The anion then removes a proton from ammonia.

The formation of the *trans*-alkene is a consequence of reducing the steric congestion in the geometrically unstable vinyl radical intermediate, **1.58**, which undergoes a rotation to form the *trans*-vinyl radical, **1.59** (rotation around double bonds in vinyl radicals is much easier than in conventional double bonds). This radical also receives a single electron from sodium to form the anion **1.60**. Formation of the alkene is complete when the anion **1.60** removes a proton from ammonia.

Further reduction to the alkane is not normally seen under these conditions; however caution must be taken as these are strongly reducing conditions and other functional groups can also be reduced.

1.4   Concluding remarks

Our survey of oxidation and reduction has been brief. It has concentrated on the reactions of functional groups that contain carbon–oxygen bonds and carbon–carbon multiple bonds. The unit has not covered functional groups such as NH_2, SH, NO_2 and SO_2R. Nevertheless, it has covered the major functional group interconversions, the key principles of reactivity and selectivity, and strategies for both oxidation and reduction. This will help you to understand why a particular oxidation or reduction has been used in a synthetic sequence and enable you to suggest a possible reagent when given a particular transformation.

Activity 1.2

At the beginning of this unit, we asked you to populate the oxidation and reduction template tables which were available on the S346 website. You should now compare your tables with Data Tables 8.1 and 8.2. You should examine the footnotes to Data Tables 8.1 and 8.2 and make sure you understand all of the exceptions.

Study note

Before moving on to Section 2, you should produce your own summary of this section and then compare it with ours. Go to Unit 6 summaries in Unit 6 resources.

2 Enols and enolates

The majority of this section is devoted to reactions involving the carbonyl group and in particular carbon–carbon bond forming reactions. Carbonyls are ubiquitous in organic synthesis because they are able to undergo an extensive variety of reactions. This is because carbonyl compounds have two opposing features, namely they possess both nucleophilic and electrophilic character. Consequently a significant part of the repertoire of reactions available to the organic chemist involves the carbonyl group acting as either a nucleophile or an electrophile.

2.1 Introduction

You may have seen examples of the carbonyl group acting as electrophiles if you have studied the Level 2 chemistry module which described how nucleophiles attack the positive carbon centres of carbonyl groups. The Grignard reaction is a good example of this as is the attack of a cyano group to form a cyanohydrin. Further examples of this will be seen in Unit 8 which reviews peptide synthesis in which amine nucleophiles attack the positive carbon atoms of carboxylic acid derivatives to give amides. However, carbonyl groups can be nucleophilic as well, opening up the possibility of an attack by an electrophile at the negative oxygen centre. Another important property of carbonyl compounds is their ability to exist in two forms – a keto form and an enol form.

keto form   enol form

(2.1)

Aldehydes and ketones are usually represented in the keto form which emphasises the electrophilic nature of the carbonyl carbon. However, they can also exist in another form called an enol that imparts nucleophilic character to the carbon adjacent to the carbonyl carbon. The structure of the enol is suggested by its name, **ene-ol**, shortened to enol. It has a double bond and an alcohol group. These two forms, the keto and the enol form, exist in equilibrium involving movement of a proton (marked in red in Equation 2.1).

■   Are these two structures resonance forms?

□   No. Resonance forms are different representations of a single structure, which only differ in the way the electrons are distributed. The actual distribution is a mix of all the resonance forms.

The keto and enol forms are isomers since they only differ by the position of the hydrogen – they are known a **tautomers** and their rapid interconversion is known as tautomerism. Most carbonyl compounds exist predominantly in the keto form, for example, propanone has 99.999 9999% of the keto form with only 0.000 0001% in the enol form.

$$CH_3-\overset{\overset{\displaystyle O}{\|}}{C}-CH_3 \quad \rightleftharpoons \quad CH_3-\overset{\overset{\displaystyle OH}{|}}{C}=CH_2 \qquad (2.2)$$

keto   enol

The percentage of the enol form for carboxylic acids, esters and amides is even less. If the enol form is such a small percentage, you might ask why we bother to consider their properties. Even though they are present to only a small extent they are very reactive, and because there is a rapid equilibrium between the keto and enol forms, all of the carbonyl compound can undergo reaction via the enol form. Thus the reactivity of enols has a big impact on the chemistry of carbonyl compounds.

2.2   Stability and reactions of enols

2.2.1   Formation of enols

Keto–enol tautomerism is catalysed by acids and bases. In the acid-catalysed process the oxygen is protonated by the acid which is followed by loss of a proton from the adjacent carbon atom. In this last step the conjugate base A^- of the acid HA acts as the base.

The base-catalysed process proceeds via the formation of an enolate ion intermediate. As you will see later in this unit, enolate ions are very important reagents for forming carbon–carbon bonds because they are relatively stable carbanions.

You met pK_a values in Unit 3.

■   Propanone has a pK_a of 20 whereas ethane has a pK_a of 50. What does this tell us about the acidity of hydrogens on carbons adjacent to carbonyl groups?

□   The smaller (or more negative) the pK_a, the more acidic the compound, thus propanone is more acidic than ethane. In propanone all the hydrogens are identical and this suggests that the hydrogens on carbons adjacent to carbonyl groups are more acidic than conventional alkane hydrogens.

The enhanced acidity of hydrogens on carbons adjacent, alpha, to carbonyls mean that when a base is added, a proton is removed from this alpha carbon atom to give an enolate ion.

Subsequent protonation of the enolate ion at the oxygen gives the enol form. Protonation occurs at the adjacent carbon as well but this just gives the keto form.

As we discussed in the Introduction, using propanone as an example, in keto–enol tautomerism the equilibrium generally favours the keto form. However, various factors such as stereo effects, resonance effects, intermolecular hydrogen bonding and solvent effects can lead to the enol form being favoured. Such a situation occurs in the keto–enol tautomerism in Equation 2.3, where the aromatic enol, phenol (**2.2**), is the preferred form.

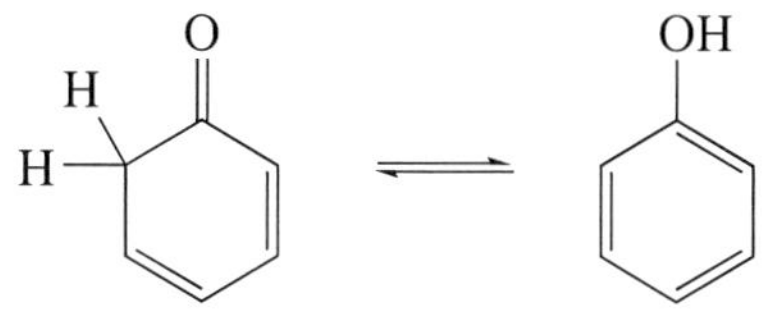

$$(2.3)$$

This is because benzene-type molecules with six π-electrons are particularly stable – there are two resonance forms of equal energy for **2.2**:

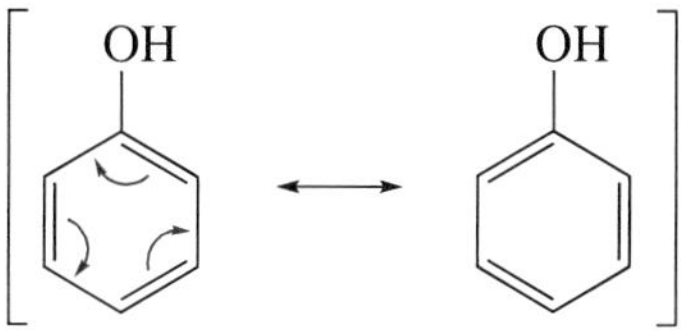

The keto form **2.1** doesn't have the cyclic system of six π-electrons and therefore lacks this 'extra' stabilisation form resonance. Any resonance form you may draw for **2.1** will involve charge separation and thus have a relatively high energy. This extra stabilisation of **2.2** is sufficient to ensure that **2.2** is the lower energy form, and thus predominates over **2.1**.

The enol content of a range of carbonyl compounds is shown in Table 2.1. Notice that generally esters have a much lower enol content than aldehydes and ketones. The table also shows that when the carbonyl is next but one, beta, to another carbonyl, the enol content is greatly increased.

Table 2.1   The enol content of some carbonyl compounds.

Compound	Enol content/%	Compound	Enol content/%
CH_3COCH_3	6×10^{-5}	$CH_3COCH_2COCH_3$	76.4
CH_3CHO	1×10^{-3}	CH_3COCH_2COOEt	8.0
CH_3COOEt	no enol found*	$EtOOCCH_2COOEt$	7.7×10^{-3}

* Less than 1 part in 10 million.

■   For example, at equilibrium, 76% of pentane-2,4-dione (acetylacetone) is in the enol form, $CH_3COCH=C(OH)CH_3$, whereas for propanone the percentage of enol is much smaller. Why does the presence of a β-carbonyl lead to so much more enol?

☐   There are two main reasons. First, and probably more importantly, in the enol form, conjugation of the C=C with the second carbonyl group lowers the energy of the enol via resonance stabilisation:

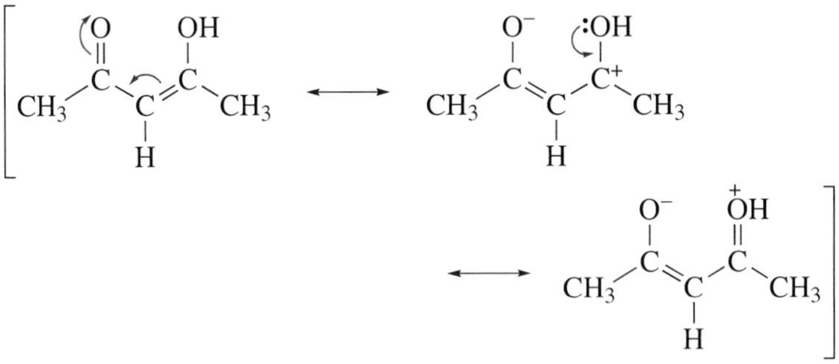

Second, the enol can often be stabilised by intramolecular hydrogen bonding in a six-membered ring structure **2.3**. No such hydrogen bonding is possible with the keto form.

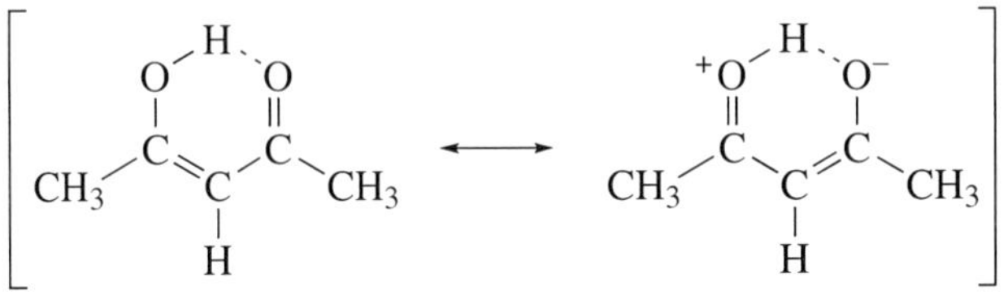

2.3

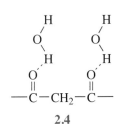

2.4

The extent to which intramolecular hydrogen bonding can stabilise the enol form with respect to the keto form is seen in the observation that, in aqueous solutions (as compared with hexane), where the water molecules can form intermolecular hydrogen bonds with the keto form as well (see **2.4**), the percentage of the enol form of pentane-2,4-dione at equilibrium falls to 15%.

Finally, we shall examine the direction of enolisation. Many unsymmetrical ketones are able to enolise in two directions; for example butan-2-one (**2.5**) can give the enols **2.6** and **2.7**.

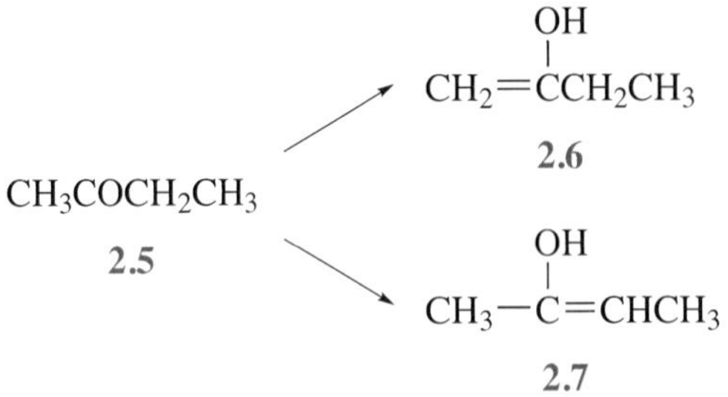

$$CH_3COCH_2CH_3$$

2.5

$$CH_2{=}CCH_2CH_3$$ with OH

2.6

$$CH_3{-}C{=}CHCH_3$$ with OH

2.7

Of course, the amount of enolisation is in any case very small, but the ratio of **2.6** to **2.7** is about 1:3, presumably because the latter enol is more stable.

■   Why is **2.7** more stable than **2.6**?

☐ Compound **2.7** is more stable than **2.6** because it is the more substituted alkene. You have met this kind of rationalisation before in the Level 2 module with Saytzeff's rule, which predicts that elimination from a neutral substrate would lead to the more substituted alkene because it would be the more stable.

2.2.2 Reactions of enols

■ What kinds of reactants do carbon–carbon double bonds usually react with, electrophiles or nucleophiles?

☐ The carbon–carbon double bond has a high electron density above and below the plane of the bond as a result of the π orbital of the double bond. Thus the double bond acts as a nucleophile and reacts with electrophiles. You may be familiar with this from the Level 2 module when double bonds react with electrophiles such as H^+ and Br^+ in the first step of the addition process.

Enols contain a carbon–carbon double bond which is particularly electron rich because of the neighbouring oxygen atom, so it should be no surprise that the predominant type of reaction that enols undergo involves attack of an electrophile at the electron-rich carbon–carbon double bond. Subsequent loss of a proton from the oxygen leads to overall substitution at the carbon alpha to the carbonyl:

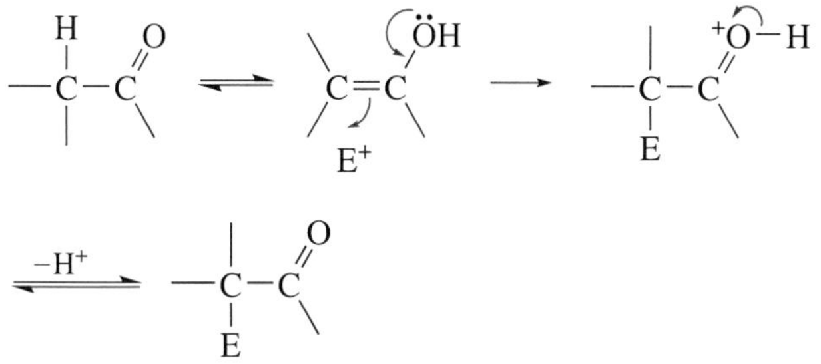

$$ \tag{2.4} $$

For example, 2-bromocyclohexanone (**2.8**) can be formed from cyclohexanone (**2.9**) by treatment of the ketone, **2.9**, with bromine in an acid (HBr).

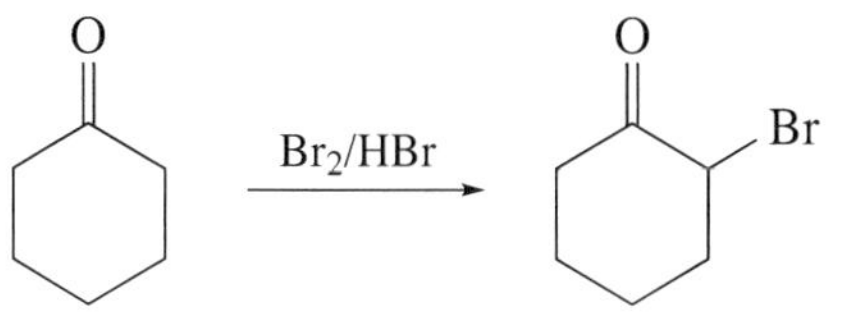

2.9   2.8

First the acid aids enolisation to give **2.10**. The enol **2.10** then reacts with the electrophilic bromine

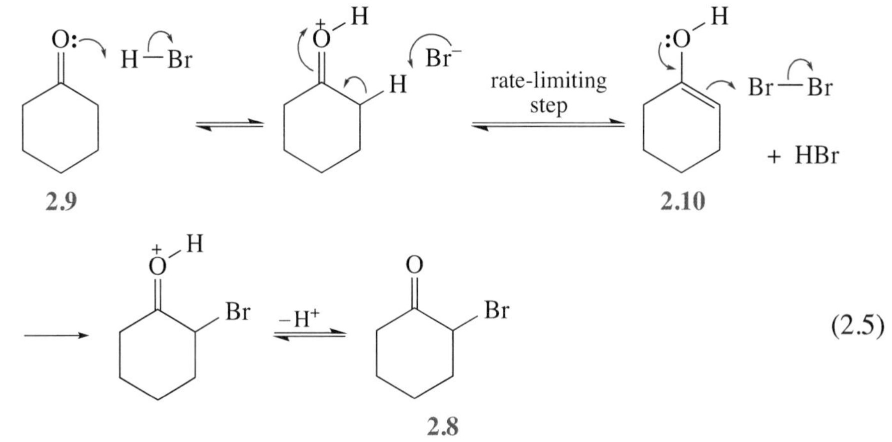

(2.5)

The last step involves loss of a proton from the oxygen to give the product. Notice that the formation of the enol is the rate-limiting step, that is, as soon as it forms it reacts with the bromine. Such α-bromoketones are synthetically useful because elimination of HBr leads to α,β-unsaturated ketones:

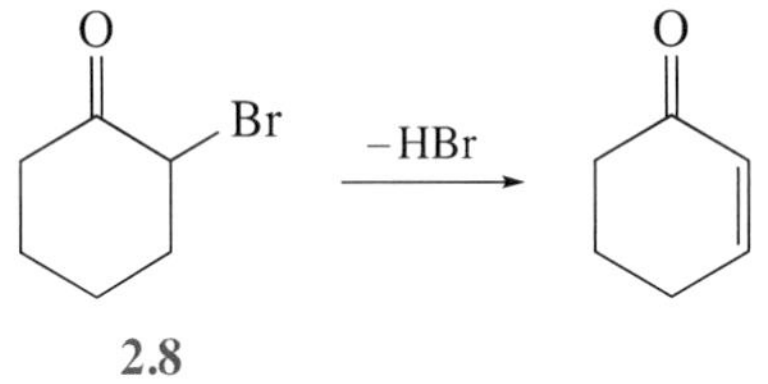

This type of enol reaction is versatile because other electrophiles can be used instead of halogens. For example, protonation of nitrous acid leads to the nitrosonium ion NO^+:

$$HONO + H^+ \rightleftharpoons H_2O + NO^+$$

The electrophilic NO^+ can be attacked by enols to give a nitroso compound, for example, **2.11**:

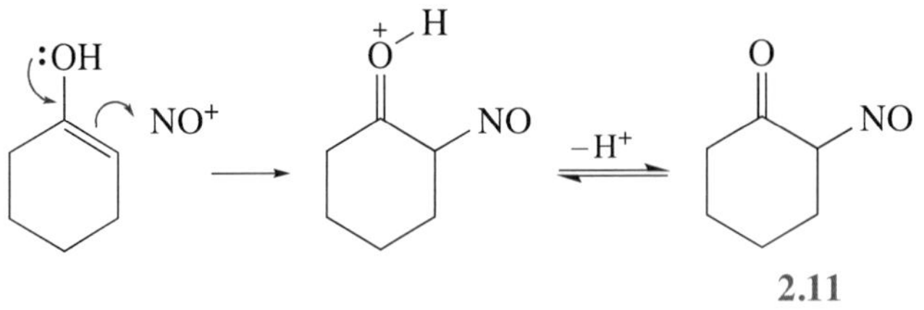

Such compounds readily rearrange to give oximes:

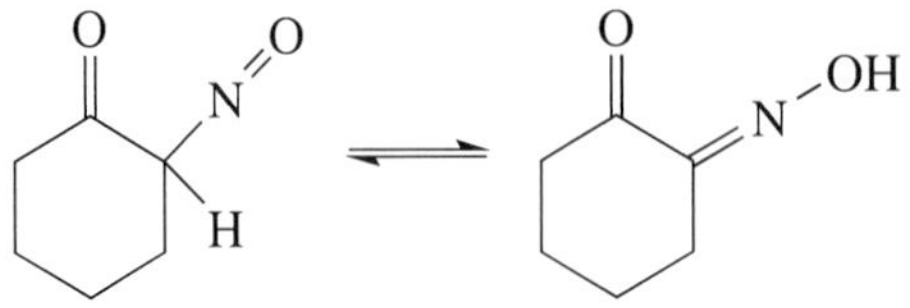

This tautomeric equilibrium is similar to keto–enol tautomerism, except that the hydroxy form predominates in this case. Hydrolysis of the oxime then leads to a diketone. (This is the reverse of oxime formation as you may recall from the Level 2 module.)

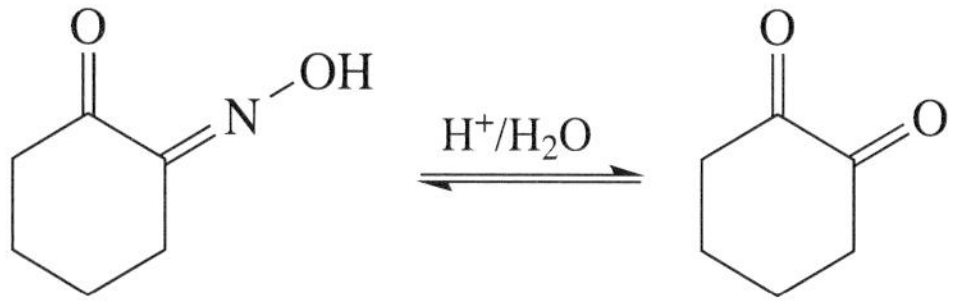

The overall transformation gives us a means of introducing a carbonyl adjacent to an existing carbonyl. This strategy was used as part of a synthesis of ceftazidime, an antibiotic where ethyl acetylacetate is nitrosated alpha to both carbonyls:

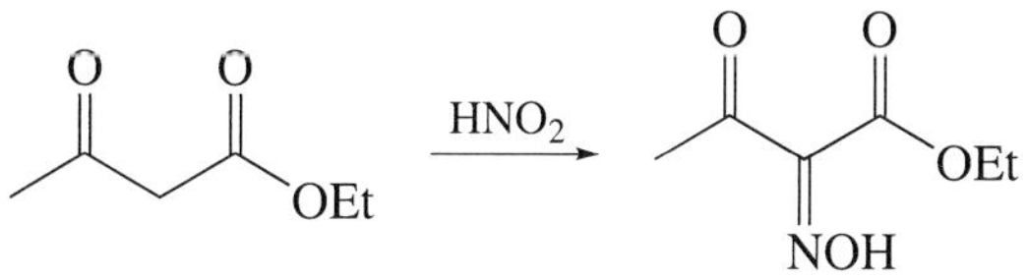

■ With unsymmetrical ketones such as **2.12** or **2.13**, α-substitution could occur at either carbon adjacent to the carbonyl. What factors will control the regiochemistry of these reactions?

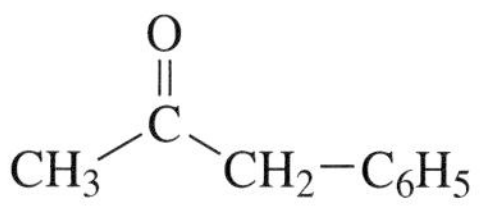

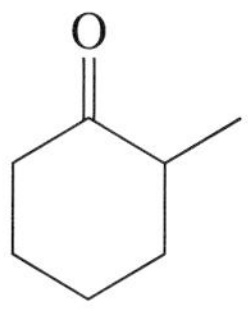

□ The site of substitution will depend on which of the enols is formed the faster, since this is the rate-limiting step.

Ketone **2.12** can form two enols, **2.14** and **2.15**. As well as being the more substituted alkene, **2.15** has the double bond in conjugation with the phenyl ring whereas this is not so in **2.14**. Thus **2.15** is more stable than **2.14**, and in this case is formed the faster.

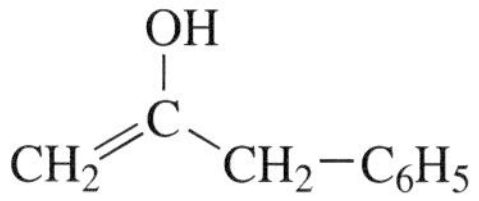

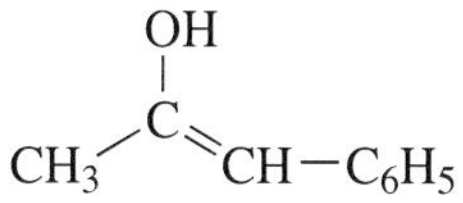

Reaction of **2.15** with an electrophile leads to substitution alpha to the carbonyl and phenyl groups, e.g. diketone formation:

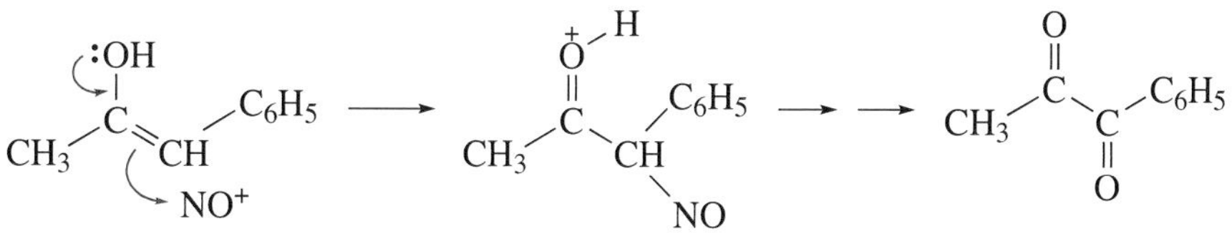

With compound **2.13**, the more substituted enol **2.16** will again be formed faster, leading to preferred substitution alpha to the carbonyl and methyl groups:

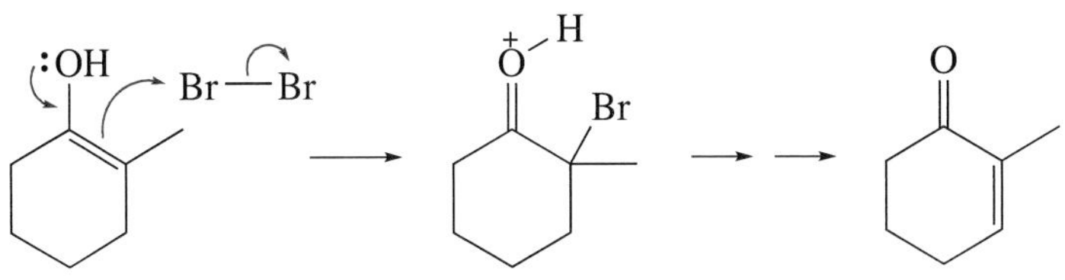

2.16

2.2.3   Derivatives of enols

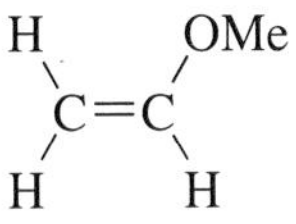

Although the enol forms of simple aldehydes and ketones have not been isolated, several of their simple derivatives are well-known stable compounds. For example, the methyl ether of the enol form of ethanal, methoxyethene (methyl vinyl ether) (**2.17**) is used industrially in the manufacture of polyvinyl ether plastics. Similarly, vinyl acetate (**2.18**) polymerises to polyvinyl acetate. Another important derivative that is used in synthesis and that we shall meet again fairly soon is the trimethylsilyl enol ether (**2.19**).

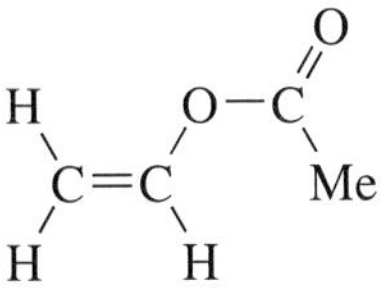

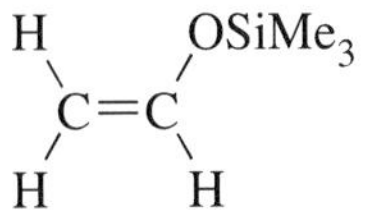

2.17

2.18

2.19

> **Study note**
>
> Before moving on to the next section, you should produce your own summary of Sections 2.1 and 2.2 and then compare it with ours. Go to Unit 6 summaries in Unit 6 resources.

2.3   Selective formation of enolate ions

Just like enols, enolate ions react with electrophiles but they are much more reactive. For example, as well as reacting with halogens they react with benzene-selenyl bromide which provides another important route to α,β-unsaturated carbonyl compounds:

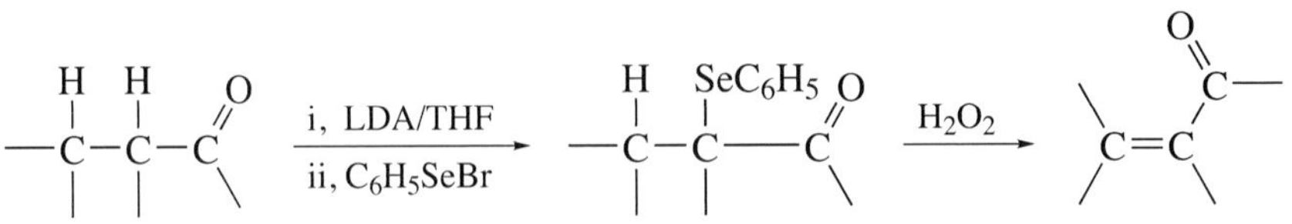

Enolate ions also react with alkyl halides, and we shall be devoting much of this unit to this type of reaction. As with enols, to rationalise the chemo- and regioselectivity of such reactions we must be aware of the relative stability of possible enolate ions. Therefore we begin this section by reviewing this topic. We shall then consider ways in which enolates are formed, and finally, how both of these factors can control the selectivity of enolate formation.

2.3.1   Stability of enolate ions

Data Table 10.1 lists the pK_a values of a range of organic compounds in water at 25 °C. From this list it is clear that carbanions adjacent to C=X bonds and other electron-withdrawing groups are stabilised by inductive and resonance effects, such that their precursors are more acidic compounds with correspondingly lower pK_a values. From these pK_a values, an approximate ordering of some substituents with respect to their ability to stabilise carbanions can be established. The suggested order is:

$$NO_2 > COR > CN \approx CO_2R > SO_2R > SOR > Ph \gg R$$

Notice that esters, such as ethyl ethanoate, are less acidic than ketones, such as propanone. Of course the presence of two such groups reduces the pK_a yet further. Let's now examine a couple of points that arise out of this order.

■   Why does pentane-2,4-dione (**2.20**) have a lower pK_a than propanone (**2.21**)?

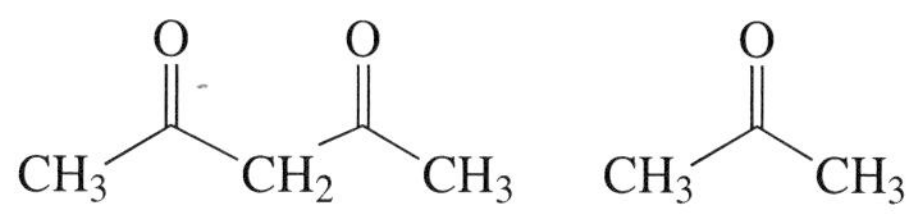

□   **2.20** is more acidic than **2.21** because the resulting anion is more stable, it has three resonance forms as opposed to two for propanone:

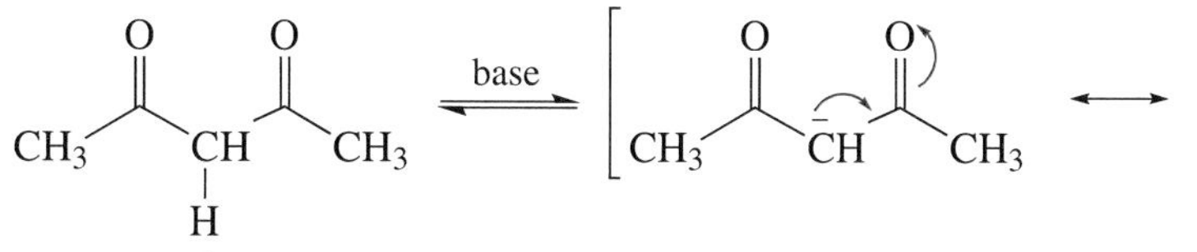

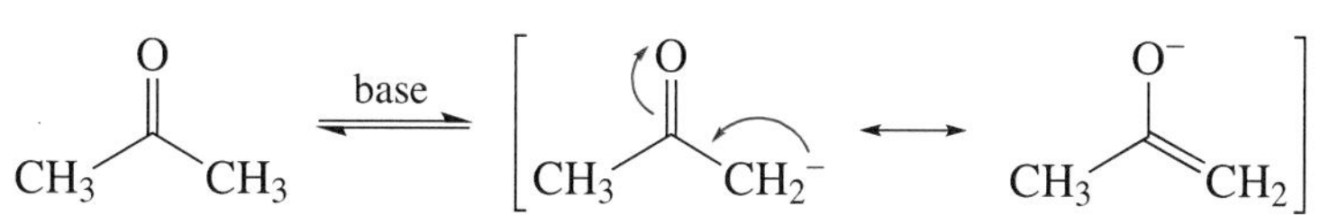

■   Why do CH_3CN and CH_3NO_2 have a very much lower pK_a than an alkane?

□   First the carbanions are stabilised by inductive electron withdrawal by the nitrogen. Secondly, and more importantly, both the carbanions from CH_3CN and CH_3NO_2 are stabilised by resonance.

$$\left[{}^-\overset{\frown}{CH_2}\!-\!C\!\overset{\frown}{\equiv}\!N \quad\longleftrightarrow\quad CH_2\!=\!C\!=\!N^- \right]$$

$$\left[{}^-\overset{\frown}{CH_2}\!-\!\overset{+}{N}\!\overset{O}{\underset{O^-}{\diagup\!\!\!\!\diagdown}} \quad\longleftrightarrow\quad CH_2\!=\!\overset{+}{N}\!\overset{O^-}{\underset{O^-}{\diagup\!\!\!\!\diagdown}} \right]$$

In each case one of the resonance forms has the negative charge on an atom (O or N). This lowers the energy of the carbanion such that CH_3CN and CH_3NO_2 are fairly acidic.

■ How will the stability of a carbanion be affected when a halogen is attached to the carbon bearing the negative charge?

☐ Halogens withdraw electrons by the inductive effect, thus spreading the negative charge and leading to a more stable carbanion.

This is borne out in practice: the acidity is increased, by about two pK_a units, when an electron-withdrawing chloro- or bromo-substituent is present as you will have seen in Unit 3.

2.3.2 Methods for the formation of enolate ions

The simplest way of making an enolate ion is by removing an acidic proton from a suitable substrate, such as a ketone. To do this we need to use a sufficiently strong base, B.

$$\underset{CH_3\quad\;\;CH_3}{\overset{O}{\underset{\|}{C}}} + B \;\rightleftharpoons\; \underset{CH_3\quad\;\;CH_2}{\overset{O^-}{\underset{|}{C}}\!\!=\!\!} + BH$$

As you saw in Unit 3, the basicity of a base is expressed in terms of how easily the corresponding species BH^+, the conjugate acid, gives up a proton:

$$BH^+ + H_2O \rightleftharpoons B + H_3O^+ \tag{2.5}$$

Clearly, with strong bases this equilibrium will lie to the left whereas with weak bases it lies to the right. Since Equation 2.5 represents a typical acid–base reaction, we can define a pK_a, where

$$K_a = \frac{[B][H_3O^+]}{[BH^+]} \tag{2.6}$$

and

$$-pK_a = \log K_a$$

■ Will the pK_a of the conjugate acid of a strong base be large or small?

☐ Strong bases will exist predominantly as BH^+, so Equation 2.6 shows that K_a will be small. Hence the pK_a of the conjugate acid will be large and positive.

Data Table 10.2 lists the pK_a values of the conjugate acids of a range of bases and solvents; strong bases appear towards the bottom of the table. By comparing the approximate pK_a values of the conjugate acids of the bases in Table 10.2 and those of the substrates listed in Table 10.1, it is possible to estimate the position of the acid–base equilibrium for a given reactant–base combination, as discussed in Section 2.2.1 of Unit 3. If the pK_a of the carbonyl compound is less than the pK_a of the conjugate acid of the base, the reaction will proceed.

■ Which anionic species will predominate in the following reactant–base combinations?

(i) $CH_3-\overset{\overset{\displaystyle O}{\|}}{C}-CH_3$ / $CH_3CH_2O^-$

(ii) $CH_2(COOEt)_2$ / $CH_3CH_2O^-$

(iii) $CH_3-\overset{\overset{\displaystyle O}{\|}}{C}-H$ / $(CH_3)_3CO^-$

(iv) CH_3CN / $Li^{+\,-}N(CH(CH_3)_2)_2$ (i.e. LDA)

☐ For combination (i), the relevant equilibrium is shown in Equation 2.7

$$CH_3\overset{\overset{\displaystyle O}{\|}}{\underset{\displaystyle CH_3}{C}} + CH_3CH_2O^- \;\rightleftharpoons\; CH_3\overset{\overset{\displaystyle O^-}{|}}{\underset{\displaystyle CH_2}{C}} + CH_3CH_2OH \qquad (2.7)$$

The pK_a of propanone, Equation 2.8, is larger than that of the conjugate acid of $CH_3CH_2O^-$, ethanol, Equation 2.9, so the reaction will not occur to any extent.

$$CH_3\overset{\overset{\displaystyle O}{\|}}{\underset{\displaystyle CH_3}{C}} + H_2O \;\rightleftharpoons\; CH_3\overset{\overset{\displaystyle O^-}{|}}{\underset{\displaystyle CH_2}{C}} + H_3O^+ \qquad pK_a = 20 \qquad (2.8)$$

$$CH_3CH_2OH + H_2O \rightleftharpoons CH_3CH_2O^- + H_3O^+ \qquad pK_a = 16 \qquad (2.9)$$

Thus ethanol is more acidic than propanone, that is, relative to their conjugate acids $CH_3CH_2O^-$ is formed more easily (i.e. is more stable) than the enolate and so $CH_3CH_2O^-$ will predominate in the equilibrium (Equation 2.7). Hence little of the enolate will be formed in the reactant–base combination $CH_3COCH_3/CH_3CH_2O^-$.

In combination (ii), the pK_a of diethyl malonate (**2.22**), 13, is less than the pK_a of ethanol, 16, and so this reaction will proceed. Relative to their conjugate acids, the enolate ion **2.23** is more stable than the ethoxide ion, so in the combination $CH_2(COOEt)_2/CH_3CH_2O^-$ the enolate ion will predominate.

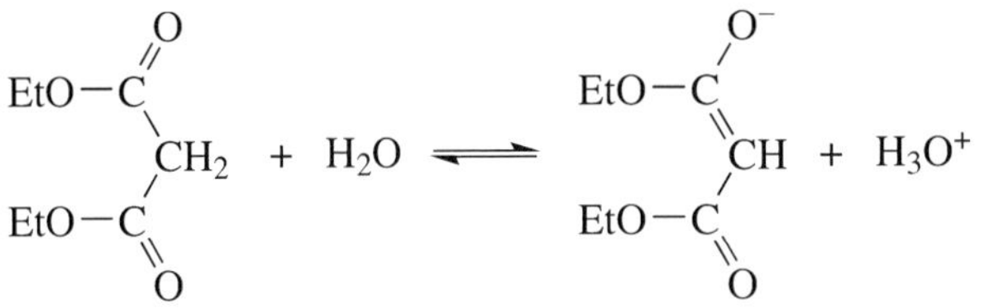

$$EtO-C(=O)-CH_2-C(=O)-OEt \ (\mathbf{2.22}) \ + \ H_2O \ \rightleftharpoons \ EtO-C(O^-)=CH-C(=O)-OEt \ (\mathbf{2.23}) \ + \ H_3O^+ \qquad pK_a = 13 \qquad (2.10)$$

$$CH_2{=}C(O^-){-}H$$

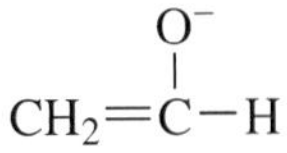

2.24

Similar reasoning shows that the enolate ion **2.24** ($pK_a = 17$) is more stable than $(CH_3)_3CO^-$ ($pK_a = 19$), and so in combination (iii) the enolate ion again predominates.

Finally, Data Table 10.2 shows that LDA is such a strong base ($pK_a = 36$) that it is able to pull a proton off CH_3CN ($pK_a = 25$) such that $^-CH_2CN$ will predominate.

■ Can you see a problem that might have occurred if HO^- had been used as the base with diethyl malonate?

☐ As well as removing a proton, the hydroxide ion could have reacted with the ester group to give carboxylic acid – a hydrolysis reaction.

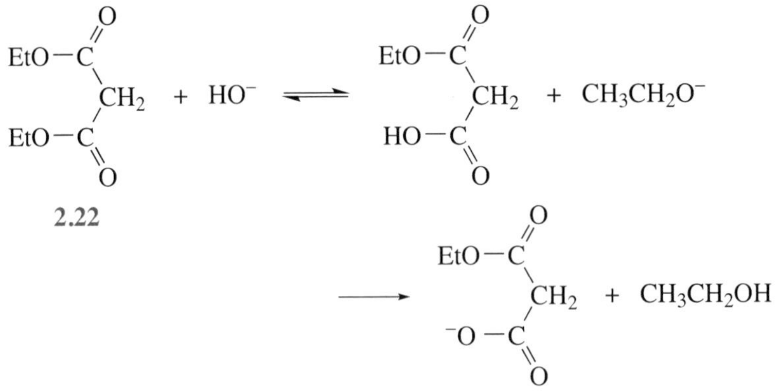

$$EtO-C(=O)-CH_2-C(=O)-OEt \ (\mathbf{2.22}) \ + \ HO^- \ \rightleftharpoons \ EtO-C(=O)-CH_2-C(=O)-OH \ + \ CH_3CH_2O^-$$

$$\longrightarrow \ EtO-C(=O)-CH_2-C(=O)-O^- \ + \ CH_3CH_2OH \qquad (2.11)$$

This is a problem you may have met before, for example in the Level 2 module; as well as being basic, hydroxide ions and alkoxide ions are also nucleophilic. For example, if CH_3O^- had been used, an ester interchange could have occurred:

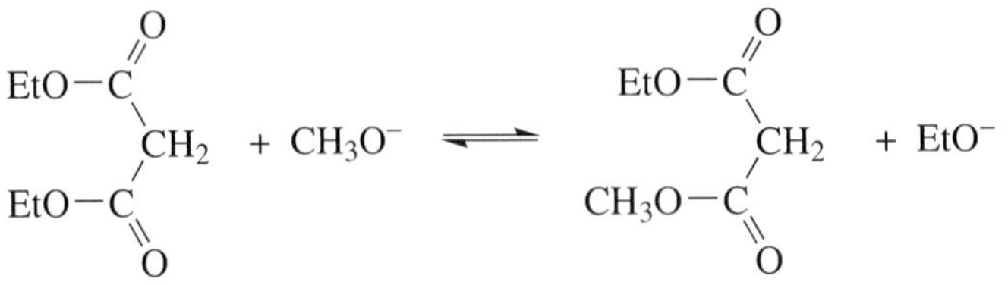

$$EtO-C(=O)-CH_2-C(=O)-OEt \ + \ CH_3O^- \ \rightleftharpoons \ EtO-C(=O)-CH_2-C(=O)-OCH_3 \ + \ EtO^- \qquad (2.12)$$

One way round this is to use an alkoxide base that corresponds to the group of the ester. This is why $CH_3CH_2O^-$ was used in (ii) above, since ester interchange just gives back the same compound. Another way of overcoming this problem is to use a hindered base. As you may remember from the Level 2 module, the tertiary butoxide anion, $(CH_3)_3CO^-$, is so bulky that it cannot form a bond to carbon in a nucleophilic substitution but can easily abstract a proton. Thus it is a good base but a poor nucleophile. Lithium diisopropylamide $Li^+ \; ^-N(CH(CH_3)_2)_2$ is another non-nucleophilic base owing to its bulky isopropyl groups. Other examples are shown in Data Table 10.3.

To complete this section we will comment on the choice of solvent for enolate formation. It is important at this stage to realise that as well as being able to dissolve the reactants, the solvent should have a pK_a higher than that of the enolate precursor. There is no point in using a base like LDA to pull a proton off acetonitrile (CH_3CN) if the solvent is ethanol. A consideration of the pK_a values for Equations 2.13 and 2.14 shows that ethoxide ion is formed in preference to $^-CH_2CN$:

$$CH_3CN + H_2O \rightleftharpoons {}^-CH_2CN + H_3O^+ \quad pK_a = 25 \tag{2.13}$$

that is, the Equilibrium 2.14 lies to the left

$$CH_3CH_2O^- + CH_3CN \rightleftharpoons CH_3CH_2OH + {}^-CH_2CN \tag{2.14}$$

In this instance, diethyl ether or tetrahydrofuran would be the preferred solvent.

2.3.3 Alternatives to proton abstraction

Enolate ions can be formed by a number of methods other than proton abstraction, such as the lithium ammonia reduction of α,β-unsaturated ketones, for example **2.25**,

The lithium reduces **2.25** to the dianion **2.26**, which removes a proton from ammonia to give the enolate **2.27**. You may encounter a similar strategy of enolate formation, based on the conjugate addition of organometallics to α,β-unsaturated ketones. Another *very* important method of generating enolate ions is by the cleavage of an enol ether derivative which can be shown schematically as:

Let's examine some examples of these reactions in detail.

- What is the product of reaction between excess methyl lithium and an ester such as ethyl ethanoate?

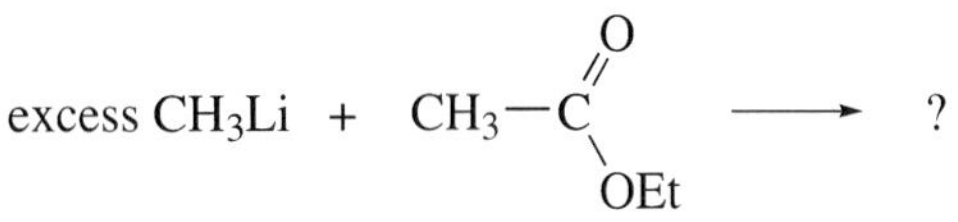

$$\text{excess } CH_3Li \quad + \quad CH_3-C\overset{O}{\underset{OEt}{\diagdown}} \quad \longrightarrow \quad ?$$

☐ In the Level 2 module you may have learnt that the methyl anion from methyl lithium first reacts with ethyl ethanoate via a substitution reaction to give a ketone and an alkoxide ion (Equation 2.15). The ketone then reacts further with more methyl lithium (Equation 2.16)

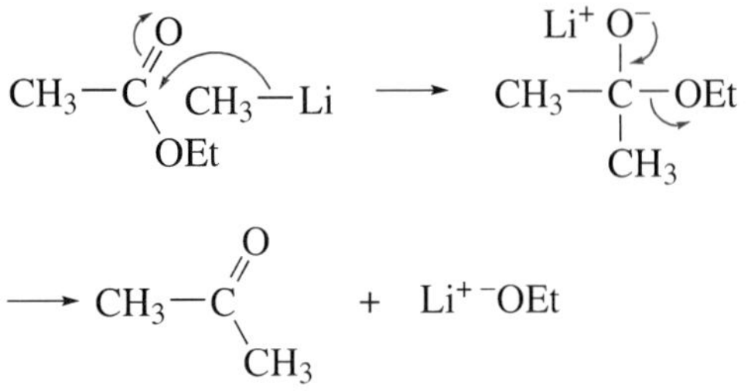

$$CH_3-C\overset{O}{\underset{OEt}{\diagdown}} \quad CH_3-Li \quad \longrightarrow \quad CH_3-\overset{Li^+ O^-}{\underset{CH_3}{\overset{|}{C}}}-OEt$$

$$\longrightarrow \quad CH_3-C\overset{O}{\underset{CH_3}{\diagdown}} \quad + \quad Li^+ \; {}^-OEt \qquad (2.15)$$

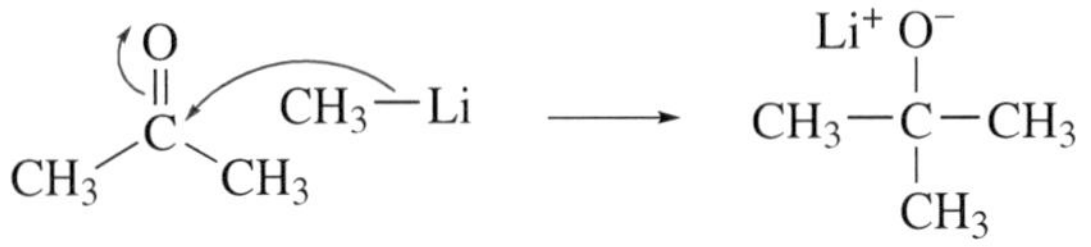

$$\underset{CH_3}{\overset{}{\diagup}}\overset{O}{\underset{\diagdown CH_3}{C}} \quad CH_3-Li \quad \longrightarrow \quad CH_3-\overset{Li^+ O^-}{\underset{CH_3}{\overset{|}{C}}}-CH_3 \qquad (2.16)$$

■ If the ester were an enol ethanoate, such as **2.28**, what would be the product of the reaction with excess methyl lithium?

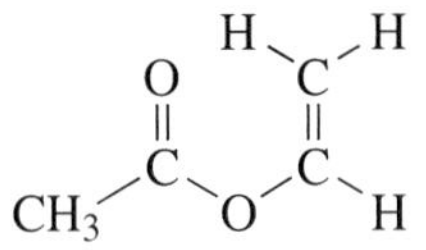

$$CH_3\overset{}{\underset{O}{\diagup}}\overset{O}{\underset{}{C}}\overset{H\diagdown C \diagup H}{\underset{O}{\diagup}}\overset{}{\underset{H}{C}}$$

2.28

☐ As well as the eventual product $(CH_3)_3CO^-$, the enolate ion **2.24** would be formed in the first step. Thus, the reaction between methyl lithium and enol ethanoates provides another route to enolate ions.

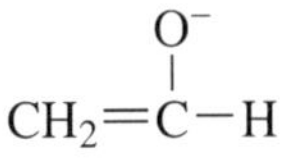

Nucleophilic substitution occurs more readily at silicon than it does at carbon, so although carbon ethers rarely undergo substitution, silicon ethers often do:

$$Nu^- \quad -\overset{|}{\underset{|}{Si}}-O-R \quad \longrightarrow \quad Nu-\overset{|}{\underset{|}{Si}}- \quad + \quad {}^-OR$$

$$\overset{O^-}{\underset{}{\overset{|}{CH_2=C-H}}}$$

2.24

This then provides us with another route to enolate ions:

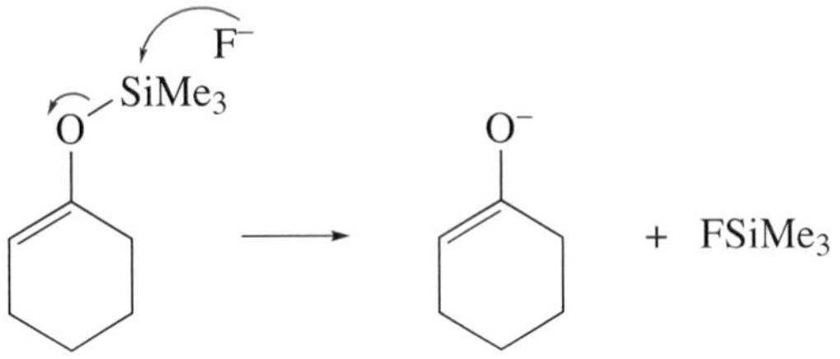

$$(2.17)$$

... $+ \; FSiMe_3$ ...

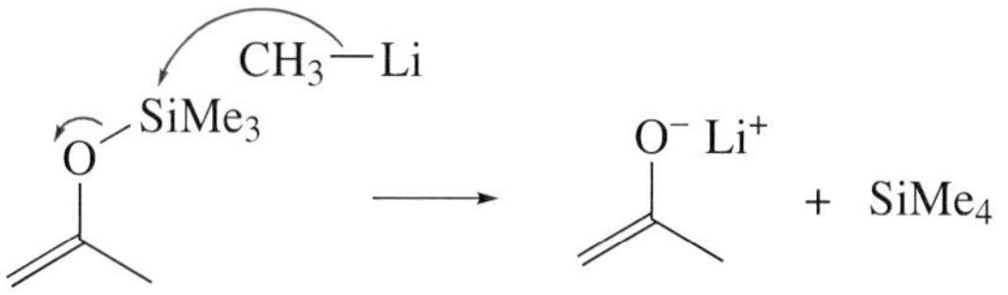

$$\text{(2.18)}$$

Of the enol ether derivatives, silyl enol ethers are more commonly used for enolate formation, particularly with fluoride ion. The silicon–fluorine bond is one of the strongest known bonds and thus provides the driving force for substitutions such as that in Equation 2.17. Such substitutions often have to be carried out in organic solvents and special reagents such as **2.29** and **2.30** have been developed which solubilise the fluoride ion in non-polar media.

$$(C_4H_9)_4N^+ \ F^- \qquad\qquad [(C_2H_5)_2N]_3S^+ \ F^-$$

tetrabutylammonium fluoride

tris(diethylamino) sulfonium fluoride

2.29

2.30

Study note

Before moving on to the next section, you should produce your own summary of Section 2.3 and then compare it with ours. Go to Unit 6 summaries in Unit 6 resources.

2.4   Selectivity in enolate formation

2.4.1   Regioselectivity

The regioselectivity of enolate formation for many compounds becomes clear when the stability of the possible enolates is examined. For example, in Equation 2.19, **2.31** will predominate because the carbanion is stabilised by resonance with both carbonyls.

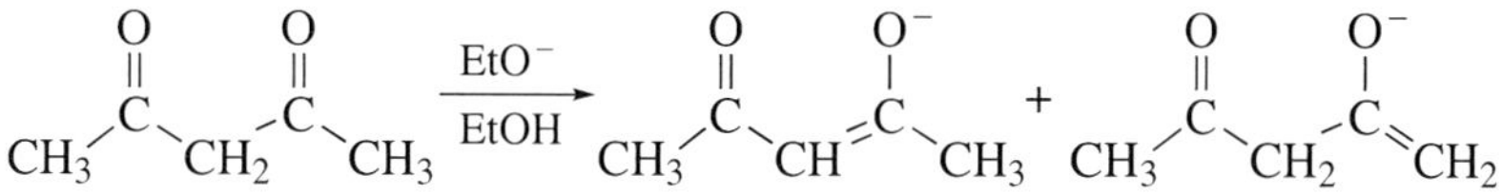

$$\text{(2.19)}$$

2.31 **2.32**

However, it isn't always as simple as this; an unsymmetrical dialkyl ketone can form different enolates on deprotonation, depending on which proton is abstracted, and it is not obvious which one will predominate:

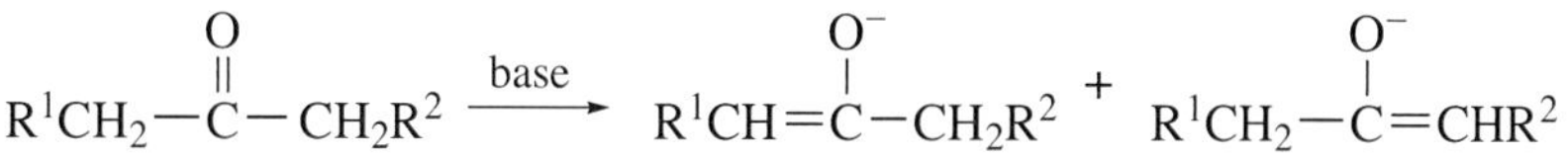

In order to exploit fully the synthetic potential of enolates it is necessary to be able to control the regioselectivity of their formation. One possibility is to generate the enolate ions as described. For example, by choosing the appropriate α,β-unsaturated ketone, we can define which enolate ion is formed in the lithium ammonia reduction:

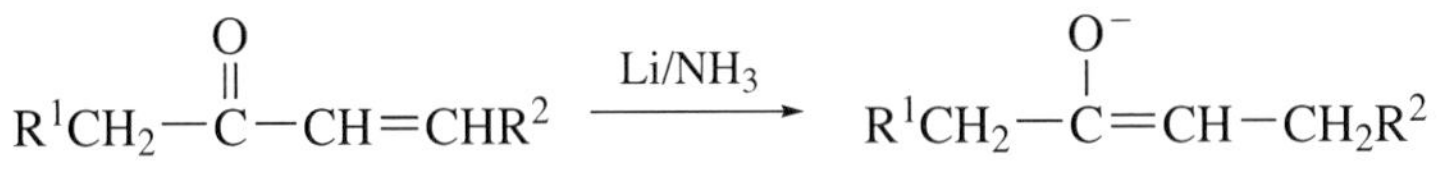

$$R^1CH_2-\overset{\overset{\displaystyle O}{\|}}{C}-CH=CHR^2 \xrightarrow{\text{Li/NH}_3} R^1CH_2-\overset{\overset{\displaystyle O^-}{|}}{C}=CH-CH_2R^2$$

Similarly, the enolate ion produced by desilylation depends on which silyl enol ether is used as the reactant:

$$R^1CH=\overset{\overset{\displaystyle O^{\nearrow SiMe_3}}{|}}{C}-CH_2R^2 \xrightarrow{F^-} R^1CH=\overset{\overset{\displaystyle O^-}{|}}{C}-CH_2R^2$$

The drawback with this approach is that the enol ether derivatives are usually prepared from the corresponding, enolate ion in the first place (Scheme 2.1).

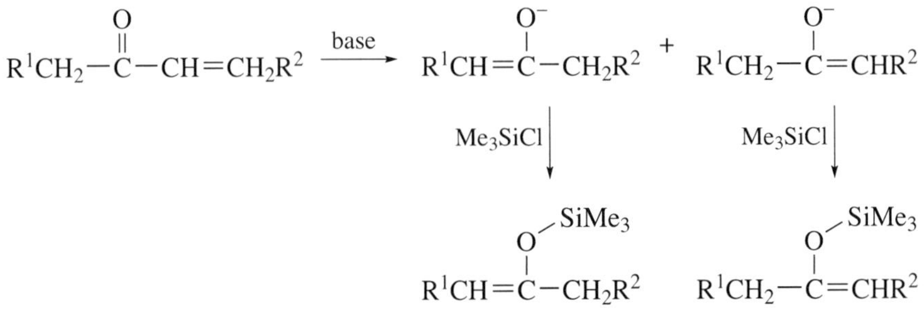

$$R^1CH_2-\overset{\overset{\displaystyle O}{\|}}{C}-CH=CH_2R^2 \xrightarrow{\text{base}} R^1CH=\overset{\overset{\displaystyle O^-}{|}}{C}-CH_2R^2 \ + \ R^1CH_2-\overset{\overset{\displaystyle O^-}{|}}{C}=CHR^2$$

Me₃SiCl ↓   Me₃SiCl ↓

$$R^1CH=\overset{\overset{\displaystyle O^{\nearrow SiMe_3}}{|}}{C}-CH_2R^2 \qquad R^1CH_2-\overset{\overset{\displaystyle O^{\nearrow SiMe_3}}{|}}{C}=CHR^2$$

mixture of regioisomers

Scheme 2.1

Because they are stable entities, a mixture of silyl enol ether derivatives can be separated by distillation or chromatography to give only one regioisomer. However, the preferential formation of the desired regioisomer is still the ultimate goal. Although in most cases it is not possible to direct deprotonation such that one regioisomer is formed exclusively, the experimental conditions can be arranged such that one is present in reasonable excess. It is this topic – how and why the reaction conditions affect the regiochemistry of deprotonation which concerns us in this section. We start by examining the process of enolate formation in a little more detail, using the following general reactions:

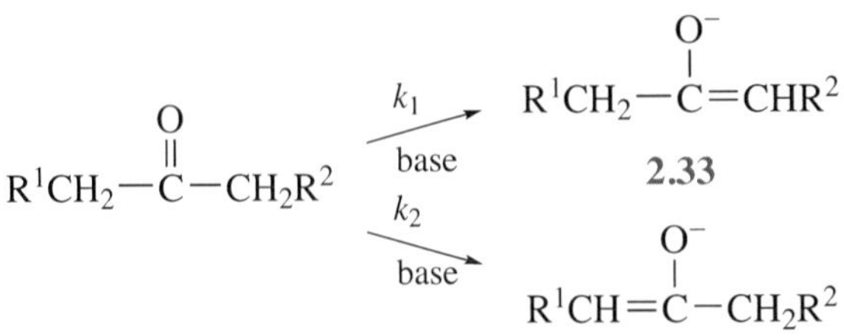

$$R^1CH_2-\overset{\overset{\displaystyle O}{\|}}{C}-CH_2R^2 \ \overset{k_1}{\underset{\text{base}}{\nearrow}} \ R^1CH_2-\overset{\overset{\displaystyle O^-}{|}}{C}=CHR^2$$

2.33

$$\overset{k_2}{\underset{\text{base}}{\searrow}} \ R^1CH=\overset{\overset{\displaystyle O^-}{|}}{C}-CH_2R^2$$

2.34

■ Enolate formation can be achieved under either kinetic control or thermodynamic control. What parameters will dictate the distribution of regioisomers under (i) kinetic control, (ii) thermodynamic control?

□ (i) If the distribution of regioisomers is under kinetic control, it is the relative rates of formation of **2.33** and **2.34** that dictate the product ratio; that is, the sizes of k_1 and k_2. (ii) If the reaction is under thermodynamic control, the distribution of isomers will depend on the relative stabilities of **2.33** and **2.34**. In essence, it is speed versus stability.

Remember, kinetic and thermodynamic control do not necessarily lead to the same distribution of regioisomers – as we saw in Unit 3, the most stable species is not always formed the fastest. In fact, with enolate ion formation from an unsymmetrical ketone, the distribution of regioisomers is reversed on going from kinetic control to thermodynamic control.

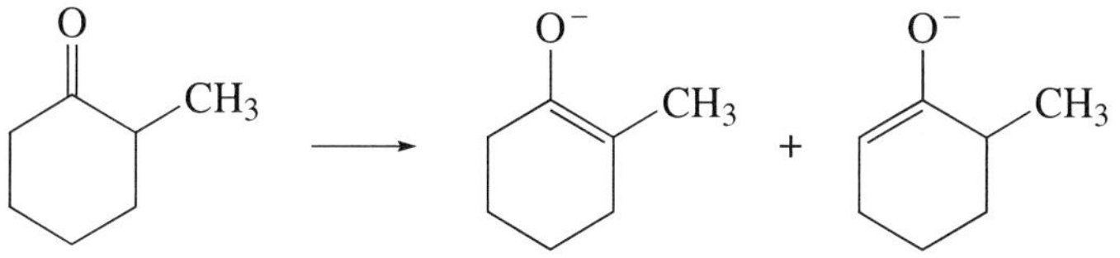

2.35

kinetic control	1%	99%
thermodynamic control	78%	22%

We can generalise that *kinetic control usually leads to the less substituted enolate*.

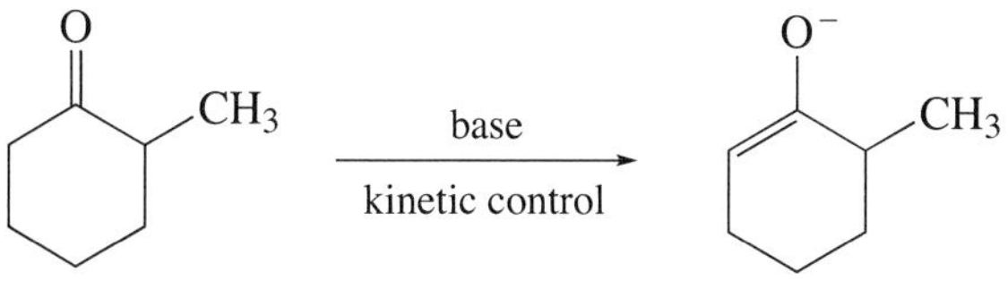

2.35

The principal reason for this is that removal of the less hindered proton is easier and therefore faster than removal of the more hindered proton. In **2.35** the base has easy access to the α-proton of the CH_2 group on the left of the carbonyl, but access to the α-proton on the right is hindered by the CH_3 substituent.

On the other hand, *under thermodynamic control it is the more substituted enolate that is usually the dominant species*. To understand why this is so, we must examine how the position of the substituent affects the stability of the resonance forms of the two possible enolates.

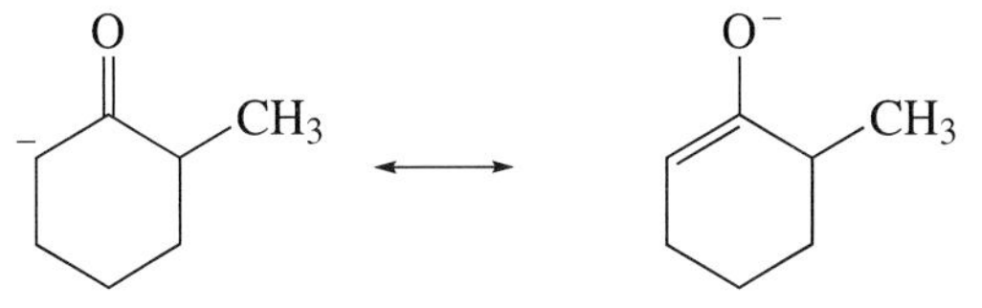

2.36   **2.37**
                            less substituted enolate

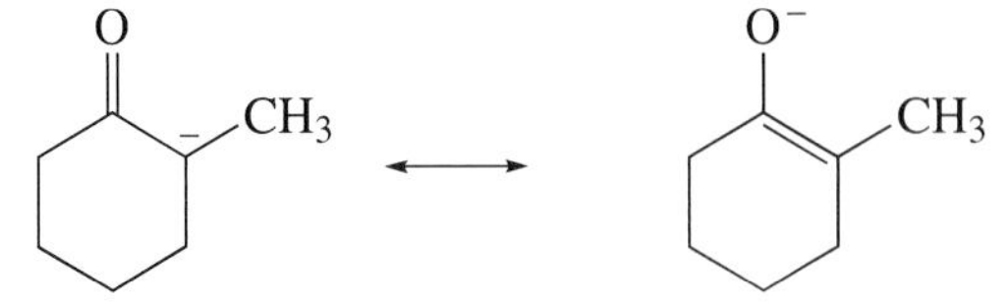

2.38   **2.39**
                            more substituted enolate

Methyl groups donate electrons by the inductive effect, hence the resonance form **2.38** will be destabilised relative to **2.36** because the charge on the carbanion becomes more concentrated. In contrast, **2.39** is stabilised relative to **2.37** because the stability of double bonds increases with increasing substitution.

It is apparent that this latter factor dominates so that at equilibrium the more substituted enolate **2.40** is favoured over **2.41**. This probably reflects the greater contribution made to the overall structure by resonance forms such as **2.37** and **2.39**, where the negative charge resides on the electronegative oxygen.

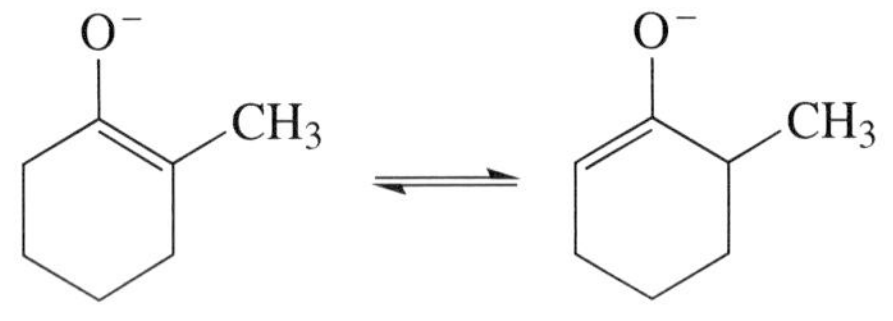

2.40   **2.41**

2.4.2   Conditions for kinetic control and thermodynamic control

Having shown that we can govern the distribution of regioisomers by performing the reaction under kinetic or thermodynamic control, the next question is:

What conditions favour kinetic control and what conditions favour thermodynamic control?

The ideal conditions for kinetic control of enolate formation are those in which deprotonation is rapid, quantitative and essentially irreversible. A rapid and quantitative removal of a proton can be achieved by using a very strong base such as lithium di-isopropylamide or triphenylmethyl-lithium ($Ph_3C^-Li^+$). To ensure the reaction is irreversible, we must use a solvent that has no acidic protons with which the enolate could react and thus equilibrate to the more stable form:

$$CH_2\!\!=\!\!\underset{\underset{CH_2CH_3}{|}}{\overset{O^-}{C}} + HS \rightleftharpoons CH_3\!\!-\!\!\underset{\underset{CH_2CH_3}{}}{\overset{O}{C}} + S^-$$

$$\rightleftharpoons CH_3\!\!-\!\!\underset{\underset{CHCH_3}{}}{\overset{O^-}{C}}\!\!=\!\! + HS \qquad\qquad (2.20)$$

HS = protic solvent

It is also important to ensure that no excess ketone is present as this also provides a route for equilibration:

$$CH_2\!\!=\!\!\underset{\underset{CH_2CH_3}{|}}{\overset{O^-}{C}} + CH_3\!\!-\!\!\underset{\underset{CH_2CH_3}{}}{\overset{O}{C}} \rightleftharpoons$$

$$CH_3\!\!-\!\!\underset{\underset{CH_2CH_3}{}}{\overset{O}{C}} + CH_3\!\!-\!\!\underset{\underset{CHCH_3}{}}{\overset{O^-}{C}}\!\!=\!\! \qquad\qquad (2.21)$$

For this reason, slow addition of the ketone to a solution of the base is preferable since this ensures that the ketone is never in excess.

The best solvents to use are aprotic solvents. You may have previously encountered protic solvents (in the Level 2 module) which contain relatively acidic atoms that enable the solvent to form hydrogen bonds. Aprotic solvents have no acidic hydrogen atoms and therefore cannot form hydrogen bonds. Examples of protic and aprotic solvents, in order of polarity, are given in Data Tables 10.4 and 10.5.

When choosing an aprotic solvent a number of factors must be considered. Obviously the solvent should be polar enough to dissolve the ionic species needed for reaction. However, the more polar aprotic solvents (such as acetone, dimethylformamide or dimethyl sulfoxide) do have protons that can be removed given a sufficiently strong base. So a compromise has to be achieved between using an aprotic solvent that is polar enough to dissolve the reactants, and a solvent that has a pK_a sufficiently different from that of the ketone generating the enolate, such that equilibration does not occur. This usually means using an ether, such as tetrahydrofuran (THF), or dimethoxyethane (DME).

A further way to ensure that equilibration is minimised is to carry out the reaction at low temperature since this will slow down the interconversion. Finally, it is better to use a base with lithium as the cation (better known as the counter-ion) rather than sodium or potassium. This is because, for reasons that we don't have time to go into now, bonds to lithium (either Li–O or

Li–C) are more covalent in character than those to sodium or potassium. Equilibration is particularly slow with lithium as the counter-ion.

So, to sum up, kinetic control can be achieved by:

1 Using a strong base, preferably with a lithium counter-ion, which quantitatively removes a proton.

2 Ensuring that, once formed, the enolate does not require low temperatures and a solvent that is aprotic, has a high pK_a and is sufficiently polar to dissolve the reactant.

3 Ensuring that the ketone is never in excess.

■ Now, under what conditions do you think *thermodynamic* control would operate?

☐ To obtain thermodynamic control, we should either use a solvent that promotes enolate equilibration or use an excess of ketone.

Examples of how the conditions can be controlled to achieve either thermodynamic or kinetic control are shown:

the effect of adding *excess ketone*:

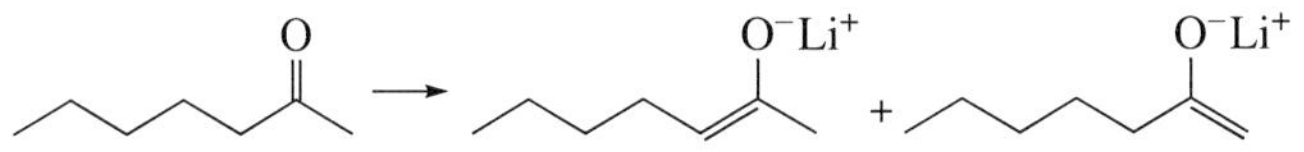

(2.22)

kinetic control	Ph₃CLi/DME	30%	70%
thermodynamic control	Ph₃CLi/DME (excess ketone)	87%	13%

the effect of using a *weak or a strong base*:

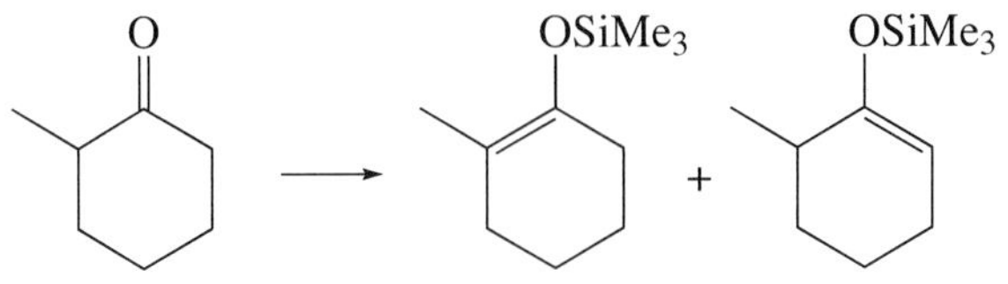

(2.23)

kinetic control	Me₃SiCl, (Me₂CH)₂NLi, DME	30%	70%
thermodynamic control	Me₃SiCl, Et₃N, DME	87%	13%

(In this instance, the enolate is silylated as it is formed.)

the effect of using a *lithium or potassium counter-ion*:

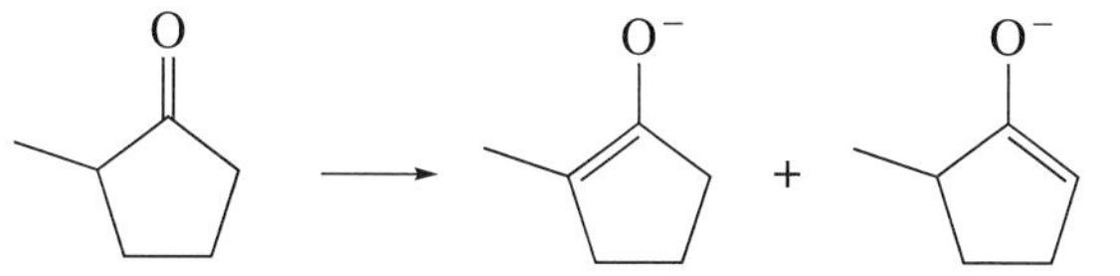

(2.24)

kinetic control	Ph$_3$CLi/DME	28%	72%
thermodynamic control	Ph$_3$CK/DME	55%	45%

Kinetic and thermodynamic effects also control which enolate is formed from deprotonation of α,β-unsaturated ketones:

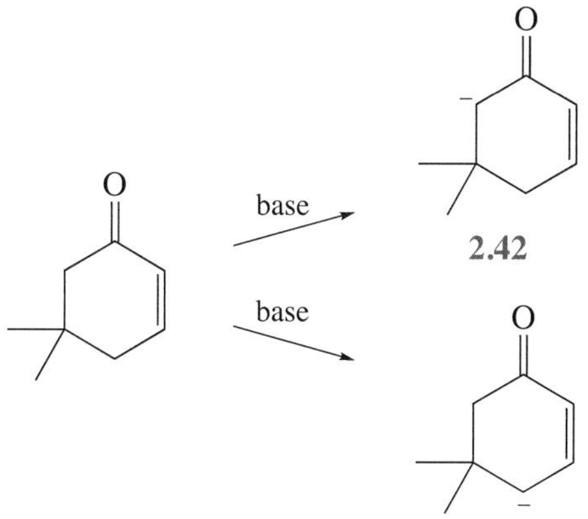

■ Which will be the more stable enolate ion, **2.42** or **2.43**?

□ The ion **2.43** has more resonance structures than **2.42** and is therefore the more stable enolate – there is a greater spreading of the charge. Hence γ-deprotonation will be the result of thermodynamic control.

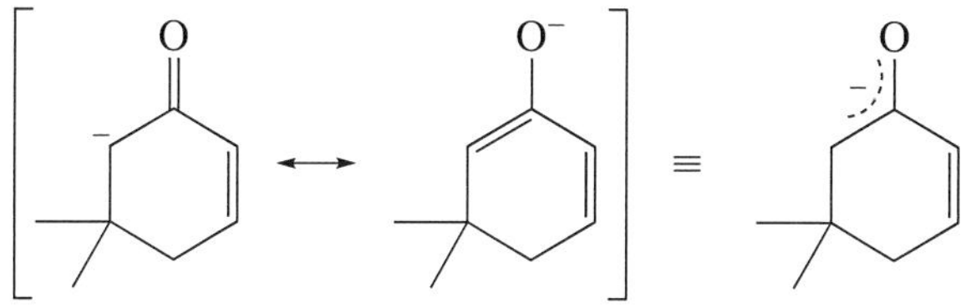

For reasons that we don't have time to consider here, under conditions of kinetic control, deprotonation occurs preferentially from the α-CH$_2$ group to **2.42**. So again we have the opportunity of controlling which enolate ion is formed by careful regulation of the reaction conditions.

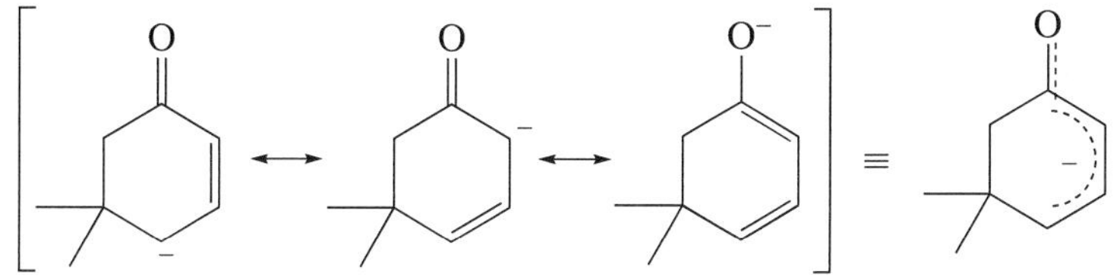

2.4.3   Stereoselectivity

Substituted enolates can have E or Z stereochemistry, but factors dictating which isomer predominates are not fully understood:

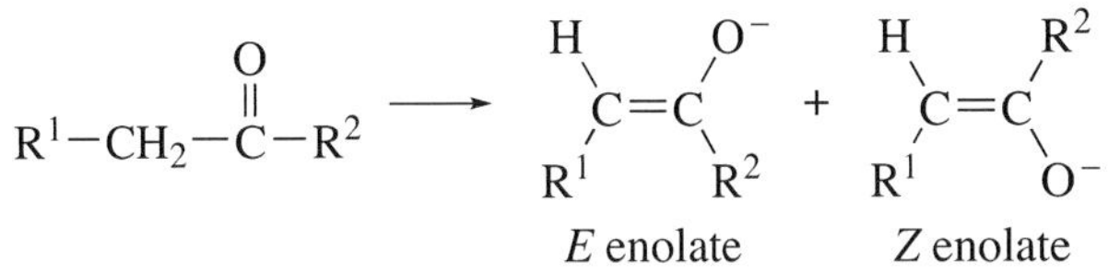

In general, the Z enolates are more stable because the R^1 group is only eclipsed by the oxygen atom whereas in the E enolates the R^1 group is eclipsed by the bulkier alkyl group R^2. Thus the Z form usually predominates under thermodynamic control, as shown in Equation 2.25.

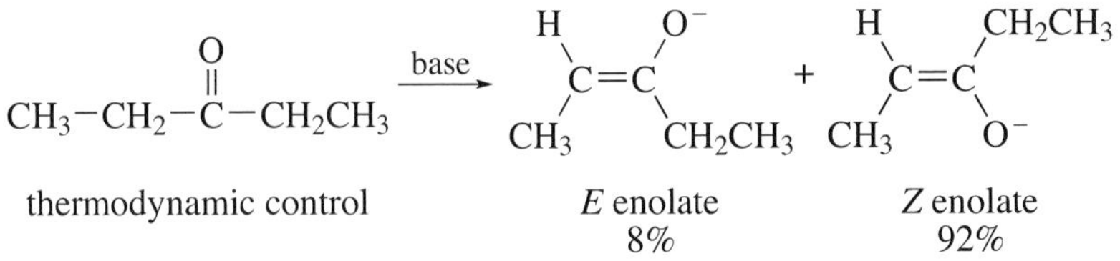

$$(2.25)$$

Kinetic control can lead to either the Z or the E enolate, depending on the alkyl groups R^1 and R^2, the nature of the base and the conditions. When R^2 is not particularly bulky, for instance an ethyl group, the E form is favoured, as shown in Equation 2.26. This is particularly true if a bulky base is employed.

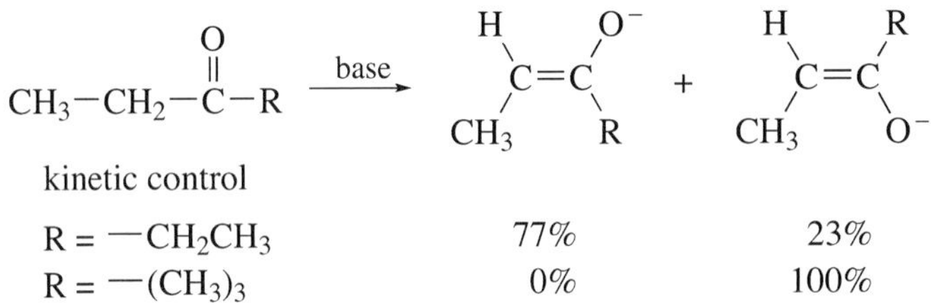

$$(2.26)$$

kinetic control

| R = $-CH_2CH_3$ | 77% | 23% |
| R = $-(CH_3)_3$ | 0% | 100% |

However, when R is large. for example t-butyl, the Z isomer is favoured, as shown in Equation 2.26. Although we don't have time to describe possible reasons for this, it is important that you recognise that reasonably stereochemically pure enolates can be prepared.

When a mixture of E and Z enolates occurs, trapping with chlorotrimethylsilane and separation by distillation or chromatography allows isolation of a stereoisomerically pure silyl enol ether (Scheme 2.2). Reaction of this with fluoride ions then generates the corresponding stereoisomerically pure E or Z enolate.

As with regioselective enolate formation, we must again ensure equilibration does not occur. Finally, it is worth noting that small-ring enolates such as **2.44** can only accommodate E stereochemistry, so in such cases only the E enolate is formed.

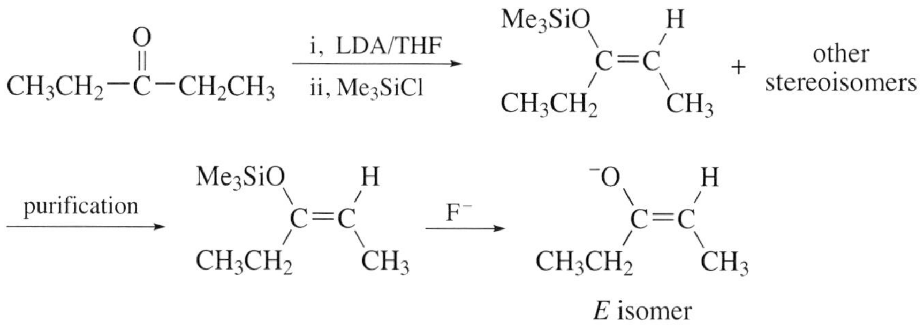

$$CH_3CH_2-\underset{\displaystyle \overset{O}{\|}}{C}-CH_2CH_3 \xrightarrow[\text{ii, Me}_3\text{SiCl}]{\text{i, LDA/THF}} \underset{CH_3CH_2}{\overset{Me_3SiO}{\diagdown}}C=C\underset{CH_3}{\overset{H}{\diagup}} + \begin{array}{l}\text{other}\\\text{stereoisomers}\end{array}$$

$$\xrightarrow{\text{purification}} \underset{CH_3CH_2}{\overset{Me_3SiO}{\diagdown}}C=C\underset{CH_3}{\overset{H}{\diagup}} \xrightarrow{F^-} \underset{CH_3CH_2}{\overset{{}^-O}{\diagdown}}C=C\underset{CH_3}{\overset{H}{\diagup}}$$

$$E \text{ isomer}$$

Scheme 2.2

$$\underset{}{\overset{O}{\bigcirc}} \xrightarrow{\text{base}} \overset{O^-}{\bigcirc}$$

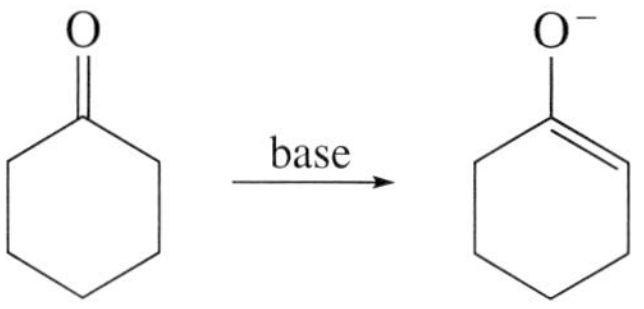

2.44

Study note

Before moving on to the next section, you should produce your own summary of Section 2.4 and then compare it with ours. Go to Unit 6 summaries in Unit 6 resources.

2.5   Reactivity and alkylation of enolates

It is the equilibrium between the keto and the enol form that makes carbonyl groups synthetically useful. This usefulness comes from the ease in which enols can be converted into their enolate anion upon treatment with a base. Deprotonation of enols is the key to their reactivity and is discussed in more detail in the following extract.

Activity 2.1

You should now read Sections 22.6 to 22.7 (pages 853–863) of *Organic Chemistry* by J. McMurry (2008). This extract (McMurry extract 1) has been provided as a PDF in the Unit 6 resources on the S346 website.

■   Which of the following two compounds A or B would you react with ethyl acetoacetate to prepare the target compound C?

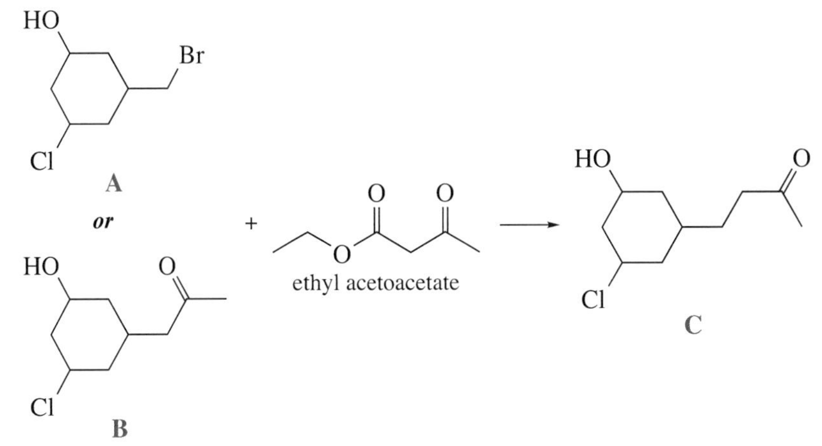

☐ You would chose the halide A to introduce the cyclohexyl ring since the carbonyl component of C would come from the ethyl acetoacetate. It adds a three-carbon chain containing the carbonyl group to the halide.

Using the appropriate combinations of carbonyl compound and alkyl halide allows the chemist to exploit the reactivity of enolates to make new carbon–carbon bonds. However there are additional features of enolates that need to be considered when planning a synthesis based on the reactions of the enolate and these are discussed in the next section.

2.6 Overcoming difficulties with the alkylation of enolates

2.6.1 The ambident nature of enolate ions

Enolate anions are **ambident nucleophiles**, that is, they contain two nucleophilic centres. They can act as oxygen nucleophiles, similar to alkoxides, as shown in Scheme 2.3, route A, or they can act as carbanions (Scheme 2.3, route B).

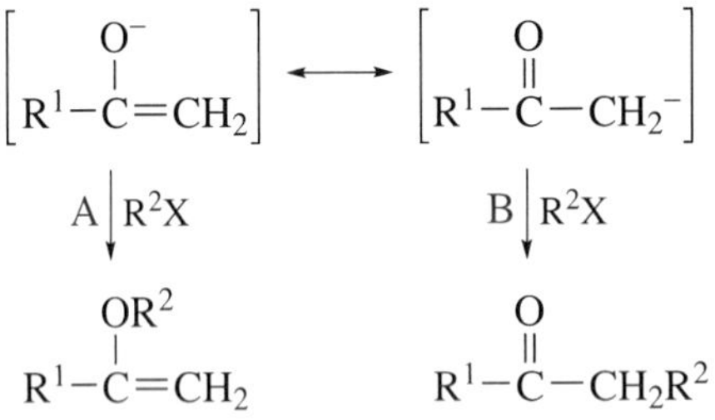

Scheme 2.3

Since oxygen is more electronegative than carbon, most of the negative charge in the enolate resides on the oxygen atom, so we might expect oxygen alkylation to dominate. However, a number of factors other than charge density can intervene so that it is possible to direct the alkylation of enolates towards the carbon centre.

First, we can vary the nature of the alkylating agent. For example, highly reactive alkylating reagents, such as $ROCH_2Cl$, α-haloketones, chlorotrialkylsilanes and acid chlorides, generally lead to reaction at the oxygen. As discussed earlier, this is important for the synthesis of enol ether derivatives.

$$R^1CH=\overset{\overset{\displaystyle O^-}{|}}{C}-H \;+\; CH_3-\overset{\overset{\displaystyle O}{||}}{C}-Cl \;\longrightarrow\; R^1CH=\overset{\overset{\displaystyle OCOCH_3}{|}}{C}-H$$

$$R^1CH=\overset{\overset{\displaystyle O^-}{|}}{C}-H \;+\; R_3SiCl \;\longrightarrow\; R^1CH=\overset{\overset{\displaystyle OSiR_3}{|}}{C}-H$$

Secondary alkyl halides are also more likely to lead to oxygen alkylation than primary alkyl halides. However, for a particular synthesis the alkyl chain to be used is often predetermined by the required product, so we have little flexibility with respect to this part of the alkylating agent. Nevertheless, we *can* vary the leaving group. For example, a higher level of carbon alkylation is observed with alkyl halides than with alkyl *p*-toluenesulfonates with the highest ratio of carbon alkylation to oxygen alkylation occurring with alkyl iodides, as shown in Equation 2.27. So, by appropriate choice of leaving group on the alkylating agent we can ensure that either oxygen or carbon alkylation predominates.

$$CH_3\overset{\overset{\displaystyle O^-K^+}{|}}{C}=CHCO_2Et \;+\; CH_3CH_2X \;\longrightarrow$$

$$CH_3\overset{\overset{\displaystyle CH_3CH_2-O}{|}}{C}=CHCO_2Et \;+\; CH_3\overset{\overset{\displaystyle O}{||}}{C}-\underset{\underset{\displaystyle CH_2CH_3}{|}}{C}HCO_2Et \quad (2.27)$$

X = OTs	88%	11%
X = Cl	60%	32%
X = Br	39%	38%
X = I	13%	71%

Secondly, we can control the site of alkylation by varying the solvent. To understand how this control is achieved, we need to spend some time examining the solvation of ions.

When strong electrolytes such as sodium chloride are dissolved in water, the anions and cations are separated from each other such that each species has little influence on the reaction of the other. Each individual ion is surrounded by several water molecules, collectively called the solvent shell. These water molecules interact with, or solvate, the cations and anions in different ways. Since the O–H bond is polarised in the sense $^{\delta-}O-H^{\delta+}$, anions can be solvated by hydrogen bonding, as in **2.46**; cations, on the other hand, are stabilised by donor interactions – the non-bonding pairs of oxygen can be donated to the electron-deficient cation, as shown in **2.45**.

2.45   **2.46**   **2.47**

Aprotic solvents with a low polarity do not solvate ions very well, which accounts for the insolubility of most ionic compounds in solvents such as hexane and benzene. When ions do dissolve in relatively non-polar aprotic solvents, they tend to form ion pairs, for example **2.47**, as a result of electrostatic attraction. Because of this close association, any reaction of one ion will be influenced by the counter-ion.

As the polarity of the aprotic solvent increases, it can solvate and shield individual ions to some extent, so that the tendency to form ion pairs decreases. However, an important property of many of the more polar aprotic solvents, such as those given in Data Table 10.5, is that they solvate cations to a greater extent than anions. This is because they contain non-bonding pairs on oxygen or nitrogen that can be donated to the electron-deficient cation in much the same way that cations are stabilised by water. However, by definition, aprotic solvents cannot solvate the anion by hydrogen bonding – they have no acidic hydrogens. Consequently, in such solvents the cation is solvated, but the anion is more 'naked'.

We can now return to the problem of oxygen versus carbon alkylation of enolates. The more concentrated negative charge on oxygen means that ion pairing or solvation by hydrogen bonding will occur mainly at the oxygen rather than the carbon. In such circumstances the more coordinated oxygen atom will then be less available as a nucleophile and carbon may become the relatively more nucleophilic site. *Hence carbon alkylation will be increased by solvation of the enolate ion or ion pairing, whereas oxygen alkylation will be preferred when the enolate ion is more naked.*

■   How might this observation explain the following results obtained with the alkylating agent diethyl sulfate?

$$\underset{CH_3\overset{|}{C}=CHCO_2Et}{\overset{O^-Li^+}{}} \;+\; (CH_3CH_2O)_2SO_2 \longrightarrow$$

$$\underset{CH_3\overset{|}{C}=CHCO_2Et}{\overset{CH_3CH_2-O}{}} \;+\; \underset{\underset{CH_2CH_3}{|}}{\overset{O}{\overset{\|}{CH_3C-CHCO_2Et}}} \qquad (2.28)$$

in t-butanol	0%	94%
in THF	0%	94%
in HMPA	83%	15%

□ *tert*-butanol can act like water and solvate both the cation (by donating the non-bonding pair of oxygen) and the anion (by hydrogen bonding). So the oxygen of the enolate ion is heavily solvated and carbon alkylation predominates. THF contains an oxygen atom that could solvate the cation to some extent but, because of its relatively low polarity, appreciable ion pairing occurs. Again, complexing of the oxygen of the enolate leads to carbon alkylation. Finally, a more polar aprotic solvent such as HMPA can solvate a cation but not an anion. In this case the enolate is naked and thus oxygen alkylation predominates.

To sum up briefly, oxygen alkylation can be maximised by using an alkyl *p*-toluenesulfonate in a polar aprotic solvent, whereas carbon alkylation can be maximised by using an alkyl iodide in a relatively non-polar or hydrogen-bonding solvent.

2.6.2 Dialkylation

Continuing with our theme of the problems associated with alkylation, you may have noticed that none of the product distributions quoted in Equations 2.27 and 2.28 add up to 100%. The missing product is the dialkylated species, whose yield can sometimes be quite high – up to 23% with bromoethane in Equation 2.27. Obviously this can be a severe drawback if it consumes precious starting material.

The problem arises when an initial monoalkylated product, such as **2.50**, is also acidic and thus can form an enolate, **2.51**, which can react with a second molecule of alkyl halide to give the dialkylation product:

$$R^1-CH_2-\overset{\overset{\displaystyle O}{\|}}{C}-CH_3 \underset{}{\overset{base}{\rightleftharpoons}} R^1-\overset{-}{C}H-\overset{\overset{\displaystyle O}{\|}}{C}-CH_3 \overset{R^2X}{\longrightarrow} R^1-\underset{\underset{\displaystyle R^2}{|}}{C}H-\overset{\overset{\displaystyle O}{\|}}{C}-CH_3$$

| **2.48** | **2.49** | **2.50** |

$$\rightleftharpoons \quad R^1-\underset{\underset{\displaystyle R^2}{|}}{\overset{-}{C}}-\overset{\overset{\displaystyle O}{\|}}{C}-CH_3 \overset{R^2X}{\longrightarrow} R^1-\underset{\underset{\displaystyle R^2}{|}}{\overset{\overset{\displaystyle R^2}{|}}{C}}-\overset{\overset{\displaystyle O}{\|}}{C}-CH_3$$

2.51

In this case the extent of dialkylation often depends on the relative acidity of the starting material **2.48** and the monoalkylated product **2.50**, since this will determine how easily each of them forms enolate ions. At the beginning of the reaction, when not much monoalkylated product has been formed, the predominant enolate ion is **2.49**. However, towards the end of the reaction, when the concentration of starting material has decreased and that of the monoalkylated product has increased, the predominant enolate ion will be **2.51** and dialkylation starts to be a problem. One way of reducing the amount of dialkylation is to use a large excess of carbonyl starting material, as shown in Equation 2.29. This ensures that, at all times, the predominant enolate ion is **2.49** and alkyl halide is used up before the relative concentration of the monoalkylated products becomes high. However, this procedure is feasible only if the starting material is readily available and easily separated from the product!

$$CH_2(CO_2Et)_2 \; + \; C_6H_5CH_2Cl \; \underset{EtOH}{\overset{EtONa}{\rightleftharpoons}}$$

$$C_6H_5CH_2CH(CO_2Et)_2 \; + \; (C_6H_5CH_2)_2C(CO_2Et)_2 \quad (2.29)$$

molar ratio 1:1	57%	43%
molar ratio 2:1	85%	15%

■ Sometimes dialkylation is desired so what conditions could favour dialkylation?

□ An excess of alkyl halide should be used, greater than the 2:1 ratio nominally required for dialkylation. At least two equivalents of base will also be needed since an enolate needs to be formed twice.

Another technique for achieving monoalkylation is to pre-form the enolate **2.49** and carry out the reaction under conditions where equilibration does not occur, so that the enolate **2.51** arising from the monoalkylated product never gets a chance to form.

■ What conditions will prevent equilibration?

□ When we discussed kinetic control we learnt that equilibration is suppressed by using a strong base with a lithium counter-ion in an aprotic solvent at low temperatures. It is important to use only one molar equivalent of base, because if it is in excess there will be some base left after formation of **2.49**. Any excess base would react with the monoalkylated product to give some of the enolate ion **2.51**, and thus lead to dialkylation.

A frequently used combination for suppressing equilibration is LDA in THF at low temperature. Once the enolate ion has been formed, addition of one mole of alkyl halide gives a high yield of the monoalkylated product. Addition of one more mole of LDA and a different alkyl halide leads to a high yield of a product where two different alkyl groups have been introduced. An example of such a reaction sequence is shown in Scheme 2.4.

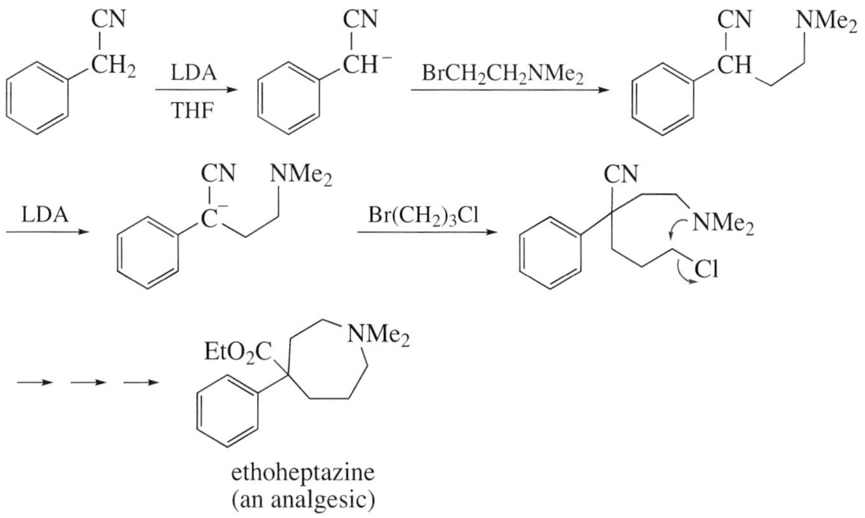

Scheme 2.4

2.6.3 Elimination versus substitution

Enolates can act as bases as well as nucleophiles, and with tertiary alkyl halides elimination predominates:

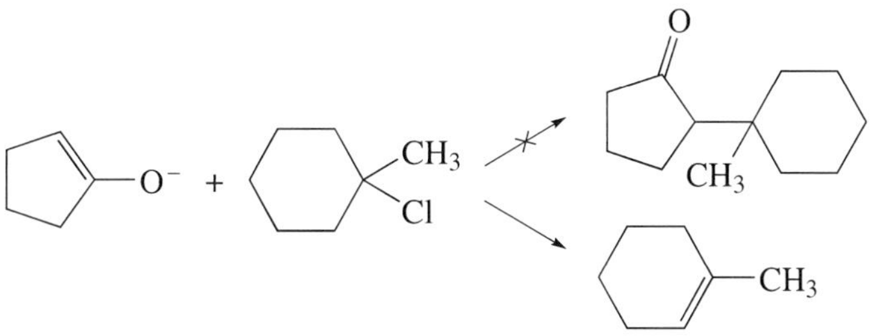

So how can we add a tertiary alkyl group alpha to a carbonyl? Such reactions can be achieved if, instead of the enolate, we use the less nucleophilic trimethylsilyl enol ether:

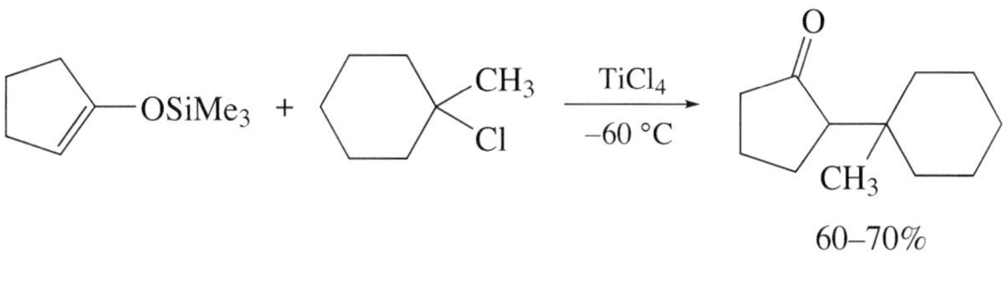

Because the enol is less reactive we need to activate the alkyl halide using a Lewis acid, thus promoting an S_N1 type process:

The carbonium ion is sufficiently electrophilic to react with the trimethylsilyl enol ether, which acts predominantly as a nucleophile:

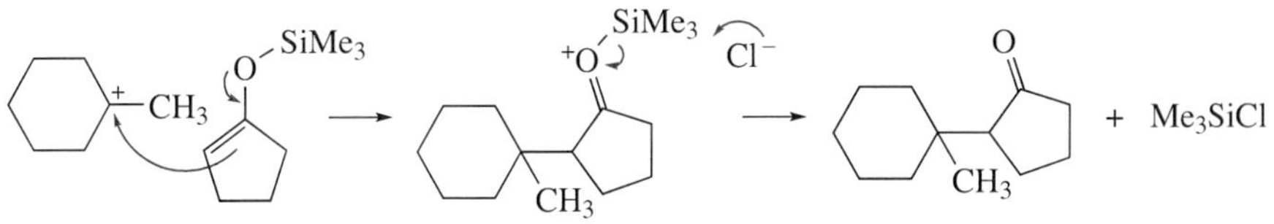

2.6.4   Self-condensation

One last problem of alkylation that we shall discuss is that of self-condensation – the reaction between an enolate and its carbonyl precursor. Just as nucleophiles undergo a nucleophilic substitution reaction with alkyl halides, they also react with carbonyl compounds to give either addition, **2.52**, or substitution, **2.53**, products.

$$Nu^- + RX \rightleftharpoons NuR + X^-$$

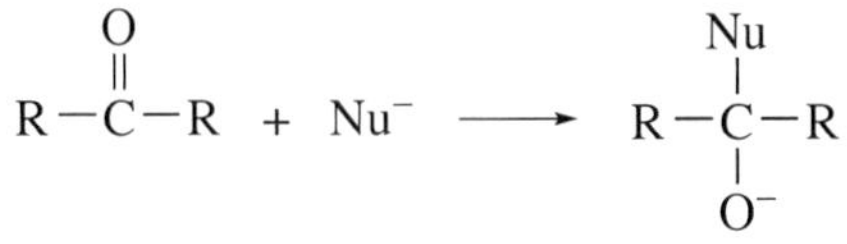

2.52

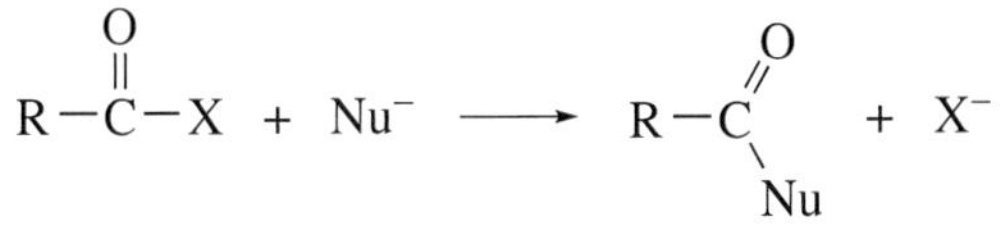

2.53

Enolates behave just like any other nucleophiles and react with carbonyl compounds in a wide range of reactions, which are extremely important in synthesis. We shall see examples of these in Units 7 and 8. Nevertheless, such reactions with carbonyl compounds do cause difficulties when the alkylation of enolates is carried out. The problem is that enolates are formed from carbonyl compounds and unless the equilibrium

$$B + CH_3-\overset{\overset{\displaystyle O}{\|}}{C}-CH_3 \rightleftharpoons CH_3-\overset{\overset{\displaystyle O}{\|}}{C}-CH_2^- + BH^+ \qquad (2.30)$$

lies well to the right, the concentration of carbonyl compound **2.54** may be sufficiently high for the carbonyl to compete with the alkyl halide as the electrophile:

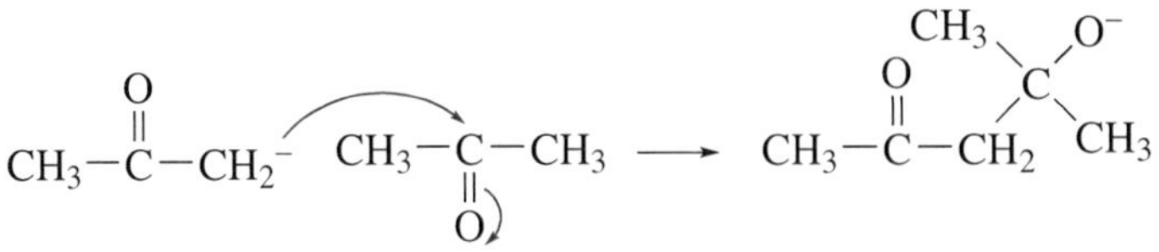

Thus, self-condensation between the enolate and the carbonyl compound can be an unwanted side reaction, which can consume a good deal of the reactant, especially if the carbonyl compound is an aldehyde.

■ One way to minimise self-condensation is to ensure that the concentration of carbonyl compound is low during the reaction. How can we achieve this?

□ Use of a strong base ensures that the equilibrium in Equation 2.30 lies well to the right and that little of the carbonyl compound remains.

It is also important that enolate formation occurs quickly. Even though the equilibrium lies to the right, a low rate of enolate formation would mean that appreciable concentrations of the enolate and carbonyl compound would be present at the same time, during enolate formation, and substantial self-condensation could occur. This can be avoided if the carbonyl compound is added slowly to the strong base, thereby ensuring that excess carbonyl is never present.

Finally, it should be emphasised that, despite the above discussion, it would be wrong to gain the impression that alkylation of enolates is fraught with problems! As we have seen, when problems do arise they can usually be overcome, and in general, alkylation has great synthetic utility.

2.6.5 Direct alkylation of propanone versus the acetoacetic ester synthesis

It might be asked: Why bother with a roundabout route like the acetoacetic ester synthesis when we could simply use propanone? A similar question could be raised about the malonic ester synthesis (Equation 2.31) which could be replaced using ethyl acetate (Equation 2.32).

$$\underset{\underset{CO_2Et}{\overset{CO_2Et}{|}}}{CH_2} \xrightarrow{\text{base}} \underset{\underset{CO_2Et}{\overset{CO_2Et}{|}}}{\overset{-}{CH}} \xrightarrow{RX} \underset{\underset{CO_2Et}{\overset{CO_2Et}{|}}}{R-CH} \xrightarrow{H_3O^+}$$

$$\underset{\underset{CO_2H}{\overset{CO_2H}{|}}}{R-CH} \xrightarrow{\text{heat}} RCH_2CO_2H \qquad (2.31)$$

$$CH_3CO_2Et \xrightarrow{\text{base}} \overset{-}{C}H_2CO_2Et \xrightarrow{RX} RCH_2CO_2Et \xrightarrow{H_3O^+} RCH_2CO_2H \quad (2.32)$$

The difficulty with using propanone or ethyl acetate is that to avoid self-condensation we need to use a strong base such as LDA, to ensure that the equilibrium lies well over to the side of the enolate and that little of the carbonyl precursor remains. LDA is fairly expensive and requires the use of special techniques to exclude water and oxygen. On the other hand, diethyl malonate and ethyl acetoacetate have much lower pK_a values, and sodium ethoxide is sufficiently basic to ensure almost complete enolate formation. Not only is sodium ethoxide less expensive, requiring no special techniques in its use, but also the less basic medium means that the alkyl halide is less likely to undergo side reactions such as elimination, which occur with LDA. Hence the malonic ester and acetoacetic ester acid syntheses are often preferable because the alkylation is more straightforward and, although they do involve a number of extra stages, these are generally high yielding.

Another reason why this indirect route is employed is because an ester group on an α-carbon is often used as an activating group to control the regioselectivity of alkylation. For example, to prepare the target molecule **2.56** we need to deprotonate the ketone **2.55** regioselectively, which may be difficult since both α-carbons are equally accessible. If instead of using the unsymmetrical ketone **2.55**, we use the keto ester **2.57**, only the more stable enolate **2.58** will be formed.

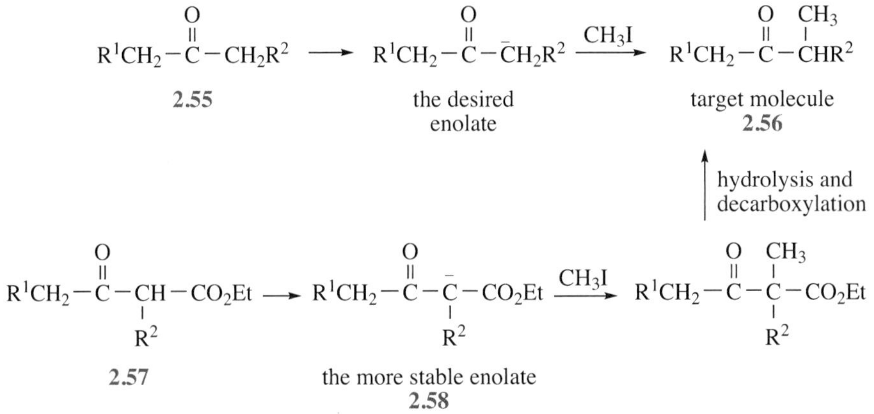

$$R^1CH_2-\overset{\overset{O}{\|}}{C}-CH_2R^2 \longrightarrow R^1CH_2-\overset{\overset{O}{\|}}{C}-\overset{-}{C}H_2R^2 \xrightarrow{CH_3I} R^1CH_2-\overset{\overset{O}{\|}}{C}-\overset{\overset{CH_3}{|}}{C}HR^2$$

$$\text{2.55} \qquad\qquad \text{the desired} \qquad\qquad \text{target molecule} \\ \text{enolate} \qquad\qquad\qquad \text{2.56}$$

hydrolysis and decarboxylation

$$R^1CH_2-\overset{\overset{O}{\|}}{C}-\underset{\underset{R^2}{|}}{C}H-CO_2Et \longrightarrow R^1CH_2-\overset{\overset{O}{\|}}{C}-\underset{\underset{R^2}{|}}{\overset{-}{C}}-CO_2Et \xrightarrow{CH_3I} R^1CH_2-\overset{\overset{O}{\|}}{C}-\underset{\underset{R^2}{|}}{\overset{\overset{CH_3}{|}}{C}}-CO_2Et$$

$$\text{2.57} \qquad\qquad \text{the more stable enolate} \\ \text{2.58}$$

Scheme 2.5

After reaction of the enolate, the ester group can be hydrolysed and then easily removed by decarboxylation. Clearly, by using this strategy, we have formed only one of the regioisomers that would have resulted from reaction of the unsymmetrical ketone.

To sum up: whenever we want to alkylate a carbonyl, consideration should be given to the use of the synthetic equivalent:

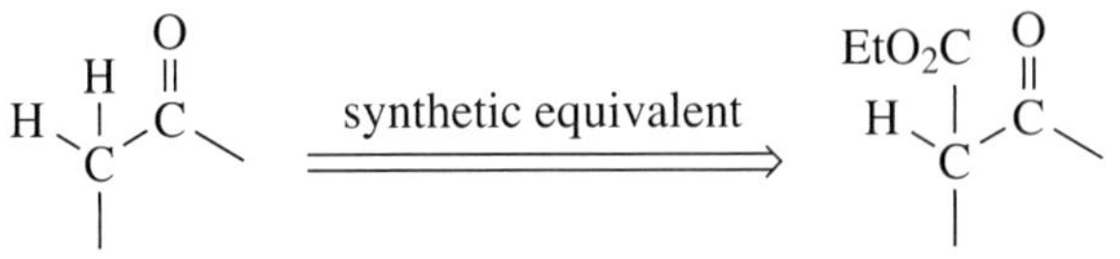

$$H\underset{\underset{|}{C}}{\overset{\overset{H}{|}}{\diagup}}\overset{\overset{O}{\|}}{C}\diagdown \qquad \xRightarrow{\text{synthetic equivalent}} \qquad H\underset{\underset{|}{C}}{\overset{\overset{EtO_2C}{\diagup}}{\diagup}}\overset{\overset{O}{\|}}{C}\diagdown$$

1   Synthesis: the aldol reaction

One of the most widely employed class of reactions used for building up the carbon framework of a new molecule involves the reaction between two carbonyl groups.

■   What do you think might happen if a base such as NaOH was added to acetaldehyde?

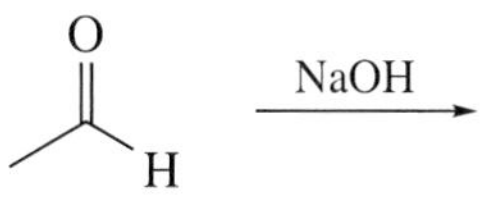

$$\text{(structure of acetaldehyde)} \xrightarrow{\text{NaOH}}$$

□   From your reading in Unit 6, you would expect that an enolate anion would be formed.

aldehyde ⇌ enolate

In fact the concentration of enolate formed is small and it rapidly reacts with an acetaldehyde in the keto form to produce 3-hydroxybutanal.

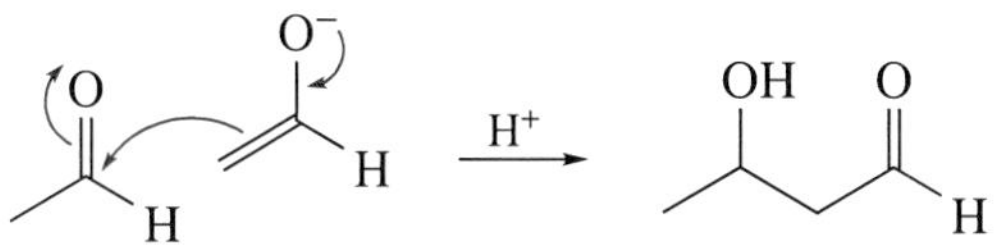

$$\xrightarrow{H^+}$$

3-hydroxybutanal

This is also known as 'aldol' since it contains both an hydroxy group and an aldehyde group and gives its name to a group of reactions of enols and enolates with aldehydes and ketones.

Activity 1.1

You should now read the second extract from *Organic Chemistry* by John McMurry (2008) (Chapter 23 up to the end of Section 23.12; pages 877–900) which explains the key principles of the aldol reaction. The extract, McMurry extract 2, can be found in Unit 7 resources.

1.1   Introduction

In this first section of Unit 7 we shall examine the aldol reaction in detail. We shall start by reviewing the mechanism of the base-catalysed aldol reaction and then examine an alternative way of carrying out the aldol reaction using acid catalysis. The final few subsections concentrate on the selectivity of the aldol reaction. We begin this aspect by discussing how the reversibility of the aldol reaction determines which products are formed. Then we describe ways of directing the aldol reaction, that is, ensuring that one carbonyl species acts as the nucleophile while the other acts as the electrophile. Finally, we spend some time looking at the stereoselectivity of the aldol reaction.

1.2   The base-catalysed aldol reaction

■   Write out the mechanism for the following aldol reaction:

$$2\ CH_3-\overset{\overset{\text{O}}{\|}}{C}-H \xrightarrow{\ EtO^-/EtOH\ } CH_3-CH=CH-CHO$$

□   First, an enolate ion is formed:

$$EtO^- \quad \overset{H}{\underset{CH_2}{|}}-\overset{\overset{O}{\|}}{C}-H \ \rightleftharpoons\ EtOH\ +\ \overset{\overset{O^-}{|}}{CH_2=C}-H$$

The nucleophilic enolate then attacks an electrophilic carbonyl group:

$$CH_3-\overset{\overset{O}{\|}}{C}-H \quad CH_2=\overset{\overset{O^-}{|}}{C}-H \ \rightleftharpoons\ CH_3-\overset{\overset{O^-}{|}}{\underset{H}{C}}-CH_2-\overset{\overset{O}{\|}}{C}-H$$

Protonation then gives the β-hydroxycarbonyl compound:

$$EtO-H \quad \overset{O^-}{|} \quad \overset{O}{\|} \\ CH_3-\overset{}{\underset{H}{C}}-CH_2-C-H \ \rightleftharpoons\ CH_3-\overset{\overset{OH}{|}}{\underset{H}{C}}-CH_2-\overset{\overset{O}{\|}}{C}-H\ +\ EtO^-$$

Depending on the conditions, either this product or the α,β-unsaturated compound can be obtained. Under slightly more vigorous conditions, such as a higher temperature, the β-hydroxycarbonyl compound loses water. This last step proceeds via an enolate ion, from which the hydroxide ion leaving group is expelled:

$$CH_3-\overset{\overset{OH}{|}}{\underset{\underset{EtO^-}{H}\ \underset{}{H}}{C}}-CH_2-\overset{\overset{O}{\|}}{C}-H \ \rightleftharpoons\ CH_3-\overset{\overset{OH}{|}}{\underset{H}{C}}-CH=\overset{\overset{O^-}{|}}{C}-H$$

$$\rightleftharpoons\ CH_3-CH=CH-\overset{\overset{O}{\|}}{C}-H\ +\ OH^-$$

Most alcohols are resistant to dehydration by dilute acid or base; however, if the hydroxy group is beta to a carbonyl, then water is readily lost.

Potentially, any aldehyde or ketone can act as the electrophilic carbonyl species in the aldol reaction, and the nucleophilic component can be formed from an aldehyde, ketone, ester, nitrile, sulfoxide or nitro compound.

One very important difference between the alkylation of enolates and the aldol reaction is that one equivalent of base is required for the alkylation reaction, whereas usually the aldol reaction requires only a catalytic amount of base; as the mechanism above shows, the alkoxide ion is regenerated. This means that, proportionally, a much smaller amount of base is employed in aldol reactions. Secondly, the alkylation of enolates often requires a strong base, such as LDA, to ensure quantitative enolate formation; this is necessary to prevent side reactions, such as the aldol reaction, from occurring. As this suggests, the aldol reaction does not require quantitative enolate formation. As shown above, weaker bases such as metal alkoxides can be employed and, even though only a small proportion of the enolate is formed at equilibrium, the reaction proceeds quite rapidly.

When choosing a solvent for an aldol reaction, we use similar criteria to those discussed for the alkylation of enolates. The solvent should be able to dissolve the reagents but it ought not to be more acidic than the conjugate acid of the base. For example, when an alkoxide is used as the base, the best solvent is usually the corresponding alcohol. However, as you will see later, a strong base such as LDA is sometimes necessary, in order to preform an enolate regioselectively or stereoselectively, and in these cases an aprotic solvent such as THF is employed.

1.3 · The acid-catalysed aldol reaction

As you have just seen, under basic conditions the reactive constituents of the aldol reaction correspond to a carbonyl compound and an enolate ion. However, such a transformation can also be carried out using acid catalysis.

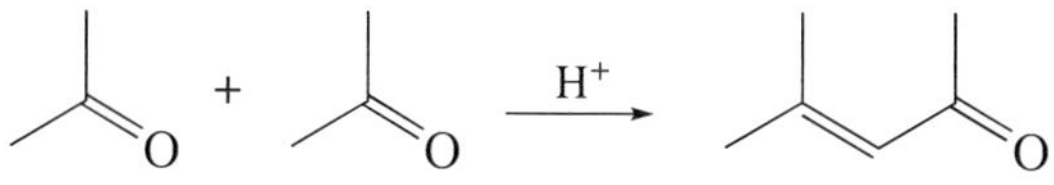

$$(1.1)$$

Under these conditions the electrophile is a protonated carbonyl compound, as is evident from the alternative resonance structure:

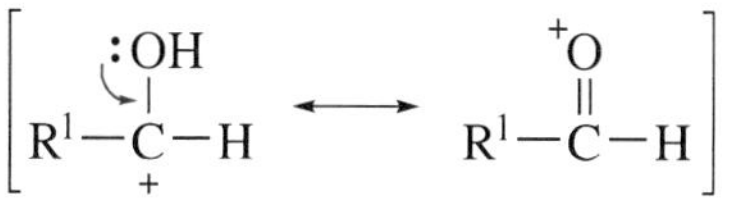

In acid, the nucleophile can be related to an enol. As you may remember from Unit 6 Section 2, enols are in tautomeric equilibrium with carbonyl compounds although they are generally only present as minor components. You also saw that they are nucleophilic and undergo reaction with electrophiles, such as bromine, at the α-carbon.

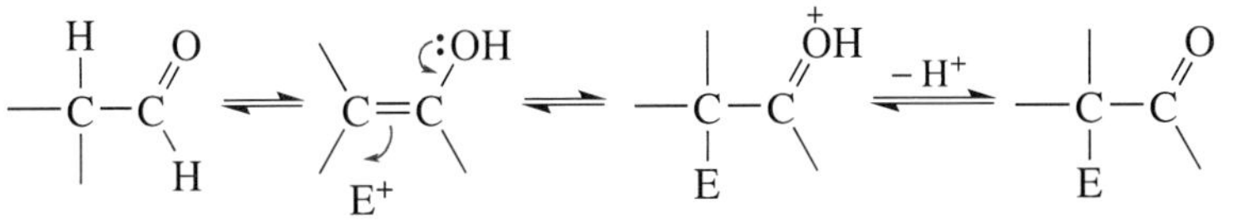

$$\tag{1.2}$$

If the electrophile is a carbonyl compound, we get an aldol-type reaction. However, because enols are not as nucleophilic as enolate ions, acid catalysis is required to enhance the electrophilicity of the carbonyl compound and thus encourage the reaction, as shown in Equation 1.3.

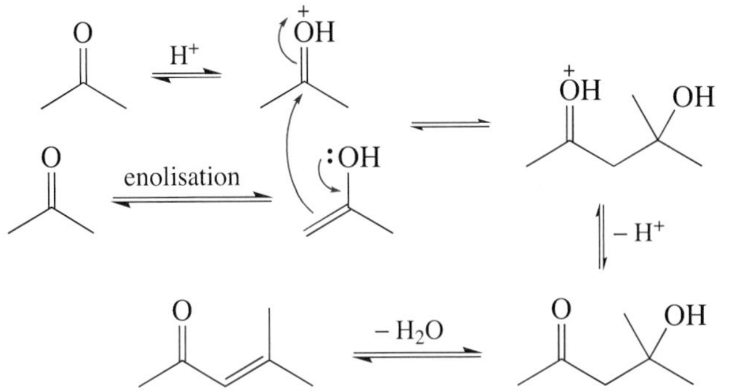

$$\tag{1.3}$$

Notice that the acid-catalysed aldol reaction proceeds via a β-hydroxycarbonyl compound, just like the base-catalysed process. In fact, retrosynthetic analysis for both processes is the same.

■ Have a go at writing out the mechanism, based on that in Equation 1.3, for the following acid-catalysed aldol condensation.

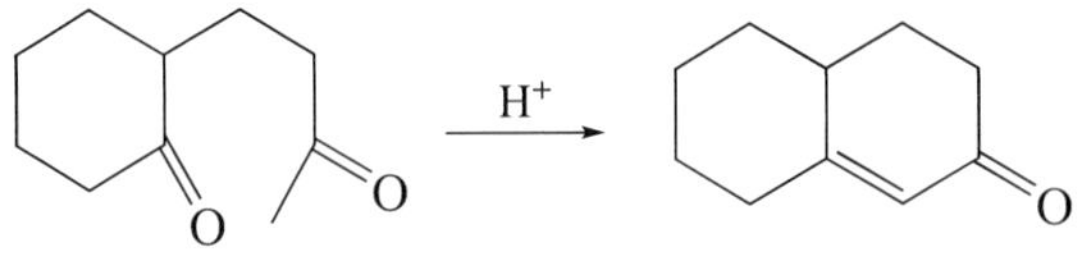

$$\tag{1.4}$$

1.1

☐ First we must identify the nucleophilic and electrophilic components. From the position of the carbon–carbon double bond that is formed in the products, the electrophilic carbonyl must be the left-hand carbonyl associated with the six-membered ring. Similarly, the enol is formed from the right-hand carbonyl. So the steps involved are as follows:

(a) Enolisation – creating the nucleophile:

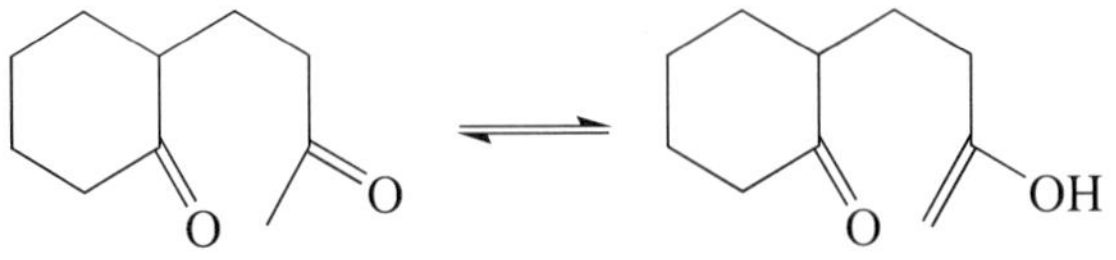

$$\tag{1.5}$$

(b) Protonation – activation of the electrophile:

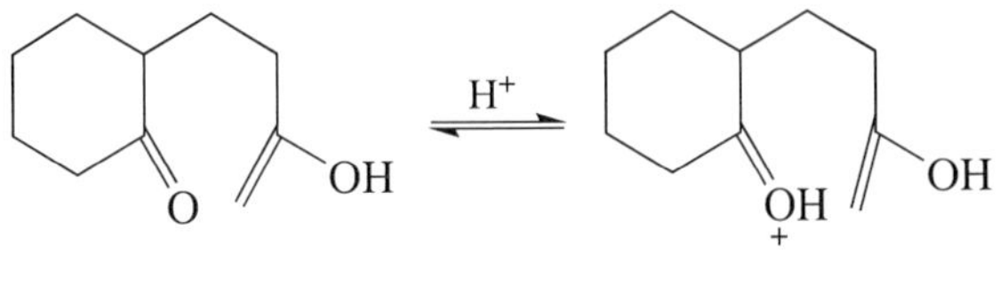

$$\tag{1.6}$$

(c) Nucleophilic addition:

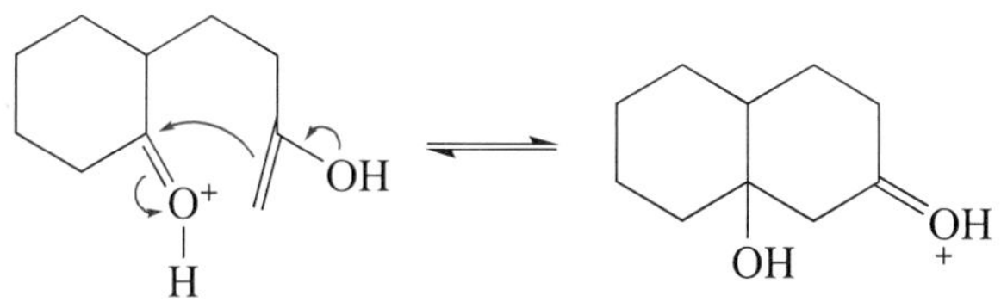

(1.7)

(d) Loss of H⁺:

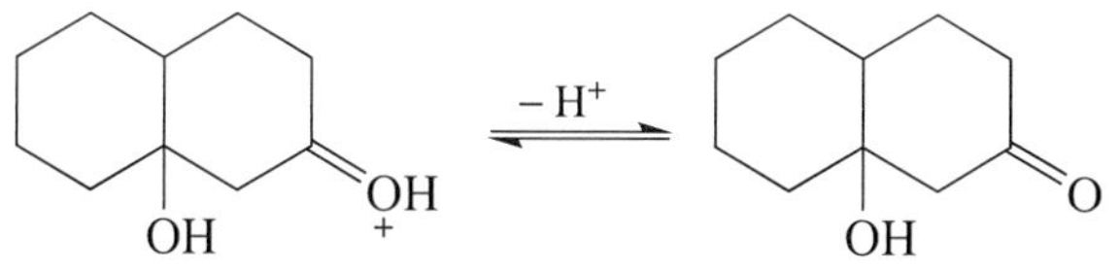

$- H^+$

(1.8)

(e) Loss of water: an enol is formed, the original hydroxyl group is protonated and water is expelled:

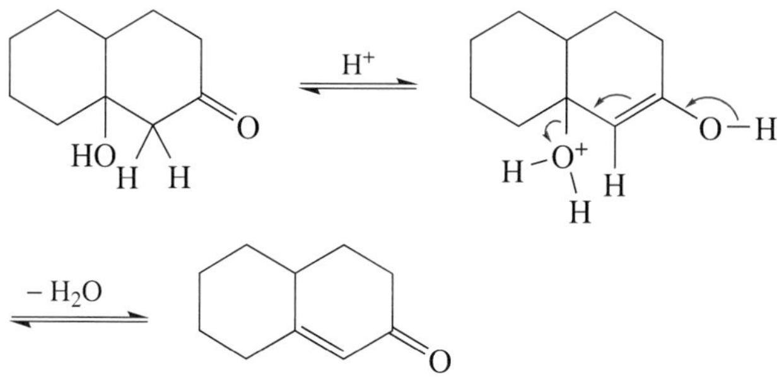

H^+

$- H_2O$

(1.9)

In fact the order of steps (a) and (b) is not important; they could be reversed.

Another way of performing an acid-promoted aldol condensation is to use a trimethylsilyl enol ether as the nucleophilic species. In this case a Lewis acid, such as titanium tetrachloride, rather than a protic acid is employed, but the various steps are essentially the same. The reaction is carried out in an aprotic solvent such as dichloromethane, usually at low temperature, and at the end of the reaction the mixture is hydrolyscd to give the required product. For example, look at the following aldol reaction:

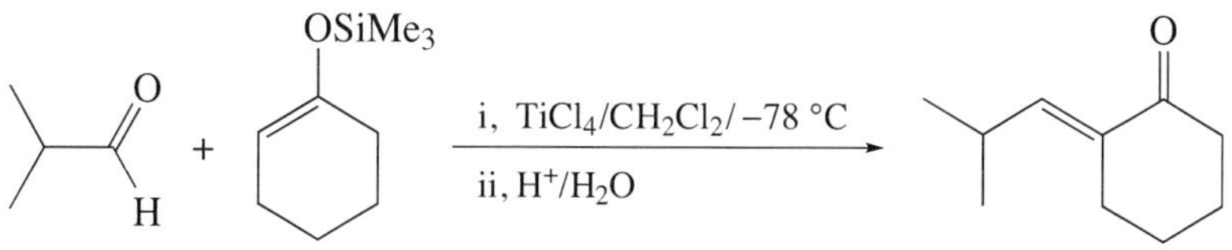

i, $TiCl_4/CH_2Cl_2/-78\ °C$

ii, H^+/H_2O

The mechanism is as follows:

(a) Activation of the electrophile by coordination of the aldehyde with the Lewis acid:

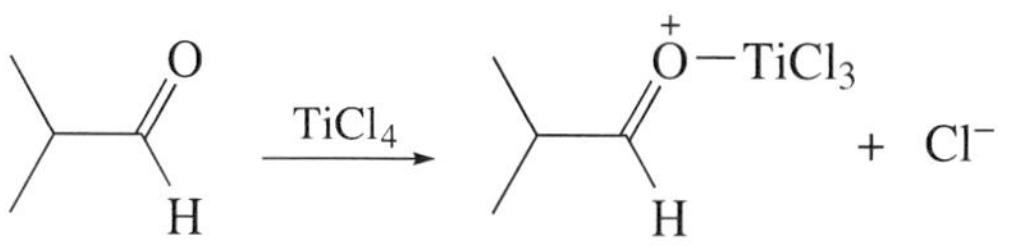

$TiCl_4$

$+ \ Cl^-$

(b) Nucleophilic addition – attack by the nucleophilic enol ether:

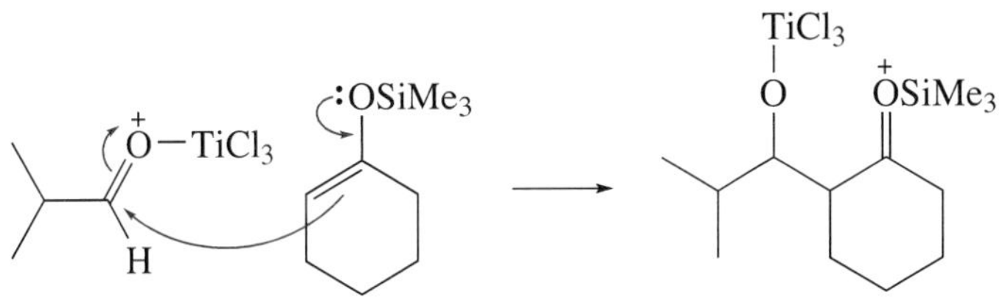

(c) Loss of the SiMe₃ group:

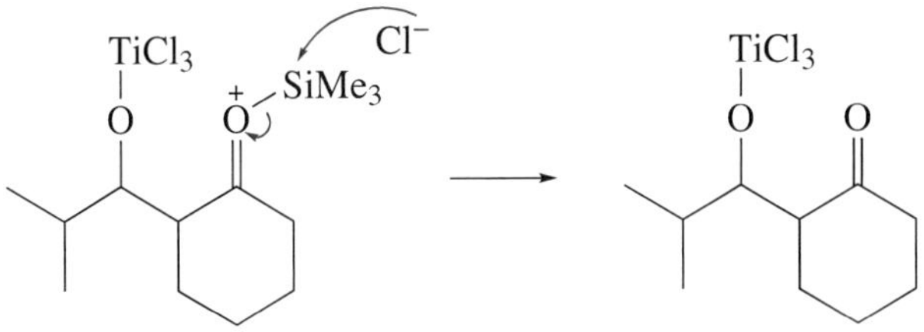

(d) Hydrolysis – formation of the β-hydroxycarbonyl intermediate:

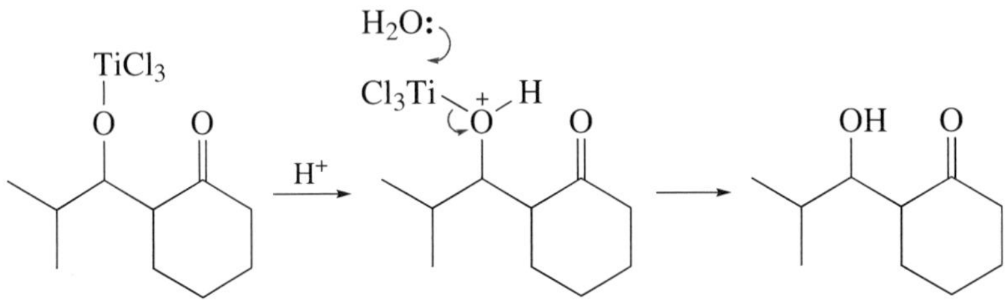

(e) Loss of water:

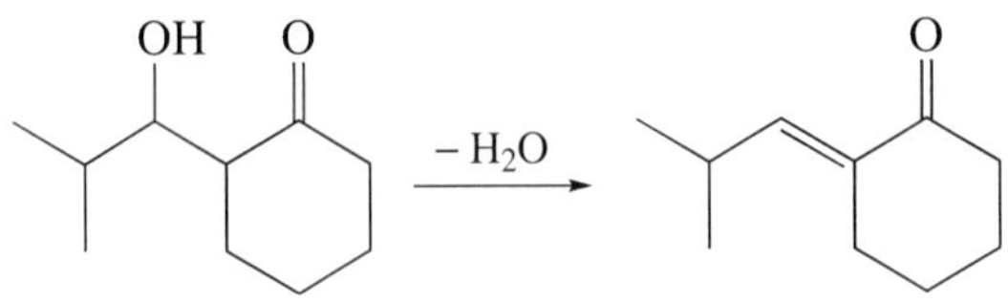

One final variation that is sometimes employed in this type of acid-promoted aldol reaction is to use acetals instead of aldehydes or ketones. This is because acetals can act only as electrophiles, and they coordinate with the Lewis acid more strongly than the parent carbonyl compound.

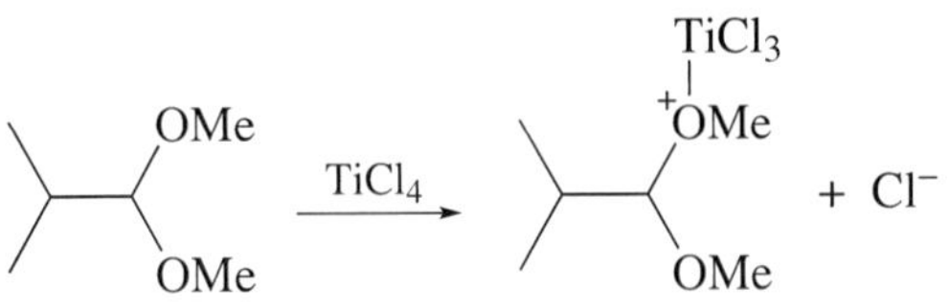

The Me–O–TiCl₃ group is a good leaving group, which can be substituted by the nucleophilic trimethylsilyl enol ether.

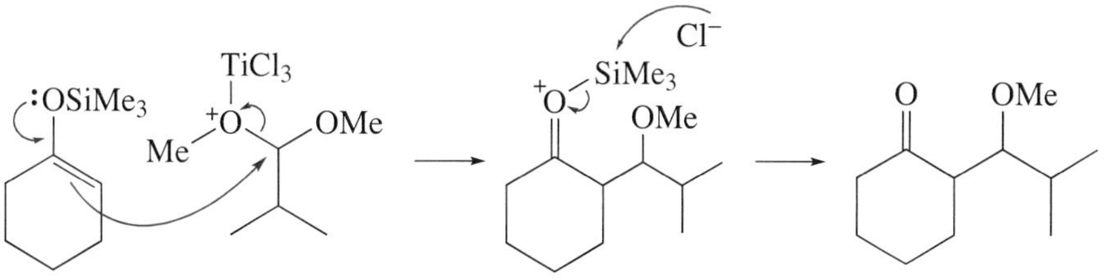

Notice that in this case the product is the ether, not the alcohol. This can be cleaved by hydrogen iodide to give the alcohol and then dehydrated to give the α,β-unsaturated carbonyl compound.

Study note

Before moving on to the next section you should produce your own summary of Sections 1.2 and 1.3 and then compare it with ours. Go to Unit 7 summaries in Unit 7 resources.

1.4   The reversibility of the aldol reaction

For the rest of this section we shall examine the selectivity of the aldol reaction. As we have discussed previously, the formation of the β-hydroxycarbonyl compound in the aldol reaction is readily reversible. The equilibrium generally favours the β-hydroxycarbonyl **1.2**, in the case of monosubstituted acetaldehydes (RCH_2CHO), but favours the starting materials for disubstituted acetaldehydes (R_2CHCHO) and for most acyclic ketones. Steric factors are probably responsible for these trends. This is generally true for both acid- and base-catalysed processes.

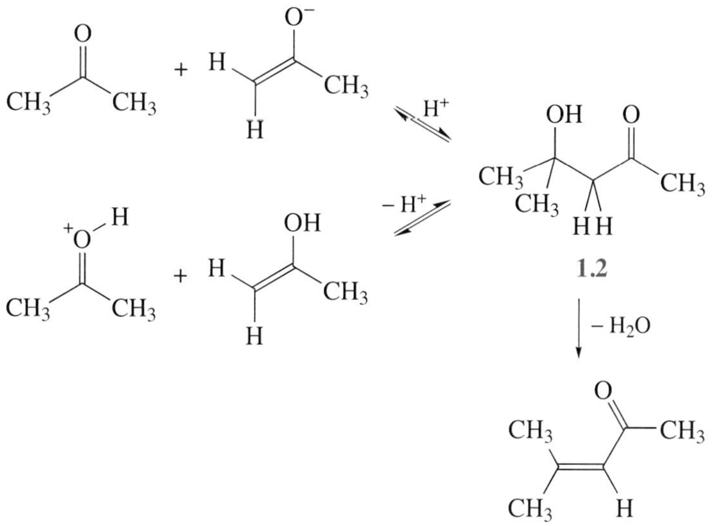

However, the equilibrium constant for the loss of water is usually very favourable because an α,β-unsaturated carbonyl is formed, which is stabilised by conjugation. Thus, this provides the driving force for the formation of the condensation product. Clearly most α,β-unsaturated carbonyl compounds can therefore be made using an aldol reaction. However, unless the carbonyl is a monosubstituted acetaldehyde, the formation of the β-hydroxycarbonyl requires special conditions; these will be described in Section 1.6.

As well as ensuring a favourable equilibrium, the ease of dehydration also has a profound effect on product selectivity, as the next two examples illustrate.

Example 1

Earlier we examined the acid-catalysed aldol condensation of **1.1**:

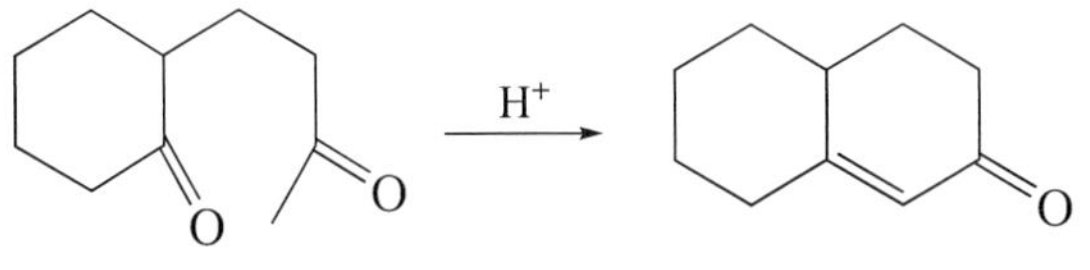

(1.4)

1.1

In working out the mechanism of this reaction, you may have noticed that enolisation of the reactant could, in principle, occur in different ways leading to four different possible compounds (Scheme 1.1). However, only one product, **1.4**, is isolated. Why do you think this is so?

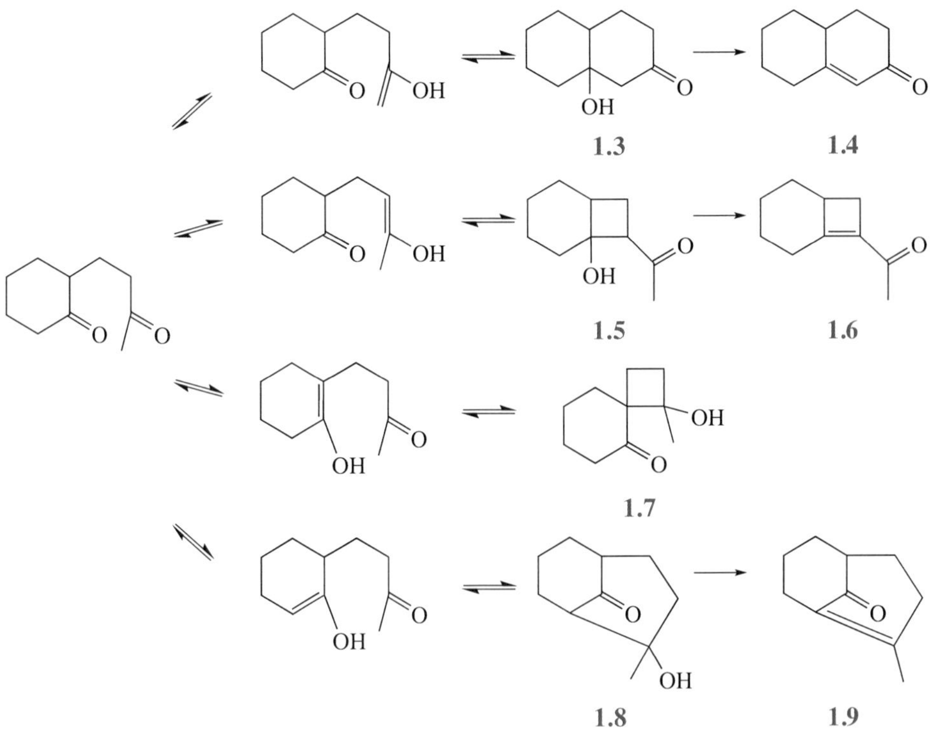

Scheme 1.1

To answer this question, we must examine the relative equilibrium yields of the β-hydroxycarbonyls, **1.3**, **1.5**, **1.7** and **1.8**, and the ease of their dehydration. Formation of **1.5** and **1.7** involves the creation of strained four-membered rings, and so the equilibrium yield of **1.5** and **1.7** will be very small indeed. Further, dehydration to give the conjugated enone that provides the driving force for product formation, is not possible with **1.7** and will be retarded with **1.5** because of the difficulty of forming sp^2 carbons in a four-membered ring. The equilibrium yields of **1.3** and **1.8** will be much more reasonable. However, with **1.8** the dehydration will be very difficult because it involves formation of a double bond at a bridgehead, which is very unlikely. Only with the β-hydroxycarbonyl **1.3** are both the equilibrium yield reasonable and the dehydration step likely.

Example 2

It is not just in bicyclic systems that the ease of dehydration has a profound effect on the regioselectivity. The condensation of butan-2-one (**1.10**) with benzaldehyde gives different products depending on whether acid or base catalysis is employed.

$$\text{PhCHO} + \underset{\textbf{1.10}}{CH_3-\overset{\overset{\text{O}}{\|}}{C}-CH_2CH_3} \quad \underset{\underset{OH^-}{\longrightarrow}}{\overset{H^+}{\longrightarrow}} \quad \begin{array}{c} PhCH=\overset{\overset{CH_3}{|}}{C}-\overset{\overset{\text{O}}{\|}}{C}-CH_3 \\[2em] PhCH=CH-\overset{\overset{\text{O}}{\|}}{C}-CH_2CH_3 \end{array}$$

Under acid conditions, two enols, **1.11a** and **1.11b**, are formed from **1.10**, but the more substituted enol **1.11b** is more stable and predominates in solution such that the branched condensation product is favoured (Equation 1.10).

$$\underset{\textbf{1.11a}}{CH_2=\overset{\overset{OH}{|}}{C}-CH_2CH_3} \qquad \underset{\textbf{1.11b}}{CH_3-\overset{\overset{OH}{|}}{C}=CHCH_3}$$

$$\underset{\textbf{1.11b}}{CH_3-\overset{\overset{:OH}{|}}{C}=CHCH_3} \quad Ph-\overset{\overset{^+OH}{\|}}{C}-H \quad \longrightarrow \quad CH_3-\overset{\overset{^+OH}{\|}}{C}-\underset{\underset{H}{|}}{\overset{\overset{CH_3}{|}}{C}}-\underset{\underset{H}{|}}{\overset{\overset{OH}{|}}{C}}-Ph$$

$$\Big\downarrow \begin{array}{l} i, \; -H^+ \\ ii, \; -H_2O \end{array}$$

$$CH_3-\overset{\overset{\text{O}}{\|}}{C}-\overset{\overset{CH_3}{|}}{C}=CH-Ph \qquad (1.10)$$

Under basic conditions, two enolates are formed which can give two β-hydroxycarbonyl compounds **1.12** and **1.13** (Scheme 1.2). However, mechanistic studies have shown that the base-catalysed dehydration of the branched-chain isomer, **1.12**, is relatively slow although the reasons for this aren't obvious. Nevertheless, because **1.13** and **1.12** are in equilibrium, reaction via the productive form **1.13** predominates, giving the linear condensation product.

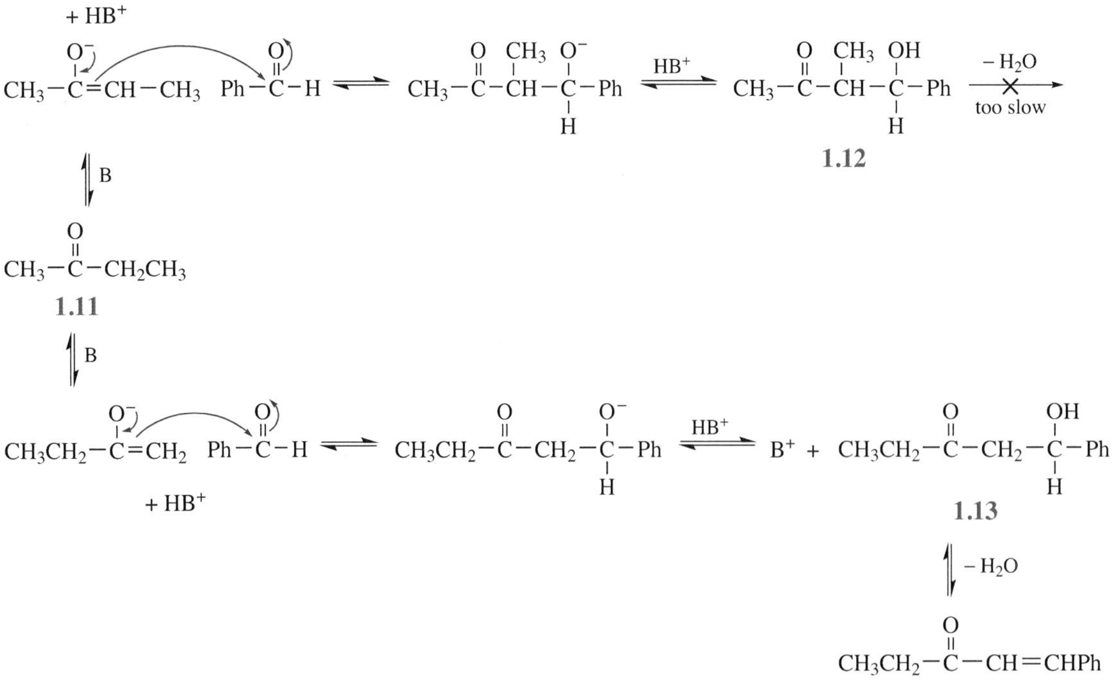

$+ HB^+$

$$CH_3-\overset{\overset{\displaystyle O^-}{|}}{C}=CH-CH_3 \quad Ph-\overset{\overset{\displaystyle O}{||}}{C}-H \rightleftharpoons CH_3-\overset{\overset{\displaystyle O}{||}}{C}-\overset{\overset{\displaystyle CH_3}{|}}{\underset{\underset{\displaystyle H}{|}}{C}}-\overset{\overset{\displaystyle O^-}{|}}{C}-Ph \overset{HB^+}{\rightleftharpoons} CH_3-\overset{\overset{\displaystyle O}{||}}{C}-\overset{\overset{\displaystyle CH_3}{|}}{\underset{\underset{\displaystyle H}{|}}{C}}-\overset{\overset{\displaystyle OH}{|}}{C}-Ph \overset{-H_2O}{\underset{\text{too slow}}{\xrightarrow{\times}}}$$

1.12

$\updownarrow$ B

$$CH_3-\overset{\overset{\displaystyle O}{||}}{C}-CH_2CH_3$$

1.11

$\updownarrow$ B

$$CH_3CH_2-\overset{\overset{\displaystyle O^-}{|}}{C}=CH_2 \quad Ph-\overset{\overset{\displaystyle O}{||}}{C}-H \rightleftharpoons CH_3CH_2-\overset{\overset{\displaystyle O}{||}}{C}-CH_2-\overset{\overset{\displaystyle O^-}{|}}{\underset{\underset{\displaystyle H}{|}}{C}}-Ph \overset{HB^+}{\rightleftharpoons} B^+ + CH_3CH_2-\overset{\overset{\displaystyle O}{||}}{C}-CH_2-\overset{\overset{\displaystyle OH}{|}}{\underset{\underset{\displaystyle H}{|}}{C}}-Ph$$

$+ HB^+$

1.13

$\updownarrow$ $-H_2O$

$$CH_3CH_2-\overset{\overset{\displaystyle O}{||}}{C}-CH=CHPh$$

Scheme 1.2

In this case, as for any system in which alternative products are possible, the structure of the final product will depend on the interplay of the rates of the various steps. In general, reaction of methyl ketones with aromatic aldehydes follows the pattern outlined above; acid catalysis leads to a branched isomer whereas base catalysis favours the linear condensation product.

1.5 Mixed aldol reactions

Although the self-condensation of a ketone or an aldehyde guarantees only one product:

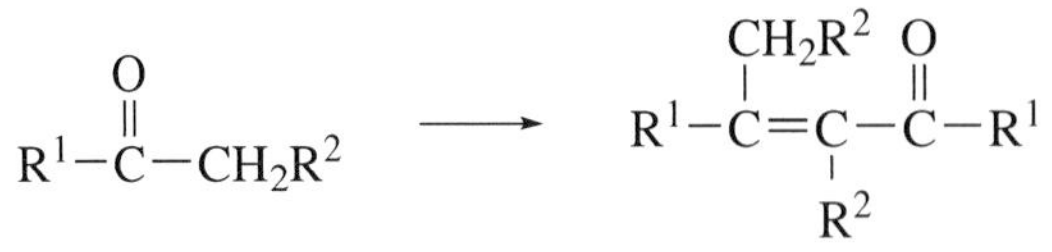

$$R^1-\overset{\overset{\displaystyle O}{||}}{C}-CH_2R^2 \longrightarrow R^1-\overset{\overset{\displaystyle CH_2R^2}{|}}{C}=\overset{\underset{\underset{\displaystyle R^2}{|}}{C}}{C}-\overset{\overset{\displaystyle O}{||}}{C}-R^1$$

it is not a particularly versatile reaction in synthesis. Usually, we would want to combine two different carbonyl compounds where one species acts selectively as the nucleophilic enol or enolate, and the other as the electrophile.

■ There is a problem with attempting mixed condensation reactions using two different aldehydes. What can go wrong?

□ Either of the aldehydes can act as the enolate or electrophilic carbonyl to give two mixed aldol products. Two 'symmetrical' aldol products also arise from self-condensation. Such a reaction would be of little practical value.

■ What two conditions would ensure a single mixed aldol product?

□ The two conditions are:

(i) One of the carbonyl components is especially acidic so that its enolate is formed preferentially:

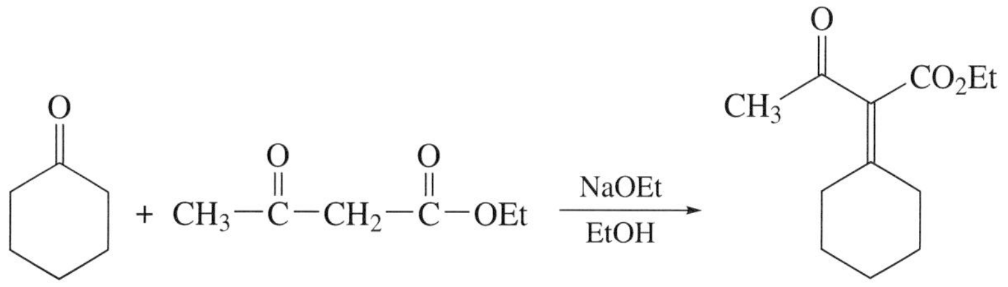

(ii) One of the components has no α-protons and so cannot act as the enolate, yet has a more electrophilic carbonyl than the other component.

In general, the carbonyls of aldehydes are more electrophilic than those of ketones for both steric and electronic reasons, and both are more electrophilic than ester carbonyls. For example, look at the following mixed aldol condensation between an aromatic aldehyde and an aliphatic ketone:

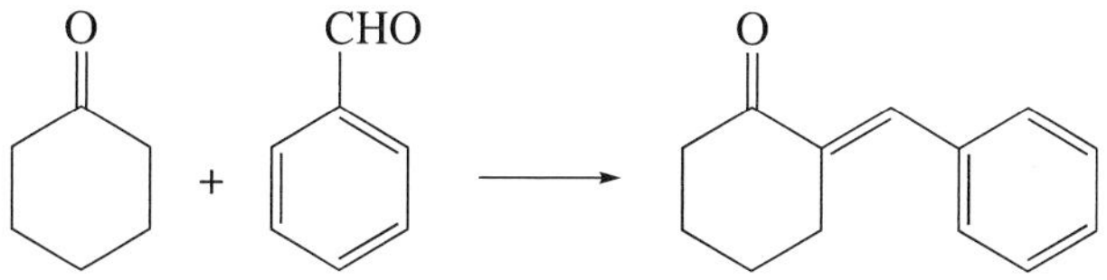

In this case, the aldehyde has no α-hydrogens and its carbonyl is more easily attacked than the ketone carbonyl.

Another reason why aromatic aldehydes generally function well as the carbonyl component is because dehydration leads to a double bond conjugated with both the carbonyl group and the aromatic ring. Even with two different aldehydes, this effect can ensure that the mixed aldol product predominates over the self-condensation product. For example, treatment of a mixture of benzaldehyde and butanal can give the mixed aldol product **1.15** or the product of self-condensation of the butanal, **1.17**.

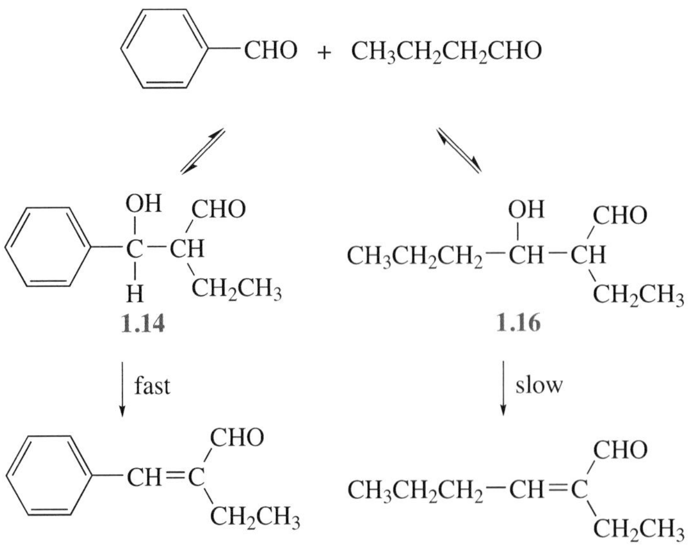

The β-hydroxyaldehydes **1.14** and **1.16** are formed together under equilibrium conditions, but dehydration of **1.14** to give the more conjugated product **1.15** occurs faster, ensuring that it predominates.

■ Now look at Reaction 1.11. Why do you think it will not work?

$$CH_3CHO \ + \ CH_3CO_2Et \ \xrightarrow{\text{base}} \ CH_3CH=CH-CO_2Et \qquad (1.11)$$
$$\textbf{1.18}$$

☐ It is easier to form enolates from aldehydes than from esters. Thus, since the aldehyde carbonyl is the more reactive of the two carbonyls, both factors favour self-condensation as the preferred route and **1.18** will be the minor product.

1.5.1   Activating groups in mixed aldol reactions

The reason why Reaction 1.11 doesn't work is because it is the aldehyde rather than the ester that forms the enolate. However, ethyl but-2-enoate (**1.18**) can be prepared if we use an activating group on the ester, which can later be removed, to ensure it preferentially forms the enolate species. In Unit 6 we studied similar methods that ensure regioselective alkylation of carbonyls – the malonic ester and acetoacetic ester syntheses:

Diethyl malonate forms an enolate under these reaction conditions whereas the aldehyde forms hardly any enolate at all. The most electrophilic species is still the aldehyde, so in agreement with the first of the conditions discussed earlier, this mixed aldol gives the required product. After hydrolysis, decarboxylation and re-esterification, our target molecule, **1.18**, can be realised. In this synthesis our overall strategy is to use the diethyl malonate as a synthetic equivalent of ethyl acetate.

So, generally:

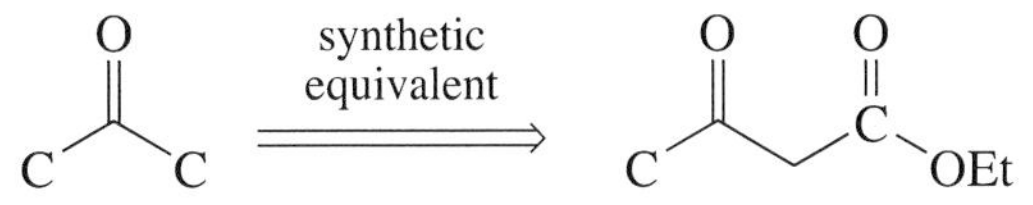

Clearly, a mixed aldol reaction between acetone and benzaldehyde will give a mixture of products. However, if we activate the required enolate species by adding a CO_2Et group which can be removed later, the reaction is successful. So in this one-stage synthesis, we use ethyl acetoacetate as a synthetic equivalent of acetone (Scheme 1.3).

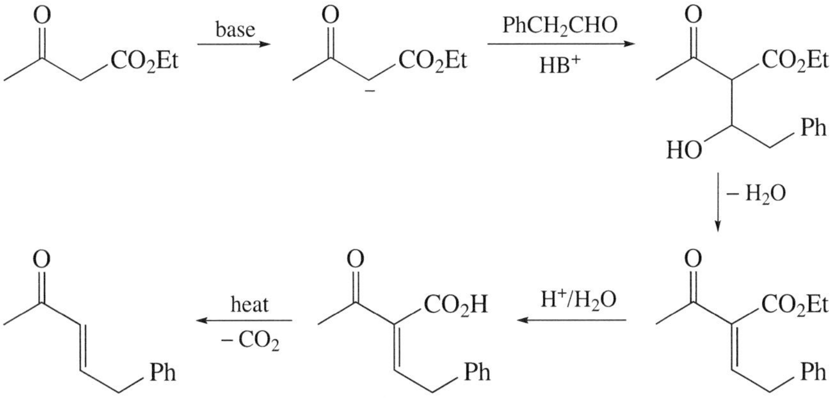

Scheme 1.3

In the next section, we shall examine ways in which chemists have been able to control mixed aldol reactions without the use of activating groups.

1.6 Directed aldol reactions

As we mentioned earlier, it is difficult to bring about a mixed aldol condensation efficiently if both carbonyls can form enols or enolate ions.

■ Compound **1.20** is needed in the synthesis of platyphyllide (**1.19**), a constituent of a variety of ragwort that is used medicinally in the Ukraine. Retrosynthetic analysis leads back to an aldol condensation between **1.21** and acetone. Can you see a problem with this reaction?

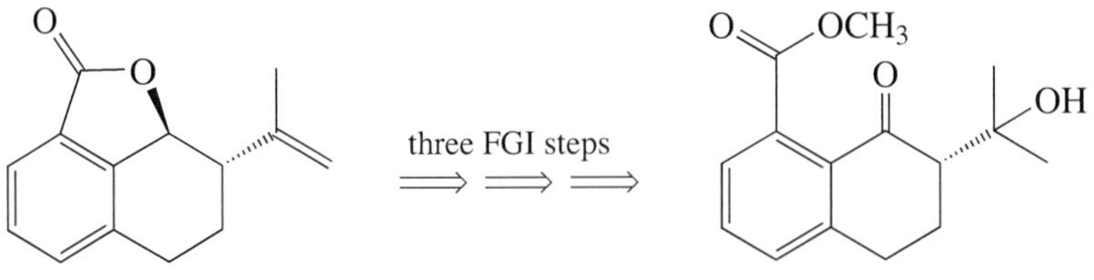

1.19 three FGI steps **1.20**

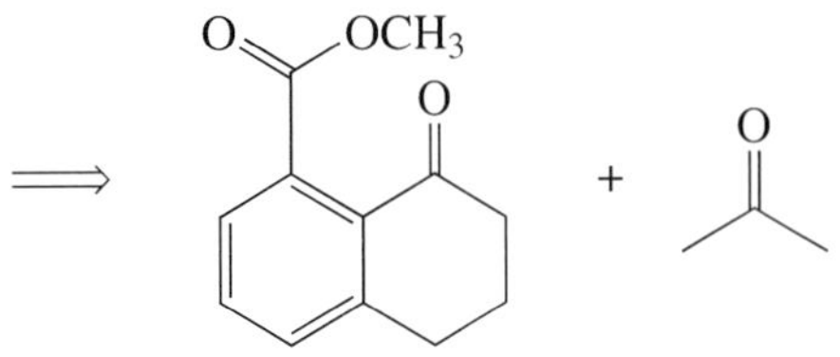

1.21

◻ Aldol condensation between **1.21** and acetone will give four products: two mixed aldols and two self-condensation products.

This type of problem can be overcome using a **directed aldol reaction**, where one species is 'compelled' to form the enol or enolate ion. In its simplest form, this involves preforming the enolate or enol of one compound on its own then treating it with the other carbonyl compound.

We shall deal in turn with two types of preformed enol or enolate (or their analogues), all of which you have already met: metal enolates and trimethylsilyl enol ethers.

1.6.1 Metal enolates

We shall discuss later in this section why such β-hydroxy ketones can be isolated.

Look at the following synthesis of α-bisabolone (**1.25**), a sesquiterpene derivative, which uses a lithium enolate in a directed aldol reaction.

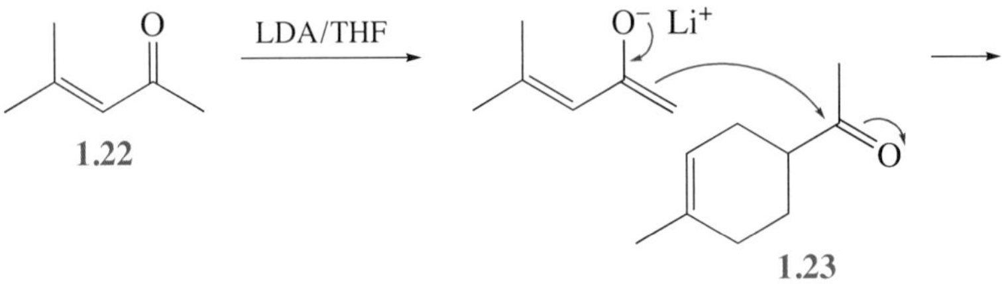

1.22   LDA/THF   **1.23**

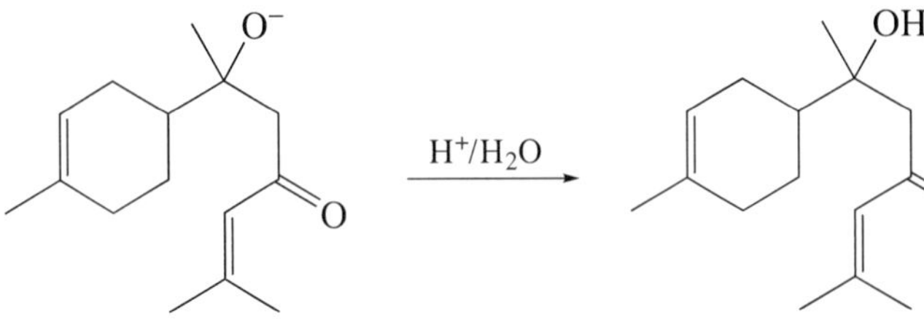

1.24   H$^+$/H$_2$O   **1.25**

The strategy involves first forming the enolate of the ketone **1.22**, then adding the carbonyl species **1.23**. We must ensure first that, during enolate formation, there is no self-condensation of the ketone **1.22** and, secondly, when we add the ketone **1.23**, that there is no equilibration of enolates, which would lead to mixed aldols:

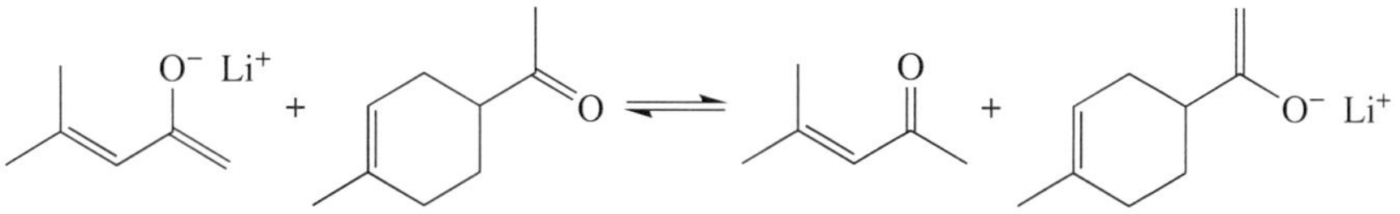

- ■ From what you have learnt regarding formation of lithium enolates under kinetic control (so-called 'kinetic enolates'), what conditions and reagents do you think would favour this approach?

- □ A strong base will be required to form the enolate so that the proton is removed quickly and quantitatively from **1.22**, thereby reducing the opportunity for self-condensation. A low temperature and an aprotic solvent are also needed to ensure that there is no equilibration of enolates.

Notice that because an aprotic solvent is employed, the β-ketoalkoxide **1.24** is the product of the aldol reaction. This is because there are no species in the solution acidic enough to protonate the O^- anion. The required product, the β-ketoalcohol **1.25**, is obtained only after acidic work-up.

In recent years, metal enolates with a range of counter-ions, **1.26**, have been developed. These can be preformed and used in directed aldol reactions.

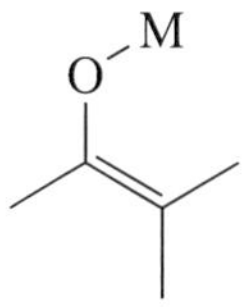

M = AlR_2, BR_2, $SnCl_3$, $TiCl_3$, ZnBr and ZrR_2Cl

1.26

One particularly important example contains a zinc counter-ion. Just as a Grignard reagent is formed by treating an alkyl halide with magnesium metal, these halozinc enolates are formed by treating an α-haloester with zinc metal:

$$BrCH_2CO_2CH_3 \xrightarrow[Et_2O \text{ or } C_6H_6]{Zn} CH_2{=}C(OCH_3)(O^- \overset{+}{Z}nBr)$$

Since this enolate is preformed, and the use of an aprotic solvent prevents enolate exchange, then addition of a carbonyl leads to a directed aldol-type reaction. Again, in an aprotic solvent, the alkoxide is the product, the conjugated ester being generated after acidic work-up.

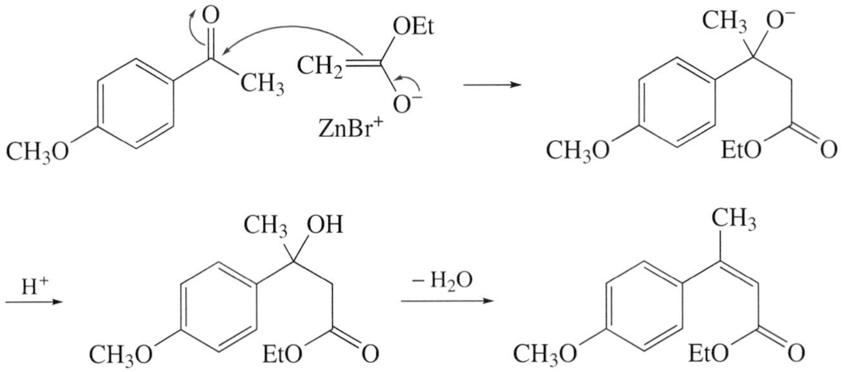

This directed aldol reaction between a carbonyl and an α-haloester in the presence of zinc is known as the Reformatsky reaction, after its discoverer Sergius Reformatsky, and has been known for over 100 years. Zinc is used in place of magnesium simply because the organozinc compounds are less reactive than Grignard reagents; they do not undergo self-condensation with the ester function but can react with aldehydes or ketones.

■   Can you see a problem in the following preparation?

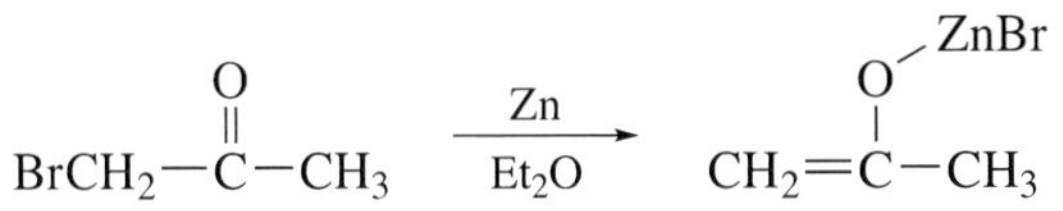

1.27

□   Since halozinc enolates react with ketones, self-condensation with the ketone **1.27** will occur. It is for this reason that the zinc metal reaction can only be used to prepare enolates of esters.

However, zinc enolates of esters, ketones and aldehydes can be prepared by adding equivalent amounts of zinc chloride to preformed lithium enolates. This enhances the usefulness of the enolate: lithium enolates are very reactive and so the condensation reaction must be carried out at −78 °C, whereas the zinc enolate reacts smoothly at about 0 °C and the laboratory conditions are more reasonable. Such a strategy has been used in the synthesis of lasalocid A, an antibiotic, using a directed aldol reaction (Scheme 1.4; just concentrate on the parts marked in red).

You may have noticed that the product of many of these 'preformed enolate' aldol reactions is a β-hydroxycarbonyl compound. Earlier we saw how the formation of the β-hydroxycarbonyl **1.28** was reversible, often unfavourably so, and a product was obtained only because dehydration to give the conjugated enone occurred:

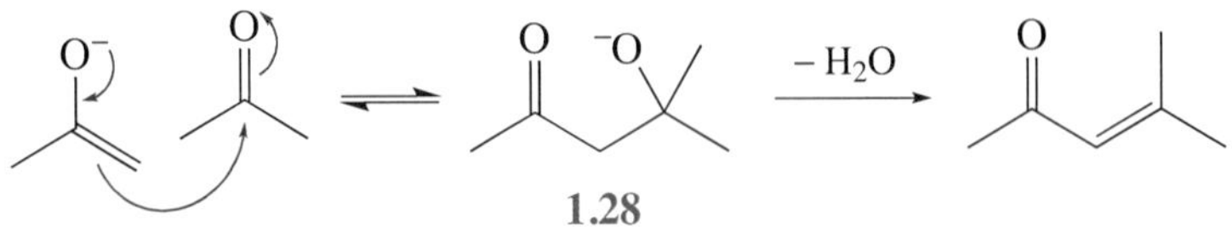

1.28

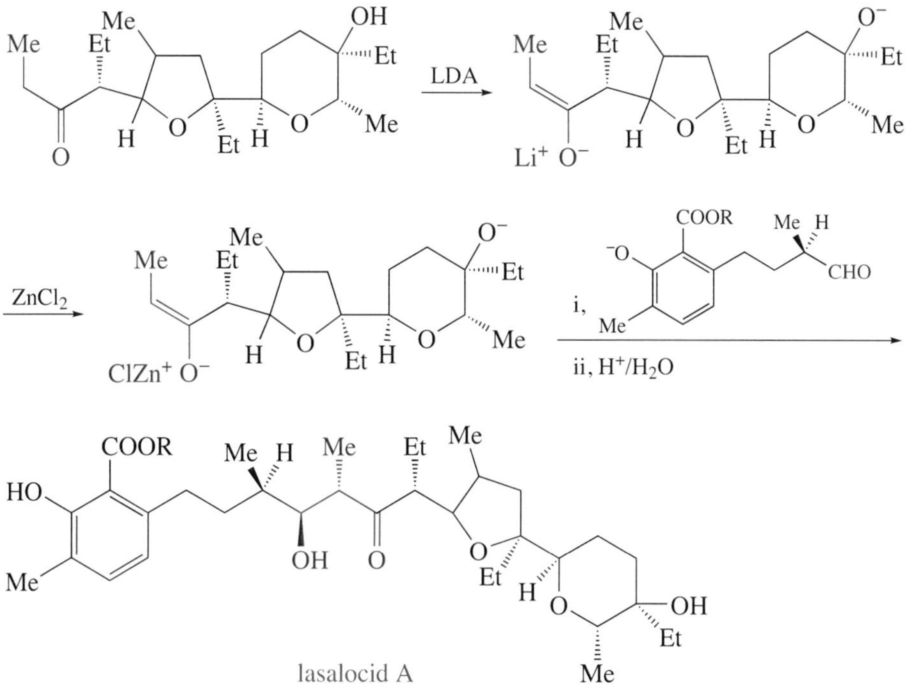

lasalocid A

Scheme 1.4

So, why should we obtain β-hydroxycarbonyls when we use preformed enolates? The answer lies in the nature of the counter-ion. When ions such as Li^+ or $ZnBr^+$ are employed at low temperature in aprotic solvents as, for example, in directed aldol reactions, the intermediate **1.28** forms a complex with the counter-ion, as a result of favourable electrostatic interactions:

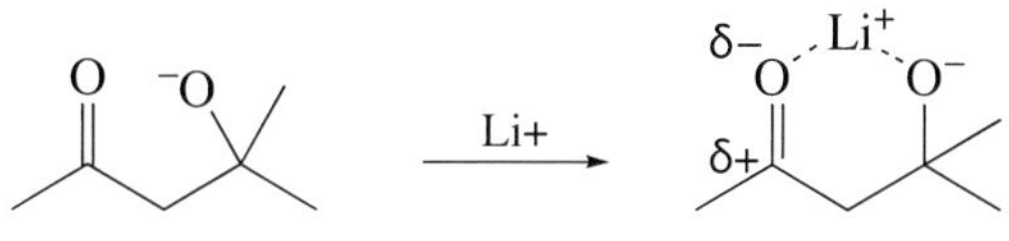

1.28

These cyclic complexes are known as **chelates** and both oxygens are coordinated to the metal atom, and the result is that the equilibrium is displaced in favour of the aldol adduct. On acidic work-up, these chelates are converted into the corresponding β-hydroxycarbonyl compounds and, as in the more conventional aldol reaction, depending on how vigorous the conditions are, the alcohol or the dehydration product can be isolated.

If the counter-ion is Na^+ or K^+, for example when the base is NaOEt or KOH, or if protic solvents are used so that hydrogen bonding occurs, chelation of the metal does not occur to any large extent and the equilibrium is not displaced towards formation of the β-ketoalkoxide. As we shall see later, chelation has another important role in controlling the stereochemistry of aldol reactions, but for now let's concentrate on our task of examining other enols or enolates that can be used in directed aldol reactions.

1.6.2   Trimethylsilyl enol ethers

We saw in Unit 6 that trimethylsilyl enol ethers can be cleaved by fluoride ions to give enolate ions. This then provides another strategy for directing aldol reactions:

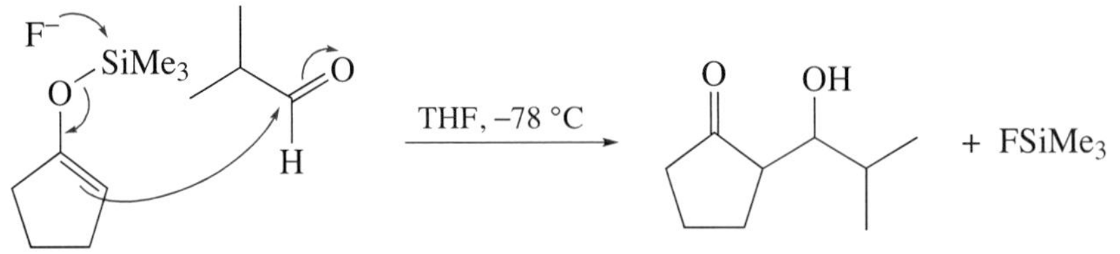

Provided that equilibration of enolates is kept to a minimum, the enol derivative can act only as the nucleophile; the absence of base ensures the carbonyl component can act only as the electrophile.

■   What other reagent could we use to catalyse the aldol reaction between a trimethylsilyl enol ether and a carbonyl?

☐   Lewis acids can be used to promote this reaction. This approach was used in the preparation of the intermediate **1.20** in the synthesis of platyphyllide (**1.19**) referred to earlier.

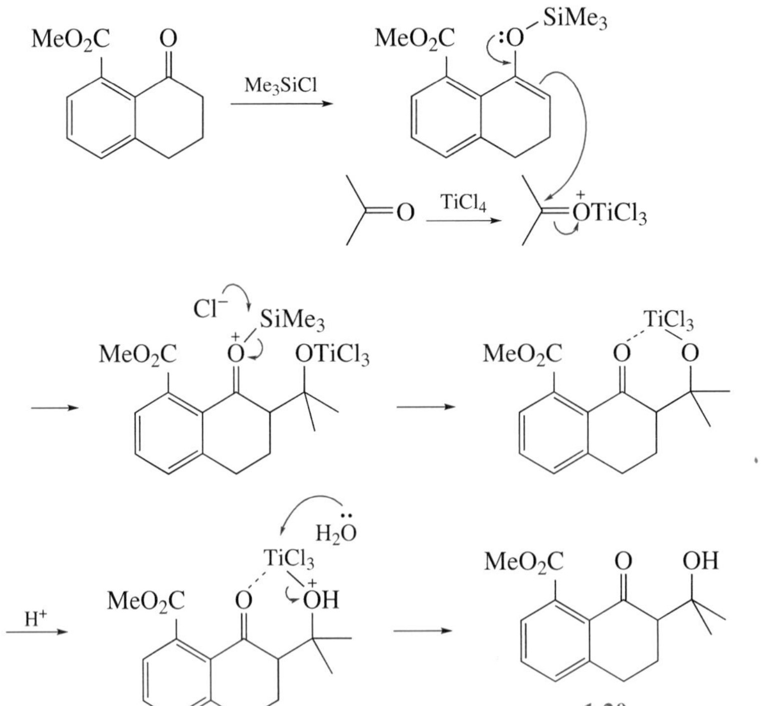

Notice that in such Lewis acid-catalysed reactions, a titanium chelate is formed, which ensures a favourable equilibrium. Notice also that in such reactions, the β-hydroxycarbonyl can be isolated.

Study note

Before moving on to the next section you should produce your own summary of Sections 1.4 to 1.6 and then compare it with ours. Go to Unit 7 summaries in Unit 7 resources.

1.7 Stereoselective aldol reactions

We now turn from chemoselectivity to examine the stereoselectivity of the aldol reaction. In the last section we saw how chelation favoured the formation of β-hydroxycarbonyl compounds, and we also alluded to the fact that chelation played an important role in controlling the stereochemistry of the products formed.

■ The following reaction proceeds via a six-membered ring chelate: draw out this mechanism. How many chiral centres are created in the β-hydroxycarbonyl?

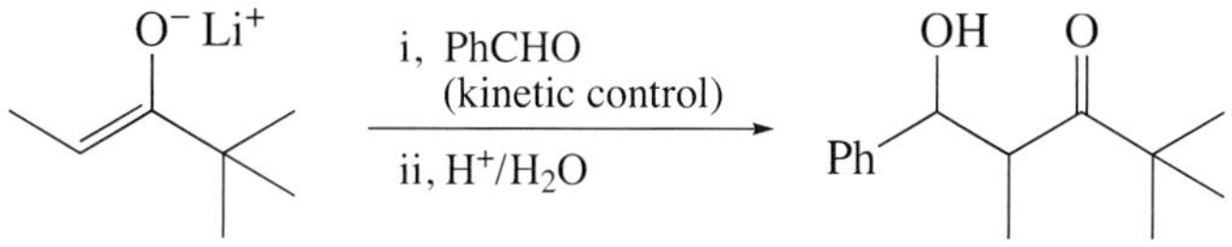

□ The reaction proceeds via a six-membered ring chelate where the two oxygens are coordinated to the lithium:

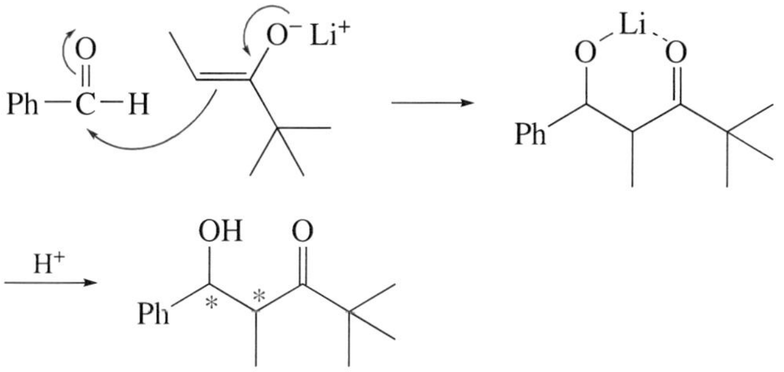

Examination of the product shows two chiral centres are created (marked with an asterisk). Two pairs of enantiomers, **1.29** and **1.30**, are therefore possible.

However, only **1.29** and its enantiomer are formed in this reaction, and we shall spend most of this section examining the origin of this selectivity. As you work through this section you might find using the molecular modelling software introduced in Unit 1 useful.

This reaction is carried out under kinetic control, so which product predominates depends on the relative rates of formation of the β-ketoalkoxide intermediates **1.31** and **1.32**.

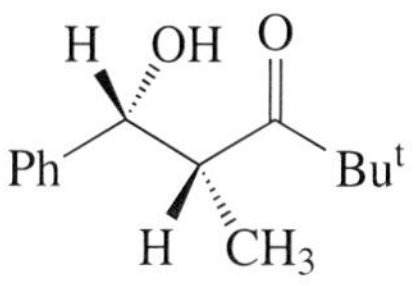

1.29
and enantiomer

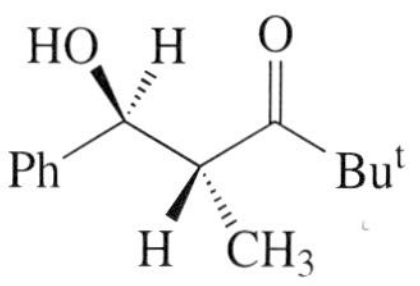

1.30
and enantiomer

The reaction scheme shows benzaldehyde (Ph–CHO) plus the lithium enolate of pinacolone reacting to form chelated intermediates:

Ph–CHO + CH₂=C(O-Li)Buᵗ →

1.31 (+ enantiomer) → H⁺ → **1.29**

1.32 (+ enantiomer) → H⁺ → **1.30**

Put another way, the stability of the corresponding transition states that lead to the intermediates determines which intermediate is formed preferentially.

Now to get an idea of the relative energies of the transition states, the Hammond postulate we encountered in Unit 3 suggests we use the two chelated intermediates **1.31** and **1.32** as models. If we examine the stereochemical features of the two intermediates, we can decide which is the more stable, and hence predict which is formed the faster and thus which product predominates.

The key feature of the stereochemistry of the cyclic intermediate chelates **1.31** and **1.32** is that they take up a chair conformation **1.33**, just like the six-membered rings you met in Unit 4. The stability of these chair conformations depends on the interactions between the substituents on the ring. As you saw earlier, bulky groups occupy equatorial positions to reduce steric strain across the ring. Unfortunately, the arrangement of groups at carbon *a* in **1.33** depends on the structure of the enolate.

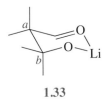

1.33

Unit 7 iFigure 1.1 illustrates that the group *syn* to the oxygen in the enolate, in this case CH₃, must always be axial in the cyclic chair transition state. For this group to occupy the equatorial position requires an equilibration of the enolate from the *Z* to the *E* form, which does not occur under the conditions of kinetic control. However, the arrangement of groups on carbon *b* depends on which way round the carbonyl component is attacked by the enolate, as shown in Unit 7 iFigure 1.2 and Unit 7 iFigure 1.3. The two corresponding intermediate chelates are shown in Unit 7 iFigure 1.4 and Unit 7 iFigure 1.5. Notice that in Unit 7 iFigure 1.4 the phenyl group is equatorial, whereas it is axial in Unit 7 iFigure 1.5. This latter arrangement is much less stable than the intermediate shown in Unit 7 iFigure 1.4. This means that the transition state leading to the intermediate with an equatorial phenyl group will have the lower energy, such that this chelate is formed the faster and this route predominates. Our last task is to deduce which product, **1.29** or **1.30**, arises from this more stable intermediate.

Thus, when chelation is important, such as when a lithium counter-ion is employed, the stereochemistry of the aldol reaction is controlled by the relative energies of the six-membered ring chair transition states leading to the chelated β-alkoxycarbonyls. The transition state with lower energy will be the one with bulky groups from the carbonyl species equatorial, and thus the corresponding product will be formed the faster; often, within the limits of detection, to the exclusion of the other diastereoisomer.

It would be very time-consuming if we were to go through this model-building exercise every time we wanted to predict the stereochemistry of an aldol reaction. Fortunately we can devise a general rule, which states that any enolate **1.34** will react with any aldehyde **1.35** to give a β-hydroxycarbonyl **1.36** via the more stable intermediate shown in Unit 7 iFigure 1.6.

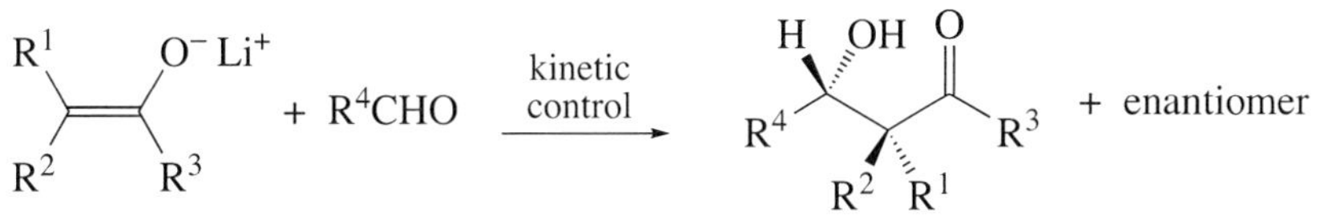

This rule is given in Data Table 10.7.

■ Use this rule to predict what will be the favoured product if **1.37**, the stereoisomer of the enolate used earlier, undergoes an aldol reaction with benzaldehyde.

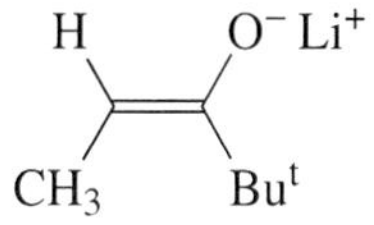

☐ In this case R^1 = H, R^2 = CH_3, R^3 = Bu^t and R^4 = Ph, so the favoured product will be:

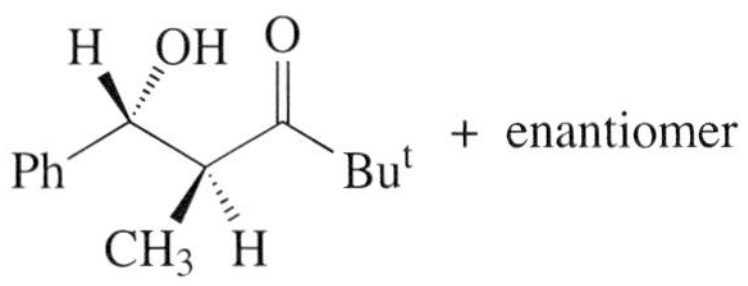

If you compare this product with that obtained earlier, **1.29**, you will see that they are diastereoisomers of each other. Thus by judicious choice of enolate stereochemistry, we can control the stereochemical outcome of the aldol reaction. This also brings us to a very important point. To get a good yield of only one diastereoisomer, the enolate must be stereoisomerically pure; that is, there must be only one isomer present. Although this model correctly predicts the stereochemical outcome of most aldol reactions when chelation is important, it should be stressed that the degree of the stereoselectivity depends on the sizes of the groups attached to the enolate and carbonyl components, and to some extent on whether the stereochemistry of the enolate is *E* or *Z*.

As well as lithium, other counter-ions such as $MgBr^+$, $ZnBr^+$ and AiR_2^+ form chelates, and the same model correctly predicts the stereoselectivity. It turns out that the use of boron enolates (**1.38**) leads to an unusually high stereoselectivity.

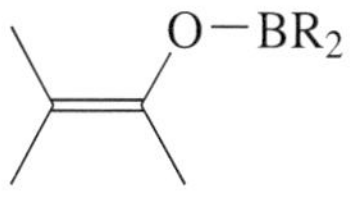

This is because the O–B and C–B bonds are short, and boron has a high affinity for oxygen non-bonding pairs. Hence, the six-membered chair transition state is more compact than with other enolates, and steric interactions between the groups around the ring are more pronounced. At the same time, bulky groups can be attached to boron to increase steric crowding,

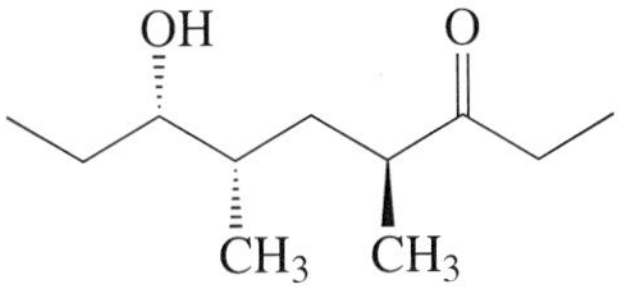

1.39

a strategy that is not possible with monovalent counter-ions such as lithium. The stereoselective reaction of boron enolates is illustrated below by one reaction step in the synthesis of the sex pheromone **1.39** of the cigarette beetle. The stereoselectivity of this step was greater than 100 : 1.

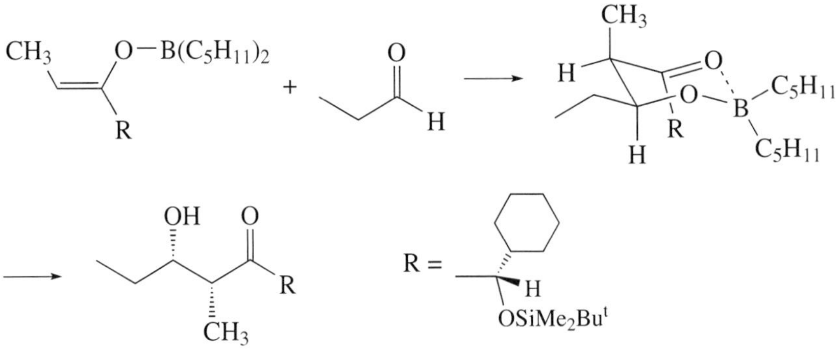

The discussion so far has centred on kinetically controlled reactions, as required for directed aldol reactions. The stereoselectivity of thermodynamically controlled aldol reactions will depend on the stability of the stereoisomers of the chelated β-ketoalkoxides. Under thermodynamic control, the enolates are in equilibrium with each other and this provides a route for ensuring that all the bulky groups can be arranged equatorially in the chair-like conformation of the chelated intermediate. For example, look at Scheme 1.5, which shows the reaction between benzaldehyde and phenyl ethyl ketone.

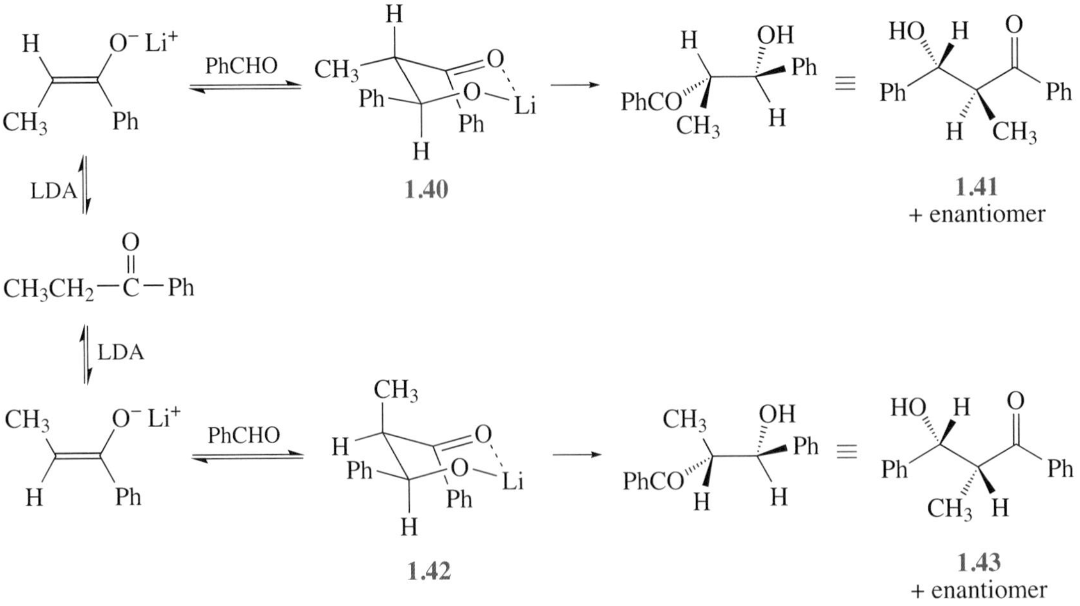

Scheme 1.5

In the intermediates **1.40** and **1.42**, the phenyl group from benzaldehyde will preferentially be in the equatorial position. Notice that, depending on the stereochemistry of the enolate, the CH_3 group can be equatorial or axial. The more stable chelated intermediate is **1.40** with both groups equatorial, and this gives **1.41** and its enantiomer as the predominant product. The general rule for this type of reaction is:

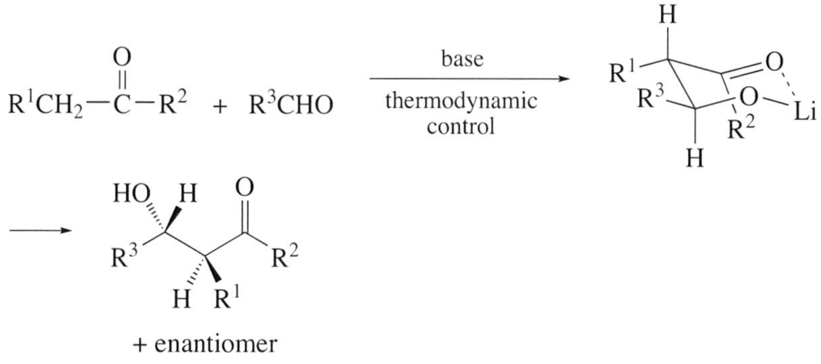

+ enantiomer

This rule is also given in Data Table 10.7.

Because the aldol reaction is such an important carbon–carbon bond-forming reaction, a great deal of effort has been invested in examining the factors that control its stereochemistry. The presence of a chiral centre in the enolate or carbonyl moiety can be used to induce asymmetry in the product. For example (and don't worry about the detail here) by applying Cram's rule (Unit 3) to the six-membered chair transition state, it is possible to predict correctly the stereochemistry of three adjacent centres.

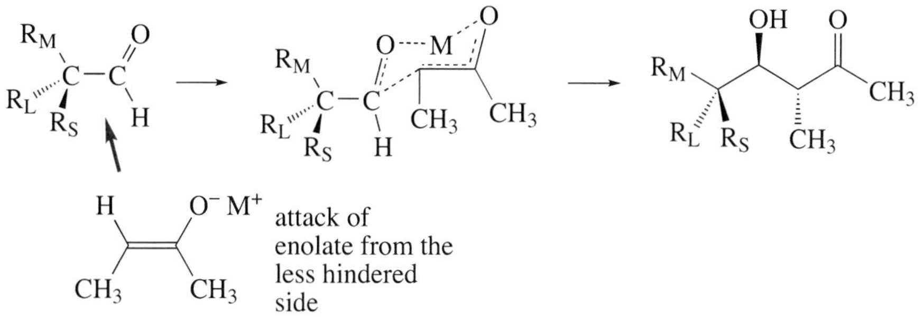

attack of enolate from the less hindered side

This kind of reasoning has been used in the synthesis of large molecules containing many such chiral centres. For example, the aldol reaction has been used to control the stereochemistry of seven of the nine chiral centres (they are marked in red) in the synthesis of rifamycin S, an antibiotic – but you won't be expected to remember or rationalise this.

Study note

Before moving on to the next section you should produce your own summary of Section 1.7 and then compare it with ours. Go to Unit 7 summaries in Unit 7 resources.

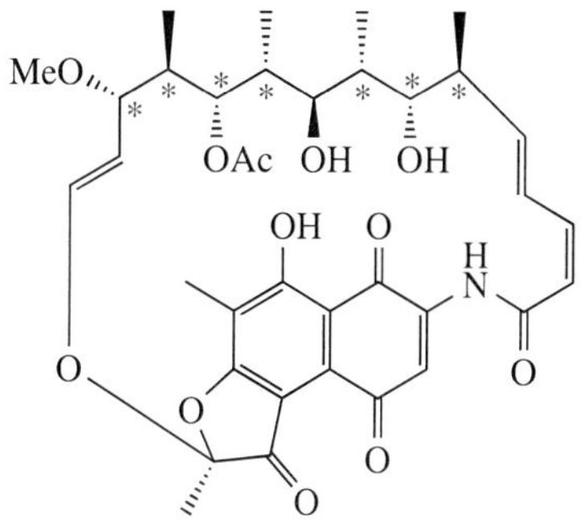

rifamycin S

1.8 Variations on the aldol reaction

When methanal (formaldehyde) is used as the electrophile in a mixed aldol reaction, something interesting and quite different happens. Firstly, the formaldehyde cannot enolise as it has no α-hydrogens and it is highly reactive. You may recall that aldehydes are more electrophilic than ketones since one of the alkyl groups has been replaced by a hydrogen. Formaldehyde has two hydrogen atoms and this makes it highly reactive, too reactive in fact for the reaction between formaldehyde and, say acetaldehyde, to stop at the simple mixed aldol.

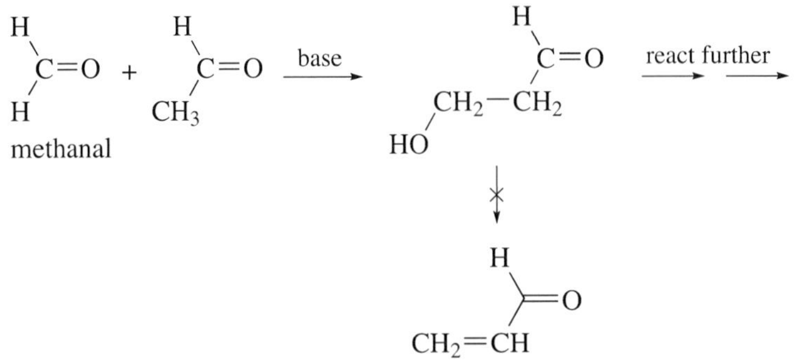

With an electrophile as powerful as formaldehyde under these conditions a second, and third molecule of formaldehyde can react with each enolisable proton on the acetaldehyde.

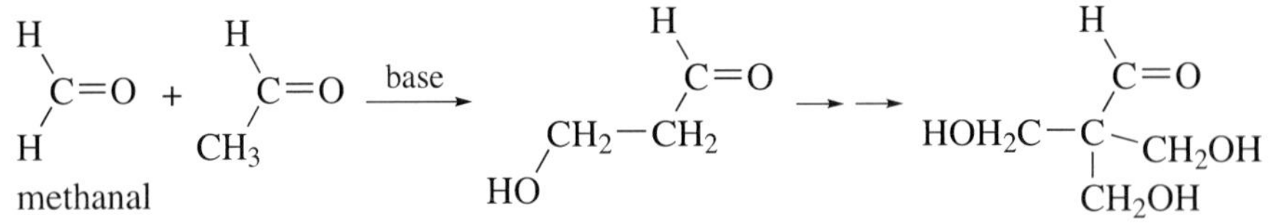

Even after the third aldol reaction it does not stop there. The hydroxide ion present then reacts with a formaldehyde to produce an anion. This anion is unstable and reacts with the aldehyde group present in the aldol product to produce a more stable carboxylic acid group and reduce the aldehyde to an alcohol group via attack of a 'hydride' ion. This reaction is known as the Cannizzaro reaction and its synthetic utility stems from the fact that it only occurs when the aldehyde loses its ability to enolise, that is, it only works with aldehydes that have no enolisable protons.

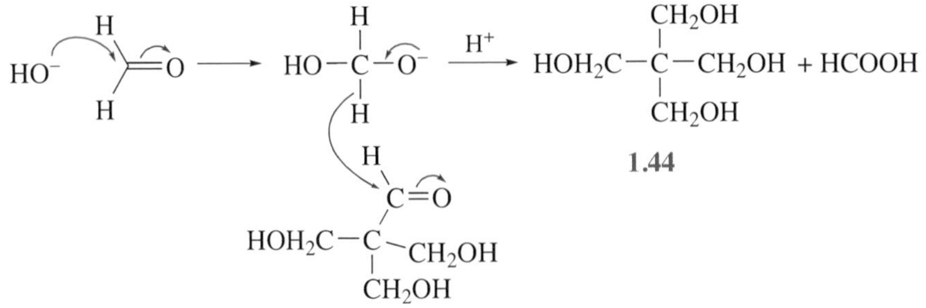

1.44

Compound **1.44** is known as pentaerythritol and about 465 000 tonnes were produced globally in 2006 for use in paints, inks, adhesives and plasticisers. The tetranitrate is used as an explosive but is also employed as a vasodilator for the treatment of angina.

This reactivity of formaldehyde has been extended to more general applicability in the reaction between formaldehyde, a secondary amine (in blue) and an enolisable aldehyde or ketone (in purple). The product of this reaction, called the Mannich reaction, is an amino ketone which is a key feature of many drug molecules. It is not strictly an aldol reaction (and this is why it is important not to classify or categorise reactions too rigidly) as only one formaldehyde molecule takes part in the reaction. It reacts with the amine to form an imine, and the imine then adds to the enol formed from the aldehyde or ketone.

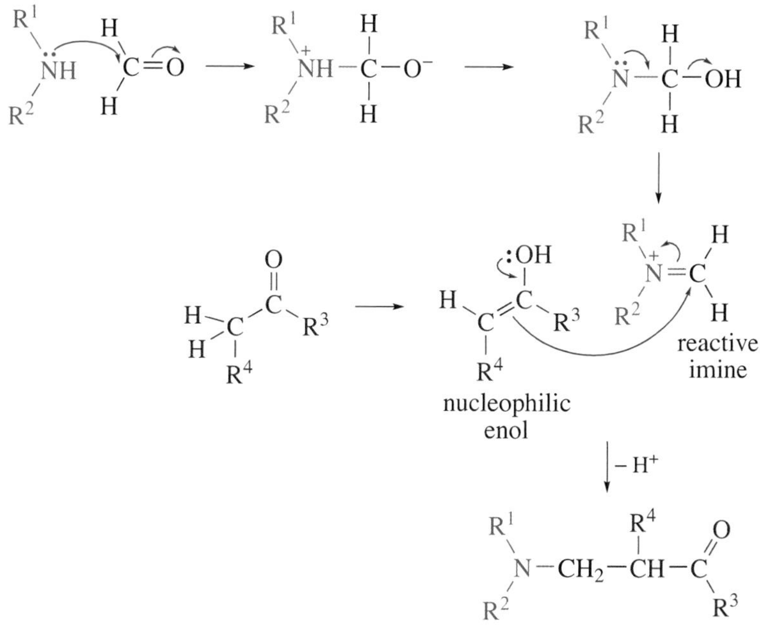

A further use of the Mannich reaction comes from the conversion of the amino ketone product, to highly reactive enones. This can be achieved by alkylating the amine, with methyl iodide then carrying out a base-catalysed elimination of the corresponding enolate.

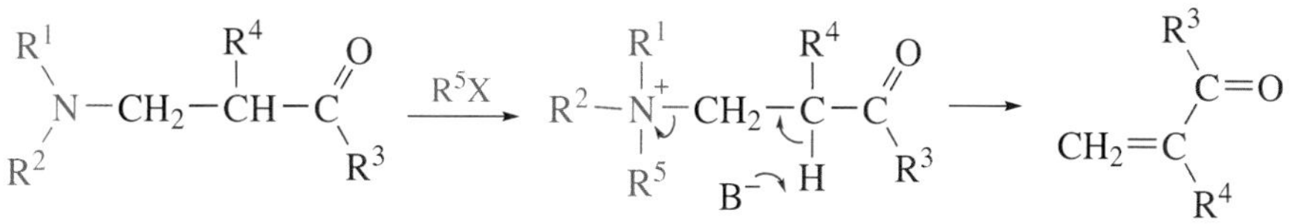

These exo-methylene compounds are very reactive and unstable but are very useful synthetic intermediates for the Michael reaction, which we will be discussing later (Section 1.10). The Mannich reaction provides a means by which these compounds can be prepared and generated in situ when needed.

1.9 Enamines

Having examined the reactions of enols and enolates with electrophiles, we now turn to their nitrogen analogues, **enamines** and **metallo-enamines**. Alkylation of enamines is a particularly useful synthetic reaction because it proceeds under very mild conditions. Metallo-enamines are very reactive, which allows some reactions to be performed that cannot be carried out using enolate methodology. As before, we start by reviewing their stability and ways of making enamines and metallo-enamines, and then we examine their reactions.

The nitrogen analogues of ketones and aldehydes are known as imines. These compounds can be prepared by condensation of a primary amine with a ketone or an aldehyde.

The mechanism for the reaction between a primary amine and cyclohexanone in the presence of an acid catalyst proceeds via the attack on the carbonyl carbon by the nucleophilic amine.

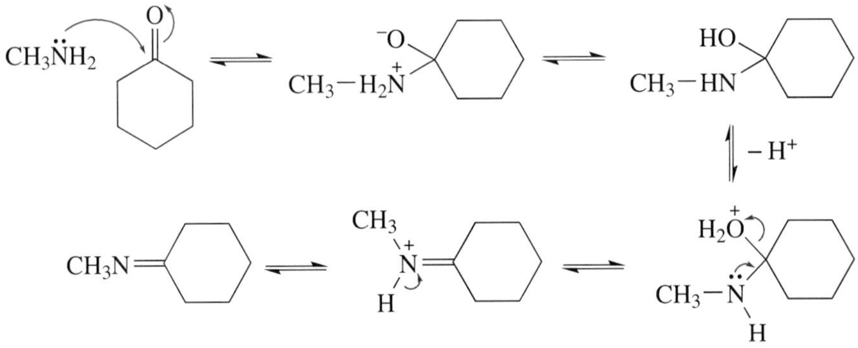

Just as ketones tautomerise to enols, so imines can undergo tautomerism to give compounds called enamines. Again the equilibrium lies well to the left, as with keto–enol tautomerism:

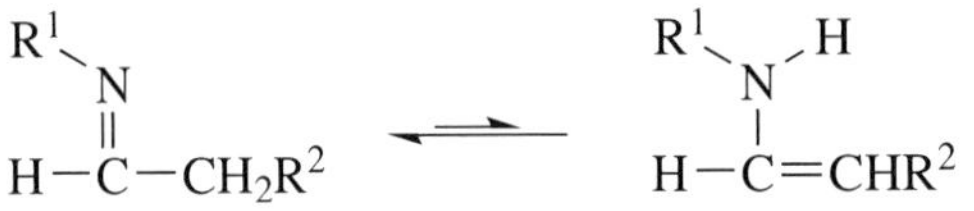

Secondary amines also react with cyclohexanone in the presence of an acid to give an aminoalcohol, **1.45**, which can be protonated and then lose water:

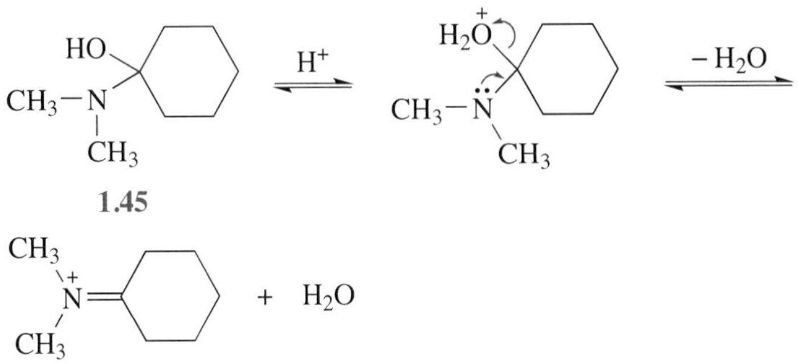

$$+ \quad H_2O \tag{1.12}$$

However, with secondary amines, the nitrogen does not carry a proton that can be lost to give the imine. In this case, an α-hydrogen is lost to give a neutral enamine which, like enol ethers, cannot tautomerise:

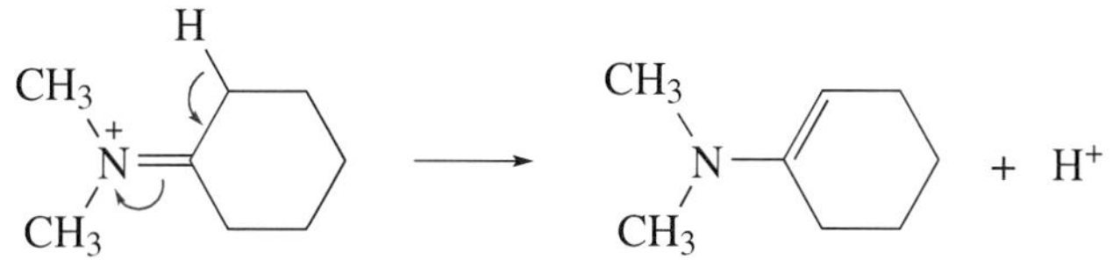

This reaction is driven to completion by removal of water, for example by using a dehydrating reagent such as titanium tetrachloride.

■ Can you see a problem with forming an enamine from 2-methylcyclohexanone (**1.46**) and dimethylamine, Me_2NH?

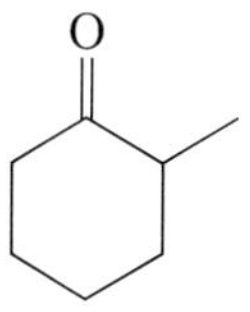

□ Enamine formation can occur in two directions:

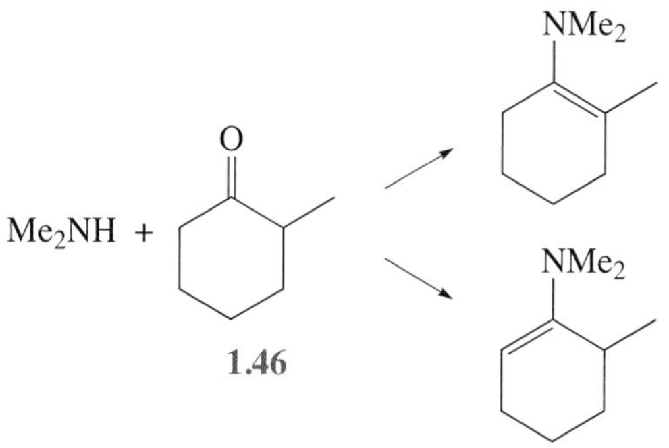

1.46

When the secondary amine is pyrrolidine, the less-substituted enamine predominates, owing to steric interactions:

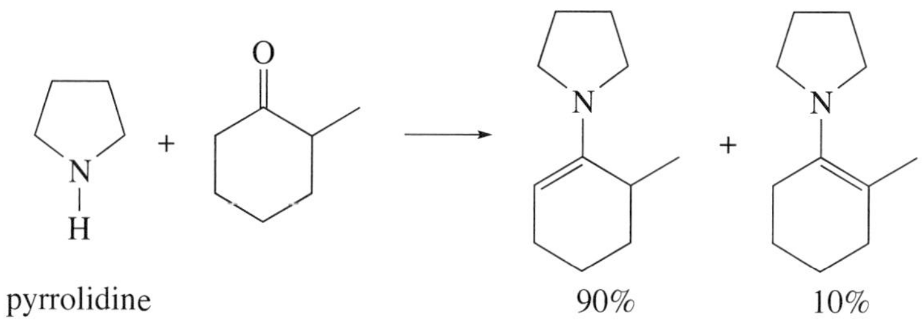

pyrrolidine   90%   10%

The non-bonding pair on nitrogen is conjugated with the π system of the double bond, ensuring coplanarity of the bonds shown in red:

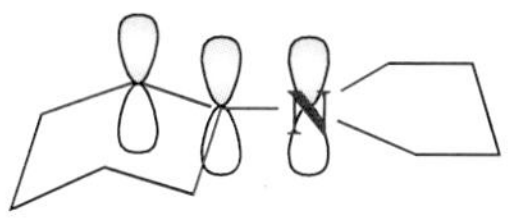

With the more-substituted enamine, there is severe steric repulsion between the CH_3 group and the CH_2 of the enamine, because they are held in the same plane:

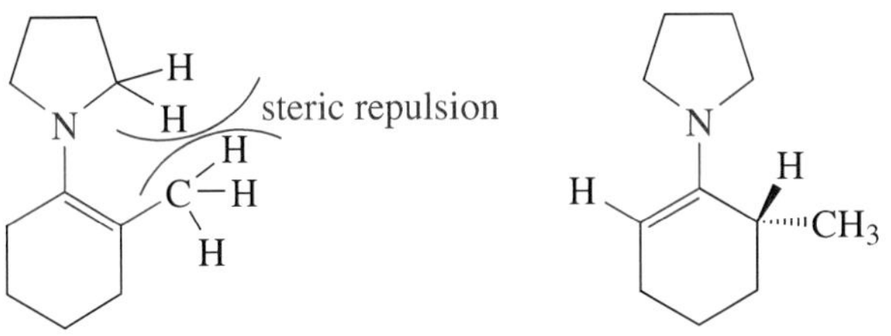

However, in the less-substituted enamine, the CH_3 group is no longer held in the same plane as the other atoms. Any steric repulsion is therefore lessened so that this isomer is more stable. (If you are unsure of this explanation, try comparing models using the modelling software Discovery Studio®.)

Of course, if the enamine can be stabilised by conjugation with an adjacent functional group, such as a carbonyl, then this will control the direction of enamine formation.

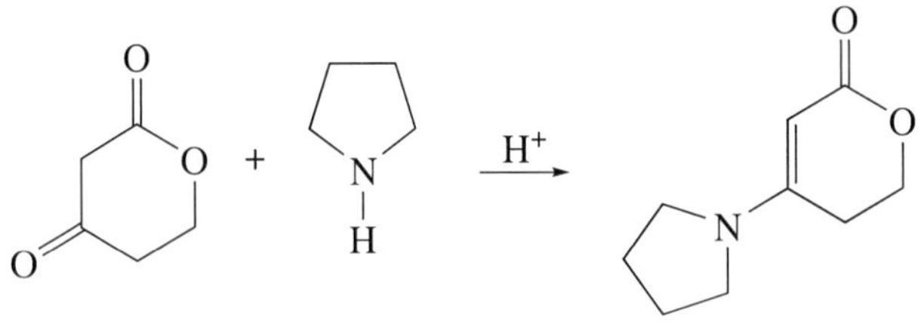

■ What are the two possible sites susceptible to electrophilic attack in enamines?

☐ As with other nitrogen compounds, the nitrogen atom is nucleophilic, and, just like enols and enolates, the second site is the alkene carbon atom beta to nitrogen.

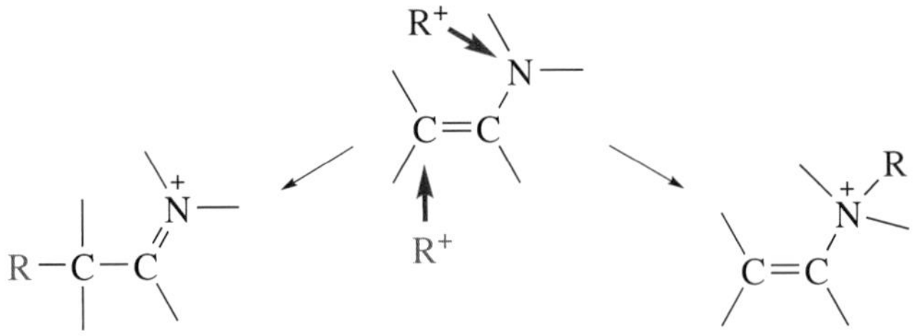

1.47

This arises as a result of conjugation with the nitrogen atom, and becomes more obvious if we examine the resonance forms. Clearly, the β-carbon bears an appreciable negative charge and can act as a nucleophile:

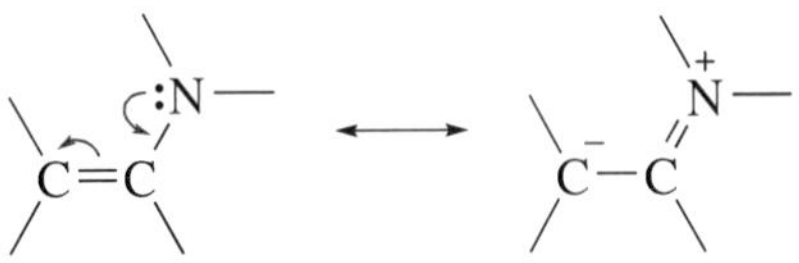

Electrophilic addition of R^+ to enamines can take place at one or both of the positions arrowed in red. In the majority of cases where the enamine is derived from a ketone, the formation of **1.47** is favoured both kinetically and thermodynamically, and we shall devote the rest of this section to this type of reaction. However, we should not forget that enamines are ambident nucleophiles, and reaction at nitrogen is sometimes a competing process. Fortunately, when this does occur, the ammonium salt so formed is often water-soluble and can be separated by extraction into water.

Let us now examine how enamines can be exploited in synthesis. One of the most important reactions of enamines is alkylation followed by hydrolysis to regenerate the ketone:

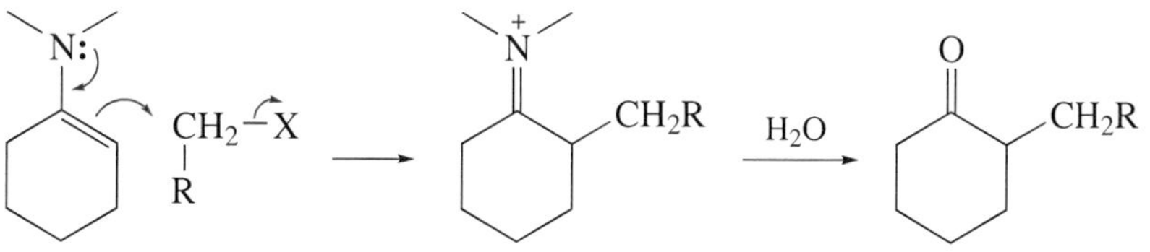

1.48

■ What is the mechanism of hydrolysis of the iminium salt **1.48**?

☐ This is just the reverse of its formation.

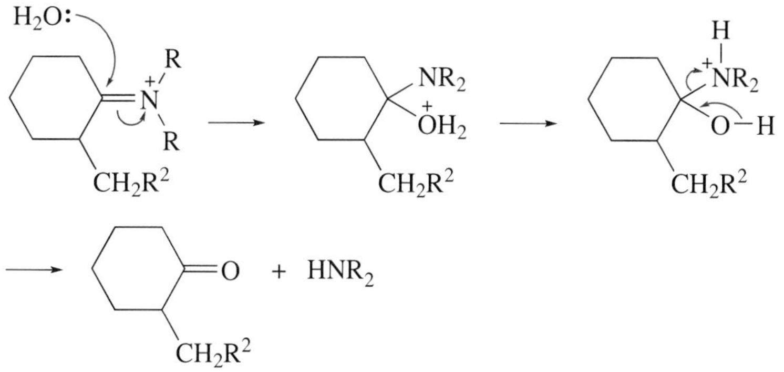

Such alkylations require relatively reactive alkylating agents, such as alkyl iodides, benzyl halides, α-haloesters, α-haloketones and α-haloethers. Of course, we could have achieved the same reaction using enolate methodology:

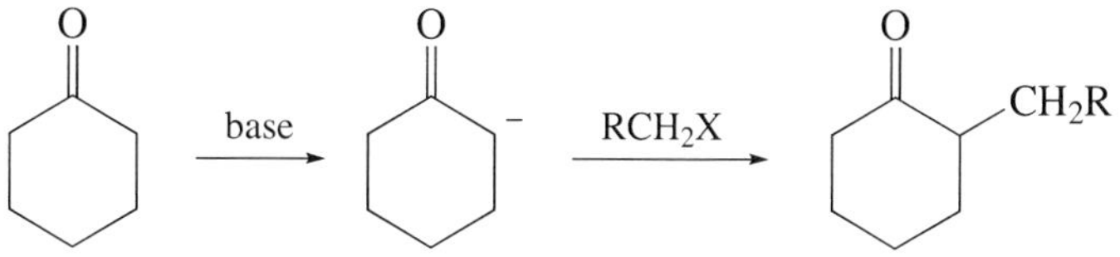

but the enamine strategy has the advantage that it proceeds under much milder conditions – no strong base is required and self-condensation is not a problem.

■ What will be the product of enamine formation and alkylation using pyrrolidine, 2-methylcyclohexanone and iodomethane?

☐ As discussed earlier, enamine formation proceeds to give mainly the less-substituted enamine, **1.49**. Alkylation followed by hydrolysis then gives the symmetrical ketone, **1.50**.

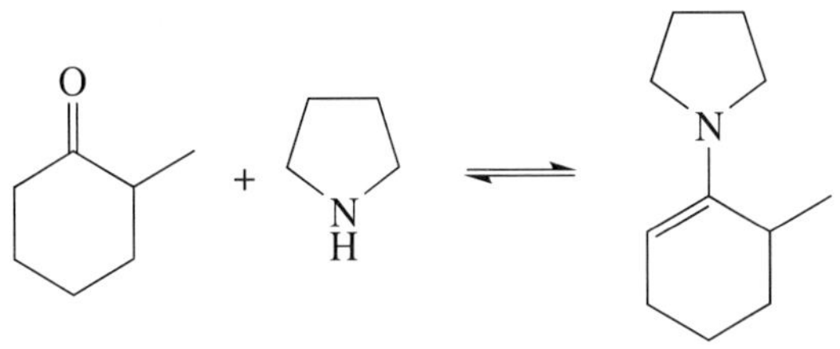

1.49

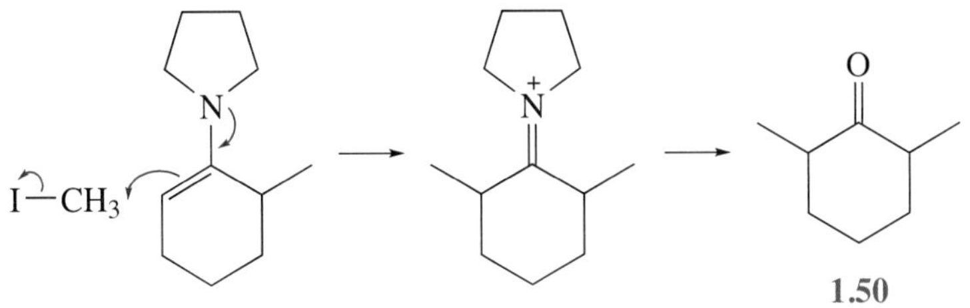

1.50

We thus arrive at the important observation that when the enamine strategy is used alkylation will occur at the less-substituted α-carbon. This compares with enolates where both patterns of regioselectivity can be observed, depending on the conditions.

Finally, we should mention that although we have concentrated on enamines from ketones, aldehydes can also be used to form enamines. In such cases, bulky secondary amines are required to form the enamine in order to reduce the amount of nitrogen alkylation.

1.9.1   Metallo-enamines

Just as enolate ions are formed by deprotonation of carbonyl compounds, the nitrogen analogue of enolate ions, metallo-enamines, can be prepared by deprotonation of imines. As with enolates, a strong base such as LDA is required.

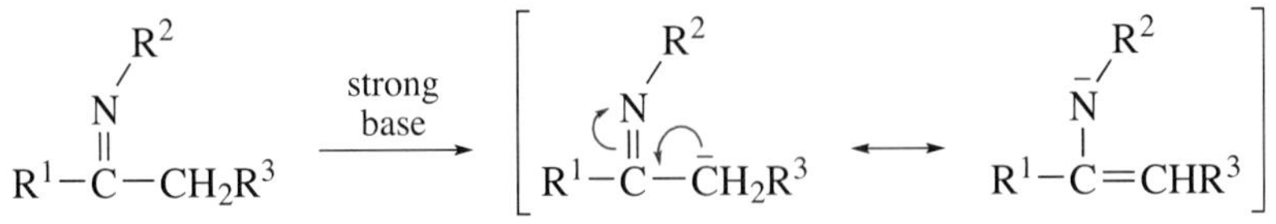

■   Will metallo-enamines be more or less reactive towards electrophiles than ordinary enamines?

☐   Just as enolates are more reactive than enols towards electrophiles, the negatively charged metallo-enamines will be much more nucleophilic than enamines. In fact metallo-enamines are even more nucleophilic than the corresponding enolate ions, and often more versatile for the alkylation of ketones and especially aldehydes – again, self-condensation is not a problem.

Just like enolate ions, metallo-enamines react with alkyl halides to give, after hydrolysis, an α-substituted ketone or aldehyde:

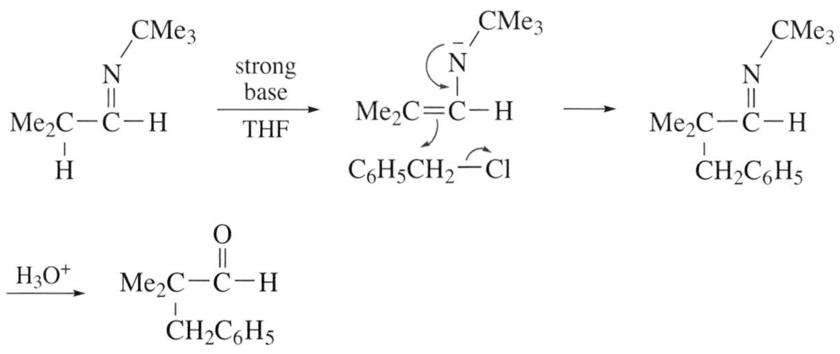

With unsymmetrical imines, metallo-enamines are formed by deprotonation from the less-substituted α-carbon, and thus subsequent alkylation also occurs at this site, just as found for enamines themselves.

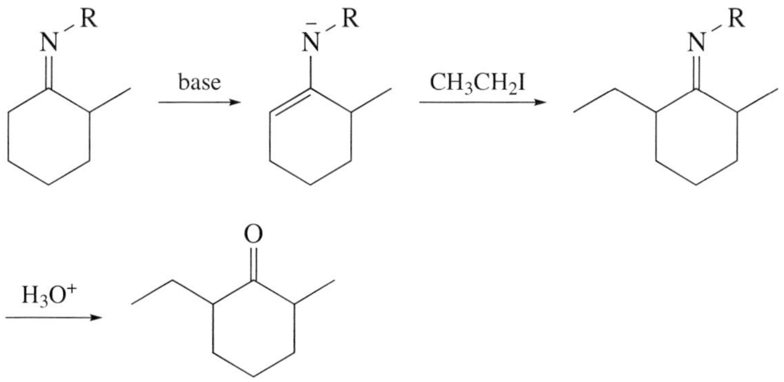

1.10   Conjugate addition of enols: the Michael reaction

So far in this unit, we have concentrated on the aldol reaction. Now we shall move on to a related reaction, the Michael reaction. Here again, an enolate attacks a carbonyl compound to form a new carbon–carbon bond, but in this case attack does not occur directly at the carbonyl and there is no subsequent loss of water.

1.10.1   Synthetic utility of the Michael reaction

α,β-unsaturated carbonyl compounds can undergo attack at two positions. Both the carbonyl carbon and the unsaturated carbon are electrophilic, leading to either 1,2- or 1,4- (conjugate) addition:

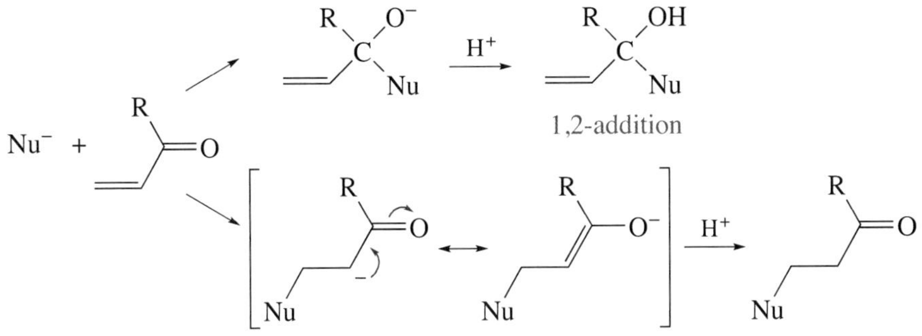

1,2-addition

1,4-addition

Just like other nucleophiles, enolates and enamines can react with α,β-unsaturated ketones, esters or nitriles via 1,4-addition. This reaction occurs in preference to the aldol reaction and is known as the Michael reaction.

■   Draw out the mechanism for the reaction between the ketone **1.51** and methyl acrylate (**1.52**), with potassium *tert*-butoxide as the base and *tert*-butanol as the solvent.

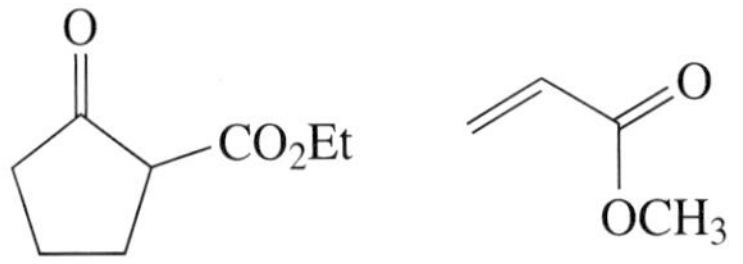

1.51   **1.52**

☐   The base catalyst removes a proton to form the stabilised enolate:

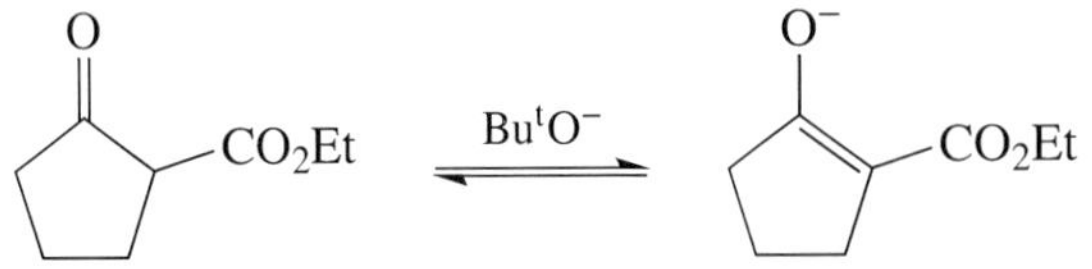

This nucleophile then attacks the α,β-unsaturated ester at the terminal CH$_2$; the product anion is a ketone enolate:

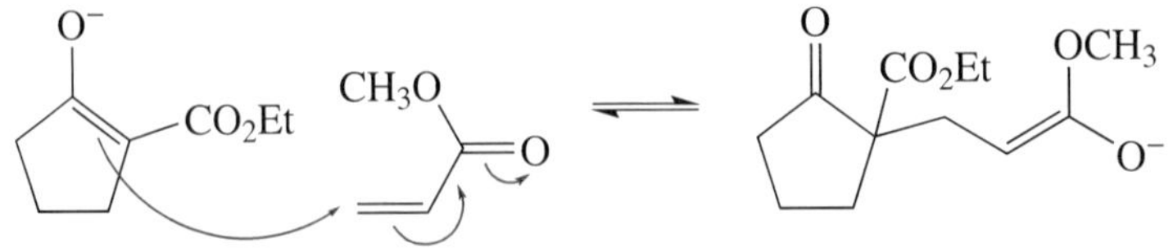

In the final step the ketone enolate abstracts a proton, either from the solvent or from the starting material. In general, as with the aldol reaction, all of these steps are reversible to some extent.

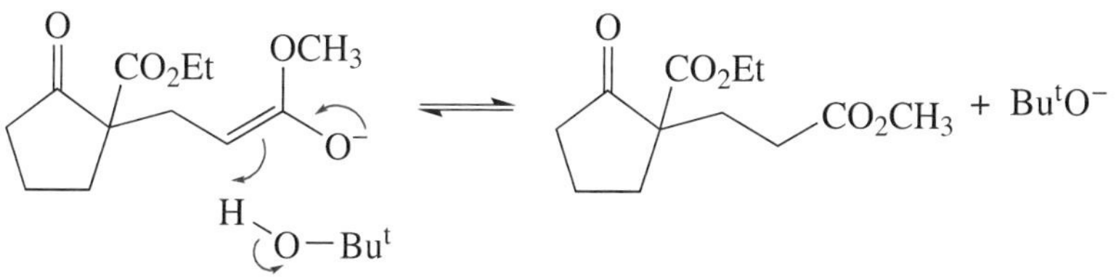

Notice that, like the aldol reaction, the Michael reaction is catalytic in base and does not require the use of a strong base. That is, quantitative formation of the enolate ion is not necessary. The reaction is applicable to a wide variety of enolates and enamines; usually stabilised enolates such as malonate esters or β-ketoesters are employed, but good yields can be obtained with simple ketones including kinetic enolates, given the correct conditions. The electrophilic component is typically an α,β-unsaturated ketone, aldehyde, ester or nitrile. Examples of this reaction are shown below in Equations 1.13 and 1.14:

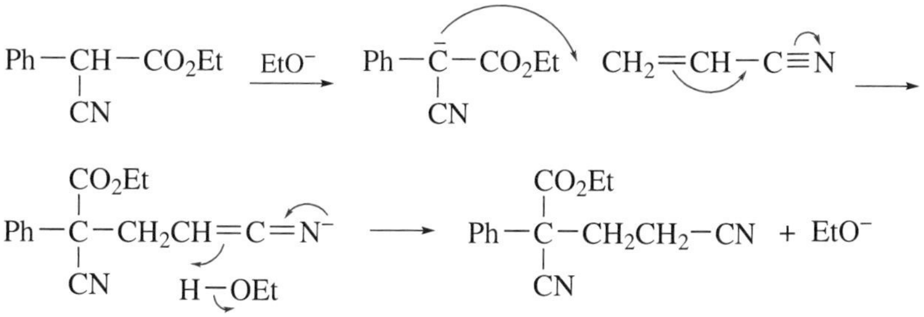

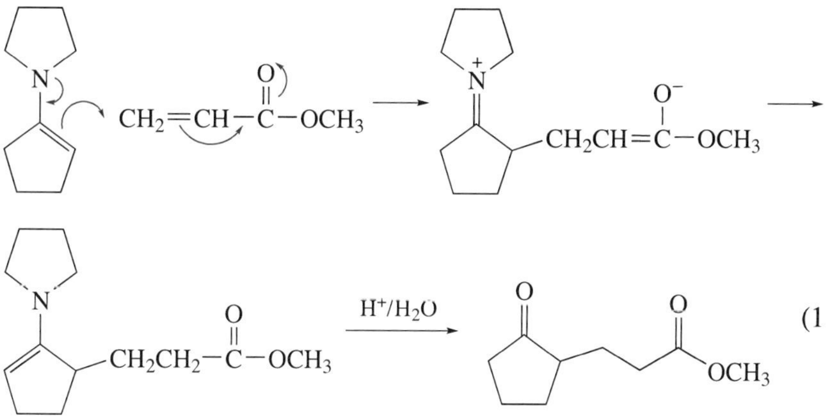

1.11 Acylation of enols and enolates: the Claisen condensation

So far in this unit we have concentrated on nucleophilic addition reactions of carbonyl compounds. However, when a good leaving group is attached to a carbonyl, as in esters, acid chlorides, etc., substitution can take place. Enolates, just like other nucleophiles, can take part in such nucleophilic substitutions and this offers a powerful method of carbon–carbon bond formation leading to 1,3-dicarbonyl compounds.

$$Y-\overset{\overset{\displaystyle O}{\|}}{C}-CH_2-R^1 \xrightarrow{\text{base}} Y-\overset{\overset{\displaystyle O}{\|}}{C}-\overset{-}{C}H-R^1 \qquad Y = \text{OR or R}$$

$$Y-\overset{\overset{\displaystyle O}{\|}}{C}-\overset{-}{C}H-R^1 \quad R^2-\overset{\overset{\displaystyle O}{\|}}{C}-X \longrightarrow Y-\overset{\overset{\displaystyle O}{\|}}{C}-\underset{\underset{\displaystyle R^1}{|}}{C}H-\overset{\overset{\displaystyle O^-}{|}}{C}-R^2$$

$$\longrightarrow Y-\overset{\overset{\displaystyle O}{\|}}{C}-\underset{\underset{\displaystyle R^1}{|}}{C}H-\overset{\overset{\displaystyle O}{\|}}{C}-R^2$$

Such reactions are known as Claisen-type condensations, and we shall focus on these reactions in this section. Generally the electrophilic carbonyl species is an ester, though anhydrides and acid chlorides can sometimes be employed. The nucleophilic component can be formed from another ester, or an aldehyde, ketone, nitrile, sulfoxide or nitro compound.

1.11.1   Bases in the Claisen condensation

■   What is the mechanism for the Claisen self-condensation of ethyl propanoate brought about by sodium ethoxide?

$$CH_3CH_2COOEt \xrightarrow{\text{NaOEt}} \quad ?$$

□   The mechanism is:

$$CH_3CH_2CO_2Et \underset{\text{NaOEt}}{\rightleftharpoons} CH_3\overset{-}{C}HCO_2Et$$

$$CH_3CH_2-\overset{\overset{\displaystyle O}{\|}}{C}-OEt$$
$$CH_3\overset{-}{C}H-CO_2Et \rightleftharpoons CH_3CH_2-\overset{\overset{\displaystyle O^-}{|}}{\underset{\underset{\displaystyle OEt}{|}}{C}}-\overset{\overset{\displaystyle H}{|}}{\underset{\underset{\displaystyle CH_3}{|}}{C}}-CO_2Et \rightleftharpoons$$

$$CH_3CH_2-\overset{\overset{\displaystyle O}{\|}}{C}-\overset{\overset{\displaystyle H}{|}}{\underset{\underset{\displaystyle CH_3}{|}}{C}}-CO_2Et \xrightarrow{\text{EtO}^-} CH_3CH_2-\overset{\overset{\displaystyle O}{\|}}{C}-\overset{-}{\underset{\underset{\displaystyle CH_3}{|}}{C}}-CO_2Et$$

1.53

Notice that **1.53** is a 1,3-dicarbonyl compound. As with the aldol condensation, the Claisen condensation is reversible up to this point. However, because the 1,3-dicarbonyl **1.53** has a very much lower pK_a than any of the other species present, including ethanol, it can easily form an enolate and this last step is essentially irreversible. So, if we use at least one mole equivalent of base, the overall reaction is effectively driven to completion by formation of the stable enolate. Acidification of the reaction mixture when the reaction is complete, usually with the weak acid ethanoic acid, then yields the β-ketoester.

■ What factors would determine the choice of alkoxide base in the Claisen condensation?

□ The alkoxide must be the same as the alcohol portion of the ester so that ester exchange is not a problem.

Notice that, as in the aldol and Michael reactions, a strong base that quantitatively forms the nucleophilic enolate in the first step is not necessarily required. Only a small proportion of the nucleophilic enolate need be formed at equilibrium for the reaction to proceed. One popular method of performing a Claisen-type condensation is to use sodium hydride as the base in the presence of a trace of the alcohol. In this case, it is likely that the effective base is sodium alkoxide formed by reaction of sodium hydride with the alcohol:

$$NaH \; + \; ROH \; \rightleftharpoons \; Na^+ \; + \; RO^- \; + \; H_2$$

$$2R^1{-}CH_2{-}\overset{\displaystyle O}{\underset{\displaystyle OR}{C}} \; + \; RO^- \; \rightleftharpoons \; R^1{-}CH_2{-}\overset{\displaystyle O}{C}{-}\underset{\displaystyle R^1}{\overset{\displaystyle -}{C}}{-}\overset{\displaystyle O}{\underset{\displaystyle OR}{C}} \; + \; 2ROH$$

As the reaction proceeds, more alcohol is produced, which reacts with sodium hydride to form more sodium alkoxide to act as the base. As well as providing the base for the reaction, the irreversible consumption of the alcohol product as it is formed also forces the reaction to completion.

■ Can you foresee a problem with the following Claisen condensation:

$$(CH_3)_2CH{-}CO_2Et \; \xrightarrow{\text{NaOEt}} \; ?$$

□ The product, **1.54**, has no protons that are alpha to both carbonyls, so the equilibrium cannot be driven to the right by the formation of a stable enolate.

$$(CH_3)_2CH{-}\overset{\displaystyle O}{C}{-}\underset{\displaystyle CH_3}{\overset{\displaystyle CH_3}{C}}{-}\overset{\displaystyle O}{C}{-}CO_2Et$$

1.54

This difficulty can be overcome by using a stronger base. If the triphenylmethide ion is used, the equilibrium for the initial formation of the reactant enolate anion is greatly favoured and the condensation proceeds in good yield.

$$(CH_3)_2CHCO_2Et \; + \; Ph_3C^- \; \rightleftharpoons \; (CH_3)_2\bar{C}CO_2Et \; + \; Ph_3CH$$

Now look at the overall reaction:

$$Ph_3C^- + 2(CH_3)_2CH-CO_2Et \rightleftharpoons (CH_3)_2CH-CO-C(CH_3)_2-CO_2Et$$
$$+ Ph_3CH + EtO^-$$

and compare this with the overall reaction for the ethoxide-induced reaction:

$$2(CH_3)_2CH-CO_2Et \underset{}{\overset{EtO^-}{\rightleftharpoons}} (CH_3)_2CH-CO-C(CH_3)_2-CO_2Et + EtOH$$

The equilibrium for the first reaction will be much more favoured than the second because the triphenylmethide ion is such a strong base. One way of illustrating this is merely to subtract the second equation from the first, when we obtain the equation:

$$Ph_3C^- + EtOH \rightleftharpoons Ph_3CH + EtO^-$$

Because Ph_3C^- is a very strong base, the equilibrium here lies well to the right.

■   What is wrong with the following Claisen-type condensation?

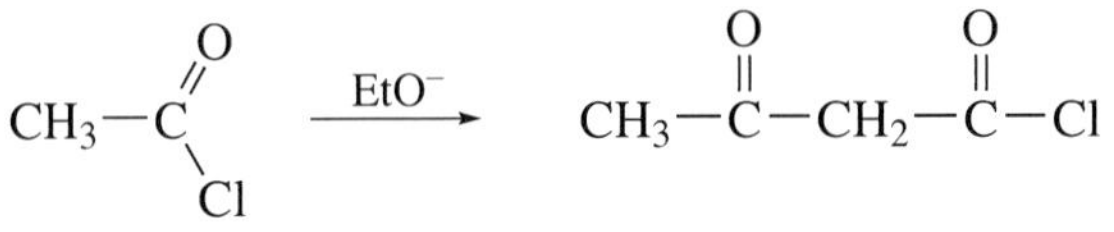

☐   Rather than abstract a proton to form an enolate, the ethoxide ion will react with the acid chloride to give an ester; thus all the base is consumed.

When an acid chloride or acid anhydride is used as the electrophilic carbonyl species in a Claisen-type condensation, a strong non-nucleophilic base is normally used to preform the enolate quantitatively before reaction with the carboxylic acid derivative:

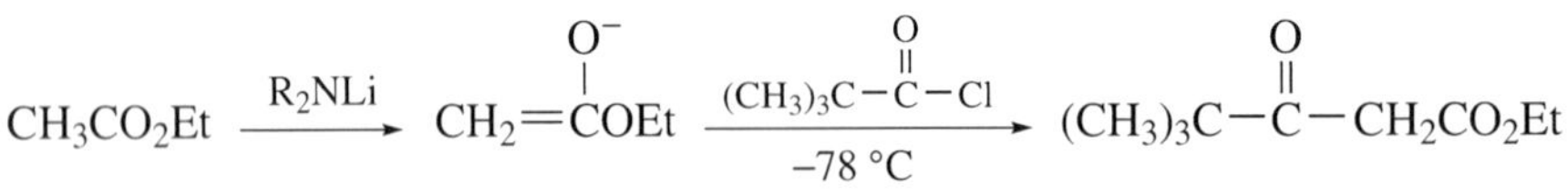

Such reactions must be carried out in non-nucleophilic solvents to prevent solvolysis of the acid anhydride or chloride. Also, the use of such highly reactive acylating agents may also lead to a good deal of oxygen acylation as a side reaction.

1.11.2 Mixed Claisen-type condensation

Now that we have reviewed the Claisen condensation in terms of mechanism and choice of base, let's examine the scope of its use in synthesis. This is often limited when attempting mixed Claisen condensations. For example, if two different esters are used, each possessing an α-hydrogen, a mixture of all four products is generally obtained and the reaction is seldom useful synthetically:

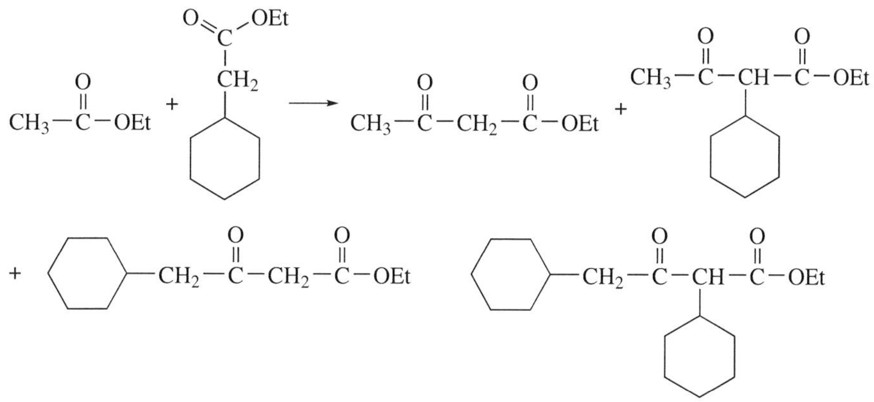

■ Under what circumstances can mixed Claisen condensations be performed?

□ Like mixed aldol reactions, mixed Claisen condensations are possible if one of the reagents has no α-hydrogens, and is relatively electrophilic. Examples of such esters with no α-hydrogens include aromatic esters, formyl esters such as **1.55**, diethyl carbonate (**1.56**) and diethyl oxalate (**1.57**).

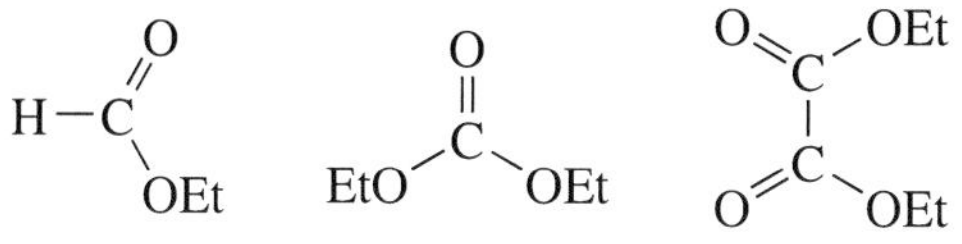

1.55   1.56   1.57

For example,

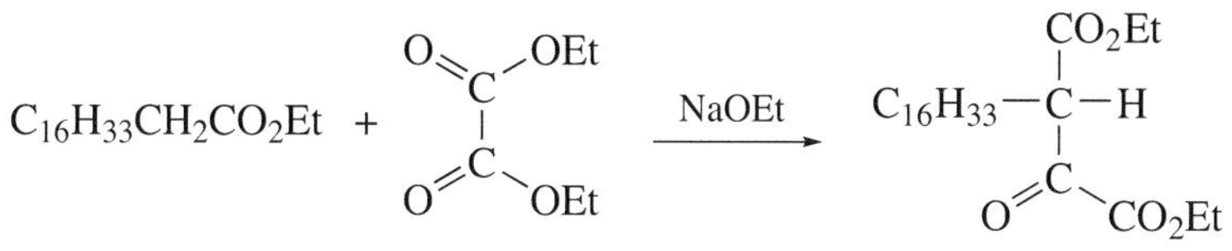

So far in this discussion, we have examined only the Claisen condensation between esters but, as we said earlier, the acylation of ketones is a good route for making 1,3-diketones. This mixed Claisen condensation works best when the ester component has no α-hydrogen atoms, but this does not need to be the case, for example:

$$CH_3\overset{\overset{\displaystyle O}{\|}}{-C}-CH_3 \ + \ CH_3(CH_2)_4CO_2Et \ \xrightarrow{\text{base}} \ CH_3\overset{\overset{\displaystyle O}{\|}}{-C}-CH_2-\overset{\overset{\displaystyle O}{\|}}{C}-(CH_2)_4CH_3$$

60%

Because the ketone is considerably more acidic than the ester, it forms an enolate more readily, which is one of the reasons why this mixed condensation product is obtained and self-condensation of the ester is not a problem. Here, of course, you might imagine that the aldol self-condensation of the ketone could be a possible side reaction. However, the aldol condensation is reversible whereas the Claisen condensation is effectively irreversible, because one mole equivalent of base is used to trap the product as its enolate ion.

Study note

Before moving on to Section 2 you should produce your own summary of Sections 1.8 to 1.11 and then compare it with ours. Go to Unit 7 summaries in Unit 7 resources.

2 The Wittig reaction

When we consider the synthesis of alkenes, it is clear that the position of the double bond does not usually pose an issue. For example, we might try and synthesise the alkene **2.1** using the dehydration of an alcohol, which could be synthesised from cyclohexanone and a methyl Grignard reagent.

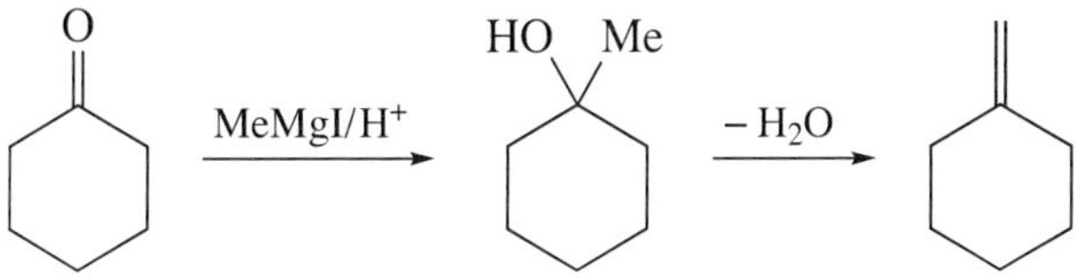

However there is a problem associated with this strategy. Elimination of the elements of water can occur in two different ways, and in practice leads to a predominance of the thermodynamically more-stable endocyclic product **2.2**.

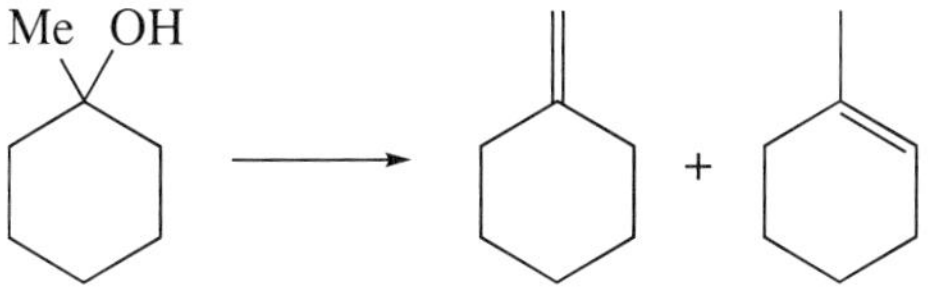

Clearly, then, this strategy has the weakness of relying on a transformation that is not completely regioselective, and in practice may not even give rise to the desired compound as the major product.

What is needed is a highly regioselective reaction that involves reagents which will not isomerise the products once formed. The ideal reaction from a synthetic viewpoint would replace the carbonyl group by a carbon–carbon double bond, so that the position of unsaturation in the product would be unambiguous. In 1953, such a reaction was developed. It became known as the Wittig reaction after its originator, the German chemist Georg Wittig. We will consider this reaction in more detail by taking as an example its use for the conversion of cyclohexanone into methylenecyclohexane (**2.1**). Nucleophilic attack by triphenylphosphine on iodomethane gives a compound called a **phosphonium salt** (**2.3**; Equation 2.1) which, on treatment with a strong base such as sodium hydride or butyllithium, loses a proton to produce the corresponding **phosphorane**, in this case methylenetri-phenylphosphorane. The bonding in phosphoranes is usually regarded as a resonance hybrid of the ylide and the so-called ylene structures (Unit 3 Section 2.6).

$$Ph_3P: + CH_3I \longrightarrow Ph_3\overset{+}{P}-CH_3 \ I^-$$

2.3

$$\xrightarrow{\text{base}} \left[Ph_3\overset{+}{P}-\overset{-}{CH_2} \longleftrightarrow Ph_3P=CH_2 \right] \qquad (2.1)$$

ylide   ylene

methylenetriphenylphosphorane

It is worth noting that the acidity of the hydrogen atoms in alkanes is very low; the butyl anion is therefore an exceedingly strong base, and butyllithium a very commonly used reagent for such reactions.

Phosphoranes are extremely reactive and the carbonyl compound is added as soon as their formation is complete. The reaction proceeds in three stages as shown in Scheme 2.1: the initial step involves nucleophilic attack of the carbonyl by the phosphorane (analogous to the Grignard reaction) to form a betaine intermediate (a dipolar molecule with charges on non-adjacent atoms); cyclisation then takes place to form an oxaphosphetane intermediate; finally, loss of triphenylphosphine oxide (**2.4**) in a concerted process gives the product alkene, which in our example is methylenecyclohexane (**2.1**).

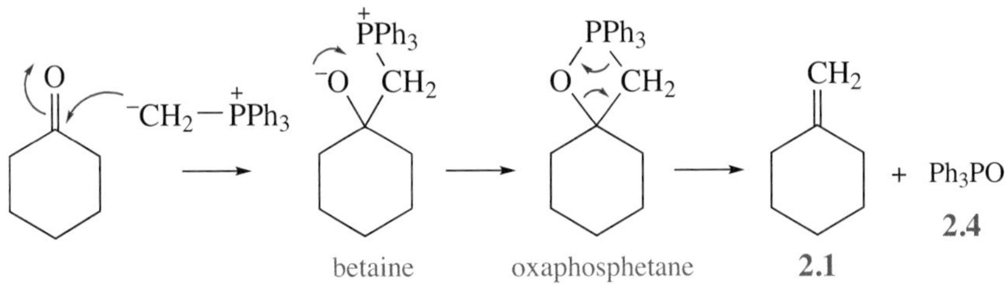

betaine   oxaphosphetane   **2.1**

Scheme 2.1

So, in the Wittig reaction only one regioisomeric alkene is formed, not a mixture as in the Grignard-dehydration method. The Wittig reaction is totally regioselective; there is no ambiguity as to the position of the double bond in the product – it always replaces the carbonyl group.

In the Wittig reaction, the phosphonium group serves to stabilise an adjacent carbanion which is the nucleophile in the reaction.

■   Nitrogen is more electronegative than phosphorus, so do you think the $Ph_3\overset{+}{N}$ group would stabilise an adjacent carbanion as efficiently as $Ph_3\overset{+}{P}$?

☐   If the only form of carbanion stabilisation in phosphoranes were inductive electron withdrawal, the answer would be yes. In fact, nitrogen ylides are not sufficiently stable to be of use in the Wittig reaction, so there must be an additional form of carbanion stabilisation present in phosphoranes. The additional stabilisation provided by phosphorus results from resonance stabilisation involving the ylene resonance structure of the phosphorane.

Phosphorus, and other elements in the third row of the Periodic Table, unlike nitrogen and other second-row elements, can expand their valence shell to ten electrons and thus stabilise an adjacent carbanion by resonance. In addition, it seems likely that at least part of the 'driving force' of the Wittig reaction is provided by the replacement of a phosphorus–carbon bond by a stronger phosphorus–oxygen bond.

2.1 Scope and limitations of the Wittig reaction

You now have an idea of the mechanism of the Wittig reaction and have also seen some of the reasons why the choice of phosphorus is so important to the success of this synthetic method. But, so far, you know very little about the range of carbonyl substrates that can be employed in the Wittig reaction, the variety of substituted phosphoranes available, or the reaction conditions that are employed. Let's discuss these points in order.

2.1.1 The carbonyl component

The carbonyl component of the Wittig reaction can be an aldehyde or a ketone (Figure 2.1). Carboxylic esters react only slowly in the Wittig reaction, and so can be present elsewhere in the carbonyl substrate and survive the reaction; this indicates the chemoselectivity of the reaction with respect to the carbonyl group.

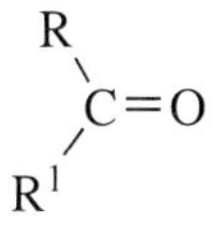

R, R^1 = H, alkyl, aryl

(compatible functional groups: alkenes, alkynes, amines, esters, ethers, acetals, nitroaryl, haloaryl)

Figure 2.1 The range of carbonyl compounds that can be employed in the Wittig reaction.

■ Why do you think esters react less readily than aldehydes or ketones?

□ They are less electrophilic due to resonance involving the alkoxy substituent, thereby making the carbonyl carbon less positive.

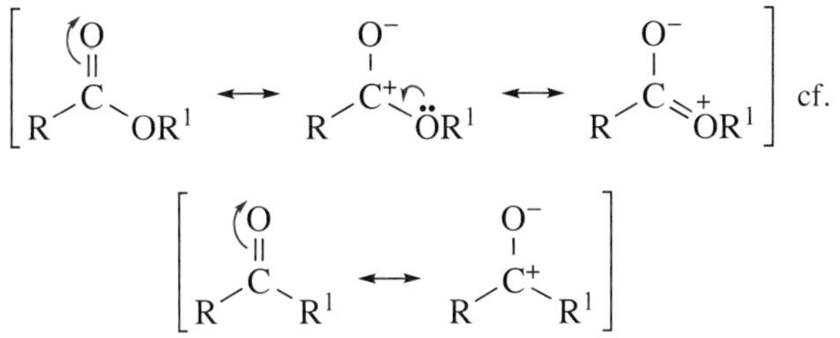

2.1.2 The phosphorane

The phosphorane is prepared by treating the corresponding phosphonium salt (itself obtained from a primary or secondary halo compound and triphenylphosphine) with an appropriate base. The types of Wittig reagent you have met so far have had R^2 and R^3 in Figure 2.2 as H, alkyl or aryl, and we refer to these as normal phosphoranes. In general, however, the same functional groups that can be present in the carbonyl component can also be present in R^2 and R^3.

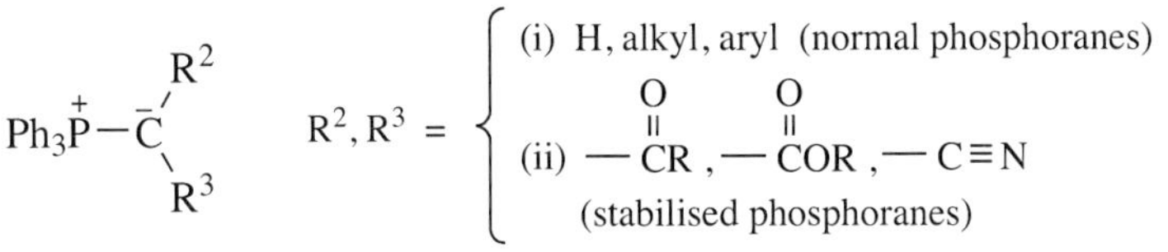

$$Ph_3\overset{+}{P}-\overset{R^2}{\underset{R^3}{\overset{|}{\underset{|}{\overset{-}{C}}}}} \qquad R^2, R^3 = \begin{cases} \text{(i) H, alkyl, aryl (normal phosphoranes)} \\[2mm] \text{(ii)} \ -\overset{\overset{O}{\|}}{C}R, -\overset{\overset{O}{\|}}{C}OR, -C\equiv N \\ \text{(stabilised phosphoranes)} \end{cases}$$

Figure 2.2 The range of phosphoranes that can be employed in the Wittig reaction.

Although ketones react with unstabilised Wittig reagents, self-condensation of reagents stabilised by ketone groups does not occur: this is because resonance reduces both the nucleophilic character of the carbanion and the electrophilic character of the carbonyl group.

Phosphoranes can also be prepared when R^2 or R^3 is capable of stabilising an adjacent carbanion by resonance, for example a directly attached ketone, ester or nitrile group. These compounds have special properties and are known as stabilised phosphoranes, for example **2.5**.

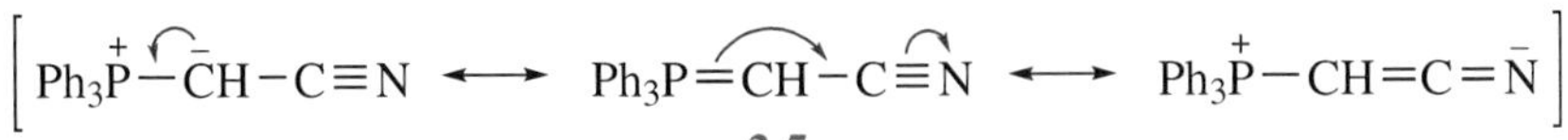

$$\left[Ph_3\overset{+}{P}-\overset{-}{C}H-C\equiv N \longleftrightarrow Ph_3P=CH-C\equiv N \longleftrightarrow Ph_3\overset{+}{P}-CH=C=\overset{-}{N} \right]$$
$$\textbf{2.5}$$

It should be noted that, though aldehydes react readily with disubstituted phosphoranes to give trisubstituted alkenes, the reaction of ketones with disubstituted phosphoranes (e.g. **2.6**) to form tetrasubstituted alkenes is often found to be of little synthetic use, presumably for steric reasons.

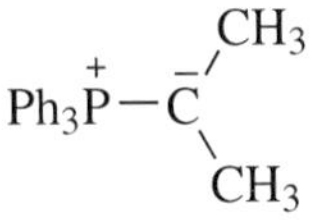

2.1.3 The reaction

2.6

Normal phosphoranes are extremely reactive and react rapidly with air and moisture as well as with ketones and aldehydes. Because of this, they are usually generated in a dry (i.e. water-free) solvent under an inert atmosphere (nitrogen or argon) by treatment of the phosphonium salt with a strong base such as butyllithium (Equation 2.2). The Wittig reaction is then carried out by immediate addition of the carbonyl compound. (Note that, in general, the reaction is only synthetically useful if one or more of R, R^1, R^2 or R^3 is H.)

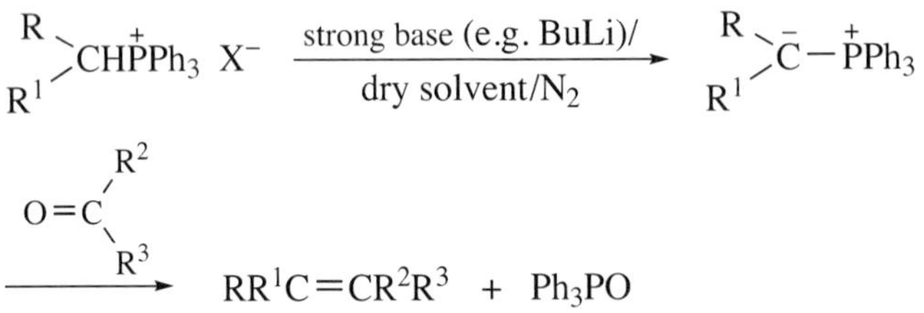

$$\underset{R^1}{\overset{R}{>}}CH\overset{+}{P}Ph_3 \ X^- \xrightarrow[\text{dry solvent/N}_2]{\text{strong base (e.g. BuLi)/}} \underset{R^1}{\overset{R}{>}}\overset{-}{C}-\overset{+}{P}Ph_3$$

$$O=C\overset{R^2}{\underset{R^3}{\overset{\diagup}{\diagdown}}}$$

$$\xrightarrow{} RR^1C=CR^2R^3 + Ph_3PO \qquad (2.2)$$

In contrast, stabilised phosphoranes are usually isolable crystalline solids which are stable to air and moisture. They also do not require such a strong base for their preparation, for example, NaOH rather than butyllithium (Equation 2.3).

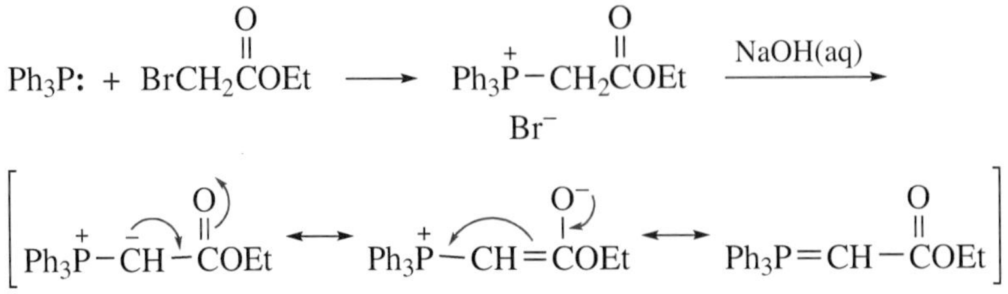

$$Ph_3P: + BrCH_2\overset{\overset{O}{\|}}{C}OEt \longrightarrow \underset{Br^-}{Ph_3\overset{+}{P}-CH_2\overset{\overset{O}{\|}}{C}OEt} \xrightarrow{NaOH(aq)}$$

$$\left[Ph_3\overset{+}{P}-\overset{-}{C}H-\overset{\overset{O)}{|}}{C}OEt \longleftrightarrow Ph_3\overset{+}{P}-CH=\overset{\overset{O^-}{|}}{C}OEt \longleftrightarrow Ph_3P=CH-\overset{\overset{O}{\|}}{C}OEt \right] \qquad (2.3)$$

2 The Wittig reaction

Because of their stability, stabilised phosphoranes can be isolated and purified prior to use. The great advantage of these reagents is that, as well as linking two molecular fragments by a double bond, they also introduce a new functional group to allow further synthetic modification of the product.

$$\begin{array}{c}\diagdown \\ \diagup\end{array} C{=}O \;+\; Ph_3\overset{+}{P}{-}\overset{-}{C}HCO_2Et \;\longrightarrow\; \begin{array}{c}\diagdown \\ \diagup\end{array} C{=}CHCO_2Et \;+\; Ph_3PO \qquad\qquad (2.4)$$

However, stabilised phosphoranes do have a drawback: the additional delocalisation of charge reduces their nucleophilicity.

■ Would you expect phosphoranes to react more rapidly with aldehydes or with ketones?

□ Ketones are less electrophilic and so aldehydes react more rapidly.

Stabilised phosphoranes, unlike normal phosphoranes, react rapidly only with aldehydes. The reaction with ketones is usually too slow to be of synthetic use. Fortunately, as you will see in the next part of this section, there is an alternative method that does allow the formation of alkenes from ketones by a related process known as the Wadsworth–Emmons reaction.

2.2 The Wadsworth–Emmons reaction

One of the limitations of the use of stabilised phosphoranes in the Wittig reaction is their very slow reactions with ketones. It was with this in mind that the Wadsworth–Emmons reaction was developed. In this process, the stabilised phosphoranes are replaced by a more nucleophilic reagent, namely the anions of phosphonate esters (for example **2.7** where Y is R^1CO-, R^1OCO- or $-C{\equiv}N$). The phosphonate esters required can be prepared by treatment of the corresponding halocompound with triethyl phosphite (the Arbuzov reaction, Equation 2.5).

$$\underset{\substack{\text{triethyl}\\\text{phosphite}}}{(EtO)_3P} \;+\; BrCH_2Y \;\longrightarrow\; EtBr \;+ \underset{\substack{\text{phosphonate}\\\text{ester}}}{(EtO)_2\overset{\underset{\|}{O}}{P}CH_2Y} \quad Y = \begin{cases} -\overset{\underset{\|}{O}}{C}R \\ -\overset{\underset{\|}{O}}{C}OR \\ -C{\equiv}N \end{cases} \qquad (2.5)$$

$$\overset{\underset{\|}{O}}{(RO)_2P}{-}\overset{-}{C}HY$$

2.7

On treatment with a strong base in a dry solvent under an inert atmosphere, phosphonate esters give a reactive phosphonate ester anion, which is reacted in situ with a carbonyl compound. Good yields are obtained with aldehydes *and* with ketones.

$$\underset{(EtO)_2PCH_2COEt}{\overset{O\quad O}{\overset{\|\quad\|}{}}} \xrightarrow[\text{benzene/N}_2]{\text{NaH/}} \underset{(EtO)_2PCHCOEt}{\overset{O\quad O}{\overset{\|\ -\ \|}{}}}$$

$$+ \ (EtO)_2PO^- \ Na^+ \qquad\qquad (2.6)$$

2.8

You can gain some idea of the relative reactivity of phosphonate ester anions and phosphoranes from the fact that the final stage in the reaction to produce **2.8** above took less than 30 minutes at room temperature and gave the product **2.8** in 70% yield. In contrast, the corresponding phosphorane, even in neat cyclohexanone, only reacted on heating to 170 °C for 10 hours!

A further advantage of the Wadsworth–Emmons reaction is that the phosphorus-containing by-product is water-soluble and hence easily separated from the organic product. This contrasts with phosphorane reactions, where the organic product usually has to be separated from the triphenylphosphine oxide by-product by distillation or chromatography.

By changing the substituents on phosphorus in phosphonate esters, reagents of varying reactivity and usefulness can be obtained, but we do not have the time or space to discuss these modifications further. The reagents we have introduced are sufficiently versatile to enable most synthetic problems requiring the use of the Wittig or Wadsworth–Emmons reactions to be solved. These reagents and their capabilities are summarised in Table 2.1.

Table 2.1 Various types of reagents used in alkene formation.

Reaction	Type of reagent	Example	Carbonyl substrate
Wittig	normal phosphorane	$\overset{+}{Ph_3P}\!-\!\overset{-}{C}HCH_3$	aldehyde or ketone
Wittig	stabilised phosphorane	$\overset{+}{Ph_3P}\!-\!\overset{-}{C}HCN$	aldehyde only
Wadsworth–Emmons	stabilised phosphonate ester anion*	$(EtO)_2\overset{O}{\overset{\|}{P}}\!-\!\overset{-}{C}HCN$	aldehyde or ketone

*Phosphonate anions which lack additional stabilisation (e.g. $(EtO)_2P(O)CH_2^-$) are not synthetically useful.

2.3 Stereochemistry of alkene formation

Clearly, with the ability to introduce a carbon–carbon double bond with complete regioselectivity, the combination of Wittig and Wadsworth–Emmons reactions represented a very significant addition to the battery of synthetic methods available to the organic chemist. However, it is often necessary not only to place a double bond at a particular position in a molecule, but also to ensure that it has a particular stereochemistry. When first investigated, the stereoselectivity of the Wittig reaction seemed to be disappointing. For example, in the synthesis of l-phenylbuta-l,3-diene from the ylide **2.9** and benzaldehyde, the product was obtained as a 1 : 1 mixture of the *E* isomer and the *Z* isomer.

1-phenylbuta-1,3-diene

Not unsurprisingly, this result did not excite a great deal of interest at the time, since it seemed to indicate that the Wittig reaction was simply not stereoselective. However, subsequent investigation showed that, depending on the structure of the ylide, the direction of coupling and the type of solvent and base used, the stereochemistry of the product varied from almost totally *Z* to completely *E*. Nonetheless, although the dependence of the alkene stereochemistry on these various factors is now very much more clearly appreciated, there is still not complete agreement as to the fundamental reasons why certain conditions give the stereochemistry found in practice.

Clearly, to understand why these results are obtained requires a detailed knowledge and understanding of the mechanism of the Wittig reaction. Unfortunately, though there seems to be general agreement that this involves a two-stage process initiated by nucleophilic attack of the ylide on the carbonyl group, many of the more detailed aspects remain controversial. As a consequence, it is not possible within the scope of this course to give a satisfactory explanation for the wide variation in product stereochemistry observed in practice. However, it is possible to give some empirical rules that allow the likely stereochemistry for a given substrate and given conditions to be predicted with a considerable degree of reliability.

It has been found that the stereochemistry of the products obtained in the Wittig reaction depends strongly on whether the ylide is 'reactive' (i.e. 'normal') or 'stabilised'. So we shall begin by considering the effect of structure on stereoselectivity before going on to look at the effect of the particular base/solvent combination used.

2.3.1   Structure of substrates

When the need to control the stereochemistry of the product alkenes formed by the Wittig reaction was realised, it soon became apparent that the structure of the phosphorane is of crucial importance. Most 'normal' phosphoranes give predominantly *Z* products whereas stabilised ones give mainly *E* products. The phosphorane discussed above (**2.9**) lies inbetween: the vinyl group,

−CH=CH$_2$, provides some resonance stabilisation but less than that of carbonyl and cyano groups. So it is perhaps not too surprising to find that, in practice, roughly equal amounts of the two possible diastereoisomers are formed.

The mechanism of the Wadsworth–Emmons reaction is thought to be broadly analogous to that of the Wittig reaction. Accordingly, since the Wadsworth–Emmons route is only practical for stabilised phosphonates, by analogy with the Wittig reaction, it is perhaps not totally unexpected to find that E products predominate.

Over the years, much detailed investigation has shown that the above broad generalisations have to be modified, often quite dramatically, depending on, for example, the particular base or solvent used, or whether the reaction is carried out homogeneously or heterogeneously. So we shall now look at the effect of some of these factors on the stereochemistry of alkene formation.

2.3.2   Reaction conditions

In the early days of the Wittig reactions, the base used to form the phosphorane from the phosphonium salt was, more often than not, butyllithium. Such reactions often gave significant amounts of E alkene even with reactive ylides. It was some time before the realisation came that it was the use of butyllithium that was affecting the $E : Z$ ratio of the products. For each millimole of butyllithium reacted, an equivalent amount of lithium ions were released. Lithium ions are now known to form strong complexes with oxygen or nitrogen atoms, particularly those bearing some negative charge.

Accordingly, it is thought that the diastereoisomeric betaines (**2.10** or **2.11**) formed initially form complexes with the lithium ions as they are released.

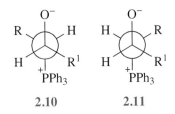

2.10   2.11

The result seems to be to cause a degree of equilibration that enhances the yield of the minor isomer. The effect of the lithium ion can be seen from the data in Table 2.2, which contrasts the relative amounts of products obtained under so-called salt-free conditions (that is, under conditions where no coordinating cations, such as Li$^+$, are present) with the effect of adding lithium iodide. The salt-free solution of the ylide was obtained by the use of sodamide, NaNH$_2$, in liquid ammonia, followed by evaporation of the ammonia, solution of the ylide in benzene and filtration to remove the NaBr by-product.

Table 2.2   Effect of lithium salts on the $Z : E$ ratio.

Conditions	Yield/%	$Z : E$ ratio
salt-free	88	24 : 1
added LiI	81	5 : 1

$$Ph_3\overset{+}{P}-CH_2CH_2CH_3 \quad \xrightarrow[\text{NH}_3(l)]{\text{NaNH}_2/} \quad Ph_3\overset{+}{P}-\overset{-}{C}HCH_2CH_3 + NaBr \xrightarrow[\substack{\text{filter off}\\ \text{NaBr}}]{C_6H_6}$$
$$Br^-$$

$$Ph_3\overset{+}{P}-\overset{-}{C}HCH_2CH_3 \xrightarrow{\text{PhCHO}} \quad \underset{H}{\overset{Ph}{\diagdown}}C=\underset{H}{\overset{Et}{\diagup}}C \quad + \quad \underset{H}{\overset{Ph}{\diagdown}}C=\underset{Et}{\overset{H}{\diagup}}C \qquad (2.7)$$
$$\text{(salt-free)} \qquad\qquad\qquad\qquad (Z) \qquad\qquad\quad (E)$$

The presence of lithium salts is found to affect the $Z : E$ ratio only when the reaction is carried out in non-polar solvents. If polar aprotic solvents such as dimethylformamide (DMF) or dimethyl sulfoxide (DMSO) are used no such effect is found and the product obtained from reactive ylides is predominantly Z.

■ Can you suggest why this should be so?

☐ Such solvents are able to coordinate with the Li^+ ions and so prevent them from forming a complex with the betaine.

Table 2.3 summarises the effect of varying the reaction conditions on the stereoselectivity of the Wittig reaction with aldehydes as substrates (the situation becomes more complex when ketones are involved). Table 2.4 shows the product ratios obtained for some specific examples.

Table 2.3   Stereoselectivity of the Wittig reaction.*

Conditions	Stabilised phosphoranes	Non-stabilised phosphoranes
polar solvent		
aprotic, e.g. DMSO	predominantly E	predominantly Z
protic, e.g. 2-methyl-2-propanol	increased proportion of Z	– †
non-polar solvent		
salt-free	predominantly E	predominantly Z
with salt, e.g. LiI	increased proportion of Z	increased proportion of E

*Intermediate phosphoranes (e.g. those stabilised by phenyl or vinyl groups) show little or no stereoselectivity under any conditions.

†Since reactive phosporanes are such strong bases, protic solvents are not used for carrying out the Wittig reaction.

Table 2.4 *Z* : *E* product ratios in the Wittig reaction.

Phosphorane	Carbonyl compound	Reaction conditions*	*Z* : *E* ratio
$Ph_3\overset{+}{P}-\overset{-}{C}HCH_2CH_3$	CH_3CH_2CHO	BuLi/DMF	95 : 5
$Ph_3\overset{+}{P}-\overset{-}{C}HCH_3$	PhCHO	NaNH$_2$/benzene	87 : 13
		BuLi/benzene/Li$^+$	58 : 42
		K$_2$CO$_3$/THF/crown ether(catalyst)	85 : 15
$Ph_3\overset{+}{P}-\overset{-}{C}H(CH_2)_3CH_3$	$CH_3CO_2(CH_2)_8CHO$	NaN(SiMe$_3$)$_2$/THF	98 : 2
$Ph_3\overset{+}{P}-\overset{-}{C}HPh$	PhCHO	PhLi/ether	30 : 70
$Ph_3\overset{+}{P}-\overset{-}{C}H(CH_2)_2CO_2Et$	$CH_3(CH_2)_3CHO$	NaN(SiMe$_3$)$_2$/THF/-78 °C	98 : 2
$Ph_3\overset{+}{P}-\overset{-}{C}HCO_2Et$	CH_3CHO	DMF	3 : 97
		DMF/Li$^+$	20 : 80
		MeOH	38 : 62
$Ph_3\overset{+}{P}-\overset{-}{C}HCO_2Et$	PhCHO	EtOH	15 : 85
		C$_6$H$_6$	5 : 95
		DMF	6 : 94
$Ph_3\overset{+}{P}-\overset{-}{C}HCOPh$	p-NO$_2$C$_6$H$_4$CHO	CHCl$_3$	0 : 100
$Ph_3\overset{+}{P}-\overset{-}{C}HCN$	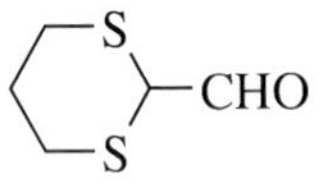 (dithiane)–CHO	BuLi/THF	0 : 100
$Ph_3\overset{+}{P}-\overset{-}{C}HCHO$	OHC–CHO	DMF/80 °C	0 : 100†

*The base is not given for stabilised phosphoranes, since they are crystalline compounds that can be purified; a wide range of bases may be used.

†Two molecules of phosphorane reacted with the dialdehyde to give (*E*,*E*)-diene product.

Study note

Before moving on to Section 3 you should produce your own summary of this section and then compare it with ours. Go to Unit 7 summaries in Unit 7 resources.

3 Metals in carbon–carbon bond forming reactions

The methods of C=C bond formation discussed in the previous section involve the addition of an organoheteroatom reagent to a carbonyl group. Such additions are also the basis of a variety of powerful methods for C–C bond formation.

■ You may have met one such method in your previous studies. Can you recall what it is?

☐ The Grignard reaction, in which reagents of the type RMgX add to aldehydes and ketones to form alcohols.

$$\begin{array}{c}
R^1 \\
\diagdown \\
C{=}O \\
\diagup \\
R^2
\end{array}
\quad
\xrightarrow[\text{ii}, H_2O]{\text{i}, \text{RMgX}}
\quad
\begin{array}{c}
R \\
| \\
R^1{-}C{-}OH \\
| \\
R^2
\end{array}$$

The Grignard reaction is a very versatile and useful synthetic transformation and for many years had few rivals in its range of application for C–C bond formation. However, it is not a universal solution – no one synthetic method ever is – and attention eventually turned to the devising of new, hopefully equally versatile, methods. One that we shall now look at derived from some experimental results obtained with the Grignard reaction that at the time were a nuisance to chemists wishing to use certain particular types of substrates, namely α,β-unsaturated carbonyl compounds.

It was observed from time to time that, with such compounds, varying amounts of an additional product (**3.1**) were formed which resulted from nucleophilic attack at the carbon beta to the carbonyl group, along with the product (**3.2**) of the normal attack at the carbonyl carbon.

$$\begin{array}{c}
\diagdown^4 \quad |^3 \quad |^2 \quad 1 \\
C{=}C{-}C{=}O \\
\diagup
\end{array}
\quad
\xrightarrow[\text{ii}, H^+]{\text{i}, \text{RMgX}}
\quad
\begin{array}{c}
| \quad | \quad | \\
{-}C{-}CH{-}C{=}O \\
| \\
R
\end{array}
\;+\;
\begin{array}{c}
\diagdown \quad | \quad | \\
C{=}C{-}C{-}OH \\
\diagup \qquad | \\
R
\end{array}$$

$$\text{3.1} \qquad\qquad\qquad\qquad \text{3.2}$$

Numbering the atoms as shown, the normal product, **3.2**, is said to be the result of 1,2-addition; the unusual product, **3.1**, is said to be the result of **conjugate addition** which is also known as 1,4-addition.

■ Can you explain why conjugate addition occurs?

□ In effect the electrophilic nature of the carbonyl group is partially transferred to the further of the two carbons in the alkene as can be seen by the following resonance structures:

$$\left[\begin{array}{c} \diagdown \\ C=C-C=O \\ \diagup \end{array} \longleftrightarrow \begin{array}{c} \diagdown \\ C=C-C-O^- \\ \diagup \end{array} \longleftrightarrow \begin{array}{c} \diagup \\ C-C=C-O^- \\ \diagup \end{array} \right]$$

In such a system then, as well as the normal 1,2-addition, 1,4- or conjugate addition becomes a possibility.

Conjugate addition involves initial formation of an enolate ion intermediate (**3.3**) which picks up a hydrogen ion to form the product (**3.1**):

$$\begin{array}{c} | \quad | \quad | \\ -C-C=C-O^- \\ | \\ R \quad H^+ \quad {}^+MgX \end{array} \longrightarrow \begin{array}{c} | \quad | \quad | \\ -C-CH-C=O \\ | \\ R \end{array}$$

$$\textbf{3.3} \qquad\qquad \textbf{3.1}$$

The net effect is addition across the C=C bond, with the carbonyl group seemingly unchanged. But, of course, the presence of the carbonyl group is essential to polarise the carbon–carbon double bond to allow nucleophilic attack to occur, a fact that is implicit in the terminology 1,4-addition rather than 3,4-addition, as you might otherwise expect.

With a particular Grignard reagent, the major factor controlling the proportions of 1,2- and 1,4-addition is the amount of steric hindrance in the α,β-unsaturated carbonyl substrate. Bulky substituents at position 4 favour 1,2-addition, whereas bulky substituents at positions 2 and 3 favour 1,4-addition, as shown in Table 3.1.

Table 3.1   Reactions of various α,β-unsaturated ketones with Grignard reagents.

Carbonyl compound	Reagent	1,2-Addition/%	1,4-Addition/%
H 4 3 2| 1 PhCH=CH—C=O	EtMgBr	100	0
CH$_3$ 4 3 2| 1 PhCH=CH—C=O	EtMgBr	40	60
Ph 4 3 2| 1 PhCH=CH—C=O	EtMgBr	1	99
Ph Ph 4 3| 2| 1 PhCH=C—C=O	EtMgBr	0	100

So, because of this large variation in the relative amounts of 1,2- and 1,4-addition, the conjugate addition of Grignard reagents is not generally a synthetically useful process which is unfortunate because, as we shall see later, a wide variety of α,β-unsaturated carbonyl compounds are available.

3.1   Organocopper reagents

In 1941, it appeared that this gap in synthetic methodology had been filled. It was discovered that Grignard reagents gave higher yields of the conjugate addition product when the reaction was carried out in the presence of a copper(I) catalyst, and in certain cases this resulted in a complete change of the regioselectivity of the reaction.

(a) MeMgBr	1.5%	98.5%
(b) MeMgBr/Cu$^+$Cl$^-$	82.5%	17.5%

Unfortunately, this modification, although an improvement, has its disadvantages: the ratio of 1,4- to 1,2-addition products is very dependent on the type and amount of the copper(I) catalyst used.

The next advance came in 1966 when the American chemist Herbert House and his co-workers investigated the mechanism of the copper(I)-catalysed Grignard reaction. They obtained evidence that suggested that organic compounds containing copper (**organocopper reagents**) were the active reagents in this reaction. This hypothesis was easily substantiated because, many years earlier, another American chemist, Henry Gilman, had devised methods for preparing such compounds from organolithium reagents and copper(I) iodide. By using organolithium to copper iodide ratios of 1 : 1 or 2 : 1, Gilman was able to prepare **organocopper(I)** (RCu) and **organocuprate** (R$_2$CuLi) **reagents**.

$$RX + 2Li \longrightarrow RLi + LiX \quad X = Cl, Br, I$$

organocopper(I) reagent

$$RLi + CuI \longrightarrow RCu + LiI$$

$$e.g.\ MeLi + CuI \longrightarrow \underset{\text{methylcopper}}{MeCu} + LiI$$

organocuprate reagent

$$2RLi + CuI \longrightarrow R_2CuLi + LiI$$

$$e.g.\ 2MeLi + CuI \longrightarrow \underset{\substack{\text{lithium}\\\text{dimethylcuprate}}}{Me_2CuLi} + LiI$$

House and his colleagues used Gilman's method to prepare methylcopper and lithium dimethylcuprate and found that these reagents undergo unusually effective conjugate addition to a wide variety of α,β-unsaturated carbonyl compounds under essentially the same conditions used for other organometallic reactions (inert atmosphere and dry solvent).

In the following discussion, we shall concentrate on organocuprate reagents, as they appear to be the reagents of choice for conjugate addition. We shall not discuss the mechanism of this process in detail, because it is still not fully understood. It seems likely that one of the reasons why organocuprates undergo conjugate addition, whereas Grignard reagents do not, may be due to the facility with which Cu(I) and Cu(II) can interconvert. At the present time a mechanism involving electron transfer is favoured, but for our purposes we can assume a mechanism analogous to the Grignard reaction in which copper polarises the reagent to provide an organic nucleophile.

Note that in this reaction, only one of the R groups of the organocuprate is used, the second R group being liberated on hydrolysis as RH.

■   Can RH be used subsequently to prepare more cuprate reagent?

☐   The preparation of R_2CuLi uses RX as starting material, and so RH cannot readily be recycled.

The introduction of organocuprates meant that the conjugate addition to α,β- unsaturated carbonyl compounds became a viable synthetic process. Before looking at some of the applications of these reagents, we must first discuss the scope and limitations of this reaction.

3.1.1   Scope and limitations of the reaction

Organocuprate reagents can be prepared from a wide variety of organic halides using the method devised by Gilman, described in the last section.

$$2RX \xrightarrow{\text{Li}} 2RLi \xrightarrow{\text{CuI}} R_2CuLi$$

R = alkyl (primary, secondary or tertiary), alkenyl, alkynyl, aryl

All of these compounds can be used in conjugate addition reactions with the exception of lithium dialkynylcuprates (**3.4**).

$(RC{\equiv}C)_2CuLi$

3.4

Lithium dialkynylcuprates can be prepared, but such is the affinity of copper for the alkynyl group that it is not transferred in a conjugate addition reaction. Figure 3.1 summarises the unsaturated substrates that have been used successfully in conjugate addition reactions, and Table 3.2 summarises the reactivity of various functional groups towards organocuprates; those classed as unreactive can be present in the organocuprate or the unsaturated substrate and survive the reaction.

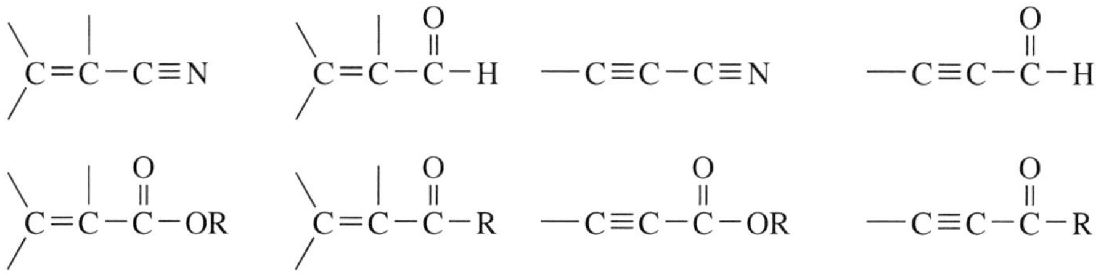

$$\text{C=C–C}\equiv\text{N} \qquad \text{C=C–C(=O)–H} \qquad \text{–C}\equiv\text{C–C}\equiv\text{N} \qquad \text{–C}\equiv\text{C–C(=O)–H}$$

$$\text{C=C–C(=O)–OR} \qquad \text{C=C–C(=O)–R} \qquad \text{–C}\equiv\text{C–C(=O)–OR} \qquad \text{–C}\equiv\text{C–C(=O)–R}$$

Figure 3.1 Unsaturated substrates that undergo conjugate addition reaction with organocuprates.

Table 3.2 Reactivity of functional groups towards organocuprate reagents.

Unreactive	Reactive
acetals	alcohols
ethers	carboxylic acids
esters	epoxides
ketones	halides
nitriles	
unconjugated double bonds	

Note that organocuprates, like Grignard reagents, only react with carboxylic acids and alcohols to give carboxylate and alkoxide derivatives. The acid or alcohol is regenerated on aqueous 'work-up' (the procedure of obtaining the pure product from a reaction mixture once the reaction is complete). However this is wasteful since it means that sufficient organocuprate reagent must be added to react with both α,β-unsaturated carbonyl compound and hydroxylic functional group.

Grignard reagents react with ketones and esters, and so you may be surprised to discover that organocuprates do not immediately appear to do so. In fact, given sufficient time, organocuprates do react with ketones and esters, but reaction with the C=C bond of a conjugated carbonyl compound is a much faster process.

When alcohol and carboxylic acid groups are present in the reactant, the organocuprate reagents need to be used in excess to ensure that after reacting with the acidic hydrogen, there is sufficient left to react with the α,β-unsaturated ketone. This is at the very least inefficient, but this waste becomes disastrous when the organocuprate is derived from a synthetically valuable reaction intermediate. Furthermore, the organocuprate reaction itself is inherently inefficient because only one group is transferred from the reagent. Of course the use of organocopper(I) or copper-catalysed Grignard reagents avoids this loss, but sometimes these alternatives are just not successful. In such cases a mixed cuprate reagent that only transfers the valuable organic group is desirable.

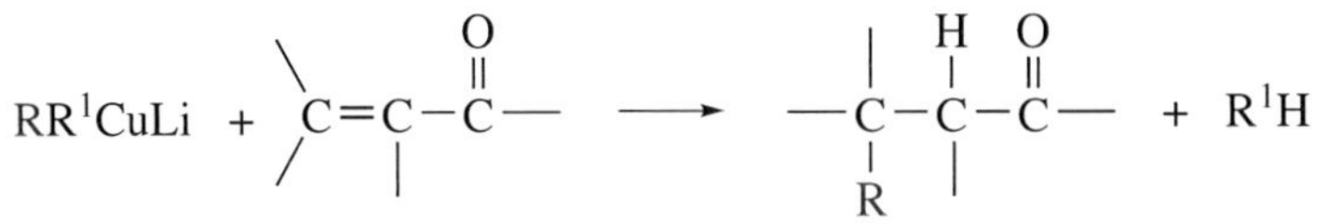

$$RR^1CuLi \ + \ \begin{array}{c} \diagdown \\ C=C-\overset{\displaystyle O}{\overset{\displaystyle \|}{C}}- \\ \diagup \ \ | \end{array} \ \longrightarrow \ -\overset{H}{\underset{R}{\overset{|}{\underset{|}{C}}}}-\overset{|}{\underset{|}{C}}-\overset{O}{\overset{\|}{C}}- \ + \ R^1H$$

■   What type of group binds strongly to copper and is not transferred?

□   The alkynyl group.

In fact, 1-pentynylcopper (**3.5**) is readily available, reasonably inexpensive and therefore ideal for use in mixed cuprate reagents:

$$CH_3CH_2CH_3C{\equiv}CCu \ + \ BuLi \ \longrightarrow \ (CH_3CH_2CH_2C{\equiv}CCuBu)Li$$

3.5

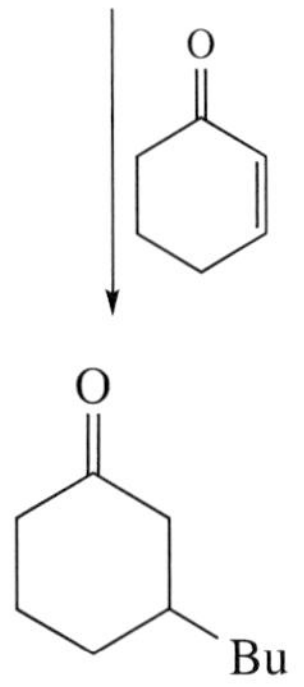

The use of non-migratory groups is especially important when the organic component is expensive or the result of a long synthesis.

The introduction of organocuprate reagents has considerably expanded the synthetic utility of the conjugate addition reaction, but these reagents have also found use in another carbon–carbon bond-forming procedure which will be discussed in Section 4.1.

Study note

Before moving on to Section 4 you should produce your own summary of this section and then compare it with ours. Go to Unit 7 summaries in Unit 7 resources.

4 Coupling reactions

So far, the methods used for forming carbon–carbon bonds have involved addition reactions at C=O or C=C bonds. The result is a molecule with either another functional group in a particular location or with the newly attached carbon-containing moiety at a particular position relative to the existing (carbonyl) functional group (as in conjugate addition). In both cases, there is a functional group present that may, or may not, be desired. Conceptually, it would be much simpler and more versatile if two carbon chains could simply be linked in the particular manner desired.

At first sight, a substitution reaction involving a halocompound and a reagent in which the nucleophilic centre is a carbon atom should do the trick.

■ Can you think of a type of reagent in which carbon is nucleophilic?

☐ Grignard reagents or organolithium compounds are polarised such that the carbon attached to the metal atom is nucleophilic.

So, in principle, reaction of a Grignard reagent with a haloalkane should give the desired product in which the two carbon chains are linked.

$$RMgBr \ + \ R^1Br \ \xrightarrow{\ ?\ } \ R-R^1 \ + \ MgBr$$

In practice, yields of this reaction are low and additional products are obtained in which the symmetrical combinations (R–R and R^1–R^1) are found.

■ Can you suggest a possible reason why this happens?

☐ One reason for this result is that the alkyl groups in Grignard reagents undergo fast exchange in such 'mixed' reactions.

$$RMgBr \ + \ R^1Br \ \longrightarrow \ R^1MgBr \ + \ RBr$$

As a result, substantial proportions of the symmetrical combinations are formed. In addition, side-reactions such as α- and β-elimination take place to a significant extent. However, these results do not mean that such reactions cannot be carried out in high yield. It is simply that Grignard reagents (and organolithium compounds) do not have the right properties. One of the most significant developments of recent years in synthetic methodology has been the investigation and exploitation of the properties of other elements, mostly metals and often transition metals, but also involving non-metals such as S, B and Si. In this section, we shall look at some of these, based on the element that you have already met, namely copper, before turning our attention to reactions based on transition metals.

4.1 Coupling reactions using organocopper reagents

Just as with conjugate addition, where high yields of 1,4-product are obtained with organocuprate reagents (in contrast to Grignard reagents which often give only low yields), so the use of organocuprates allows the linking of two hydrocarbon chains to take place in high yield, a process called a **coupling reaction**.

$$C_{10}H_{21}Br \quad \xrightarrow{(C_4H_9)_2CuLi} \quad C_{14}H_{30}$$
$$(80\%)$$

4.1.1 Direct substitution coupling reactions

The reaction takes place readily at or below room temperature, to give high yields of products from the replacement of iodine or bromine not only in haloalkanes, but even in haloalkenes and haloarenes. Primary alkyl tosylates also give good yields of the required product. Secondary haloalkanes often do not give particularly good yields using 'standard' cuprates, with formula R_2CuLi, but the use of so-called higher order organocuprates with formula $R_2Cu(CN)Li_2$ enables this problem to be circumvented. These can be formed in situ by reaction of two molar equivalents of the requisite organolithium compound with $Cu_2(CN)_2$. Similarly, the use of higher-order cuprates containing secondary alkyl groups gives higher yields.

$$(89\%)$$

■ Reaction of lithium diphenylcuprate, Ph_2CuLi, with $(-)$-(R)-2-bromobutane gives optically active 2-phenylbutane with predominant inversion of configuration. What does this suggest about the mechanism involved?

☐ This suggests that this reaction may proceed via a concerted displacement that is stereochemically S_N2-like. The corresponding iodo compound gives a racemic product, however, indicating a different mechanism.

■ Does the fact that haloalkenes (i.e. where the bromine or iodine atoms are attached to one of the carbons of the double bond) or haloarenes are good substrates surprise you?

☐ Such compounds do not usually take part in nucleophilic substitution. This also suggests that the mechanism of these substitutions may well be different from the normal S_N1 or S_N2 displacements.

Whereas reaction with haloalkanes gives inversion, the reaction of organocuprates with haloalkenes gives the product alkene with retention of configuration of the double bond. Alternatively, the use of alkenylcuprates also gives product with retention of configuration.

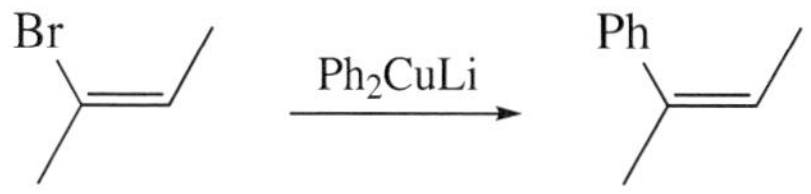

Little is known about the detailed mechanism of these reactions. However, this has not prevented their extensive use in the synthesis of alkenes and alkadienes with very high stereoselectivity.

The data in Table 4.1 show the versatility of this synthetic procedure.

Table 4.1 Coupling reactions involving organocuprates.

Substrate	Cuprate/conditions	Product	Yield/%
$CH_3(CH_2)_4CH_2OTos$	$(C_4H_9)_2CuLi/ether/-75\ °C$	$CH_3(CH_2)_8CH_3$	98
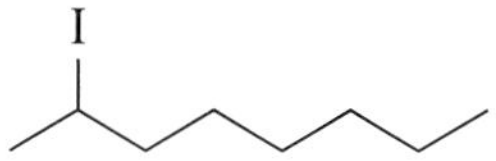	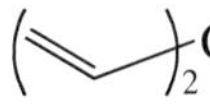 $\left(\diagup\diagdown\right)_2Cu(CN)Li_2/THF/0\ °C$	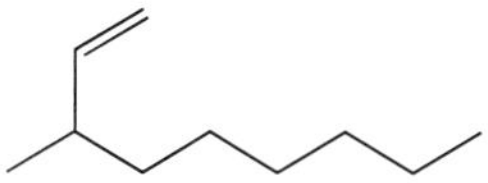	90
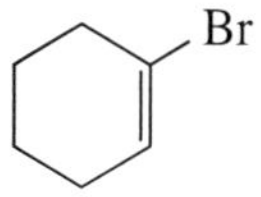	$(C_4H_9)_2CuLi$	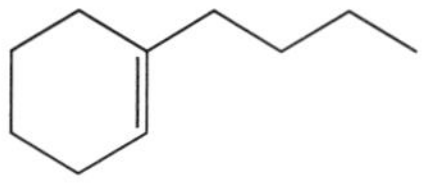	80
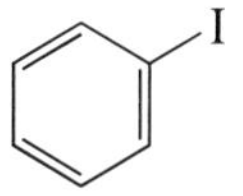	$(C_4H_9)_2CuLi$	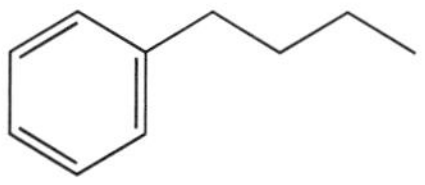	75
$I(CH_2)_{10}CO_2H$	$(C_4H_9)_2CuLi$ (excess)	$CH_3(CH_2)_{13}CO_2H$	82
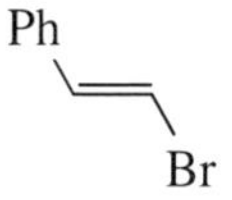	$Me_2CuLi/ether/0\ °C$	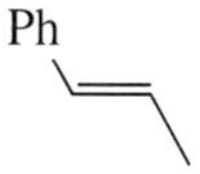	81

The use of acid chlorides gives ketones, and epoxides form alcohols by attack at the less-substituted carbon atom. As with secondary haloalkanes, better yields are obtained by the use of higher-order cuprates, for example $R_2Cu(CN)Li_2$.

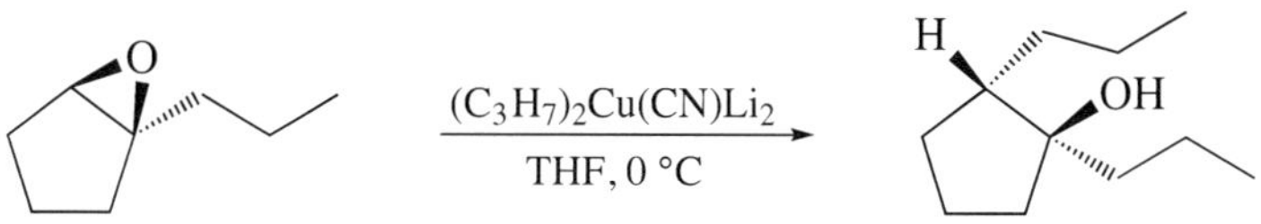

For any coupling reaction, two routes, in principle, can be employed, each halo compound being used as it is or being converted into the cuprate.

$$R^1X \longrightarrow R^1Li \longrightarrow R^1{}_2CuLi \xrightarrow{R^2Li} R^1-R^2$$

$$R^2X \longrightarrow R^2Li \longrightarrow R^2{}_2CuLi \xrightarrow{R^1Li} R^1-R^2$$

■ Why is the organocuprate reagent usually derived from the more readily available halo compound?

☐ This minimises the loss of the more valuable intermediate (only one of the R groups transfers) and leads to a more convergent synthesis.

4.1.2 Carbometallation

The necessary haloalkanes and haloarenes are readily obtained by conventional substitution reactions. However, the synthesis of the required haloalkenes or alkenylcopper reagents cannot be achieved by direct substitution. The key to their preparation is a process called **carbometallation** in which an organometallic reagent adds to an alkyne to form the requisite alkenylmetal intermediate. This reaction is possible with a wide variety of metals. The addition takes place *syn* with virtually complete stereoselectivity. Furthermore, as we have already seen, by careful control of the conditions, it is possible to retain the stereochemical integrity of the reagent during reaction with a halo compound. So the final product of the subsequent step is generally also formed as essentially a single stereoisomer.

63% yield (95% Z)

Note that carbometallation is regioselective; the copper becomes attached to the less-substituted carbon (contrast this with boron addition to alkenes). Carbometallation of alkynes is particularly efficient with copper derivatives; both organocopper(I) reagents produced from Grignard reagents, $RCu.MgBr_2$, and organocuprates, R^1R^2CuLi, can be used. Each has advantages and disadvantages.

Organocuprates are only useful for reactions with acetylene itself. The resulting reagent from a symmetrical organocuprate contains two alkenyl groups, both of which can be used in subsequent reactions.

Although less reactive in conjugate addition reactions, organocopper(I) reagents are more reactive in carbometallation. Even so, they are limited to reactions with 1-alkynes of the form $RCH_2C{\equiv}CH$.

4.1.3   Alkenylcopper reagents

The alkenylcopper reagents are very versatile synthetic intermediates and can take part in a wide variety of useful reactions. For example, reaction with iodine or *N*-bromosuccinimide (NBS) gives the corresponding haloalkenes.

$$C_6H_{13}\equiv CH \xrightarrow{\text{EtCu.MgBr}_2} \underset{C_6H_{13}\quad H}{\overset{Et\quad Cu}{C=C}} \xrightarrow{I_2} \underset{C_6H_{13}\quad H}{\overset{Et\quad I}{C=C}}$$

$$PhC\equiv CH \xrightarrow[\text{THF/}-50\,°C]{\text{EtCu.MgBr}_2/} \underset{Ph\quad H}{\overset{Et\quad Cu}{C=C}} \xrightarrow{NBS} \underset{Ph\quad H}{\overset{Et\quad Br}{C=C}}$$

These can be employed in the stereoselective formation of conjugated dienes. Note that bromine, Br_2, cannot be used in this reaction as it causes oxidation preferentially.

Alternatively, hydrolysis gives rise to alkenes and alkylation gives di- or tri-substituted alkenes.

$$PhC\equiv CH \xrightarrow[\text{THF/}-20\,°C]{C_6H_{13}Cu.MgBr_2/} \underset{Ph\quad H}{\overset{C_6H_{13}\quad Cu}{C=C}} \begin{array}{l} \xrightarrow{NH_4Cl(aq)} \underset{Ph}{\overset{C_6H_{13}}{C=CH_2}} \\[2em] \xrightarrow{CH_3I} \underset{Ph\quad H}{\overset{C_6H_{13}\quad CH_3}{C=C}} \end{array}$$

Acylation using acid chlorides represents a convenient route to α,β-unsaturated ketones.

$$C_6H_{13}\equiv CH \xrightarrow{\text{MeCu.MgBr}_2} \underset{Me\quad Cu}{\overset{C_6H_{13}\quad H}{C=C}} \xrightarrow[\text{HMPA}]{CH_3COCl} \underset{Me\quad CO-CH_3}{\overset{C_6H_{13}\quad H}{C=C}}$$

In all these reactions, the substituted group replaces the copper with retention of the stereochemical integrity. The main limitations on the scope of these reagents is their thermal lability. Even when stabilised by additives such as HMPA, trialkyl phosphites or dimethyl sulfide, the alkenylcopper(I) species are only stable up to room temperature. The intermediates formed from the Grignard-mediated method are even less stable than those from organocuprates. Chloro compounds, ethers and esters are inert under these reaction conditions and so the corresponding functional groups may be present elsewhere in the R groups.

The very high stereoisomenic purity possible by this method has resulted in their extensive application in the area of pheromone synthesis. A number of pheromones contain a *Z* double bond and their action in certain cases is totally inhibited by the presence of even a small amount of the *E* isomer. Other pheromones are conjugated dienes and the possibility that alkenylcopper reagents could react with haloalkenes for the synthesis of such unsymmetrical dienes was soon realised and widely investigated.

Unfortunately, while *alkyl*copper(I) or cuprate reagents couple readily with a wide range of halocompounds, RHal, where R can be alkenyl and aryl as well as alkyl and alkynyl, *alkenyl*copper or cuprate reagents only react with the latter two types. Whenever direct alkenyl–alkenyl coupling was attempted, only low yields were obtained, and the stereochemical integrity was largely lost. However, the use of $ZnBr_2$ and a catalytic amount of $Pd(PPh_3)_4$ gives high yields of conjugated dienes with virtually complete stereoselectivity.

4.2 Coupling reactions using transition metals

The use of heteroatom reagents incorporating metals, in particular copper lithium and boron and, more recently, palladium and ruthenium, have allowed greater selectivity to be achieved. It was the discovery that Grignard reagents gave higher yields of the conjugate addition product when the reaction was carried out in the presence of a copper(I) catalyst that led to the introduction of these metals. In certain cases this resulted in a complete change of the regioselectivity of the reaction and confirmed the useful role metal ions could play in enhancing the degree of control that could be placed on a reaction outcome. Here we look at how transition metals have enabled advances in drug synthesis and consider two of the most widely employed reactions – the Stille reaction and the Suzuki reaction.

4.2.1 The advantages of transition metal catalysts

Considerable progress has been made using organocopper and organolithium reagents and they still remain a useful methodology for the synthetic chemist to form carbon–carbon bonds, particularly where 1,2- and 1,4-addition reactions can be employed. However, the conditions employed can be relatively harsh. Added to this, the need to obtain an even greater degree of stereochemical control over reactions has increased. This is a particularly important factor for the synthesis of drugs where complex structures are dictated by the need to bind to specific receptor sites. Their synthesis requires milder conditions both to prevent undesirable side reactions of a synthetic intermediate, and to allow the precise structure and shape of the target molecule to be produced exclusively. The use of transition metals such as palladium has, in recent years, greatly aided chemists in meeting these objectives and we will focus on some examples of synthetic reactions that use palladium metal to achieve carbon–carbon bond formations that might otherwise be impossible.

The formation of C–C and C–X bonds can be readily achieved using nucleophilic and electrophilic combinations, as you will have seen if you have studied the Level 2 module and in the examples that have been discussed in Units 6 and this unit. All these transformations, be they simple or complex, operate on the same basic principles with electrons moving from a source (nucleophile) to a destination (electrophile), to form a bond with selectivity governed by thermodynamic and kinetic factors. Based on these principles it seems that some reactions simply will not occur, yet the literature contains examples of seemingly impossible reactions occurring that break all the rules of the functional group chemistry that we have developed so far.

■ Would you expect benzene and an unconjugated alkene to react with nucleophiles or electrophiles?

□ They both would react with electrophiles. This suggests that forming a new carbon–carbon bond between an alkene and benzene would be very difficult using the principles developed so far in this unit.

The reaction between bromobenzene and the alkene **4.1** should therefore be difficult to achieve.

However, if a transition metal is added as a catalyst, the reaction is able to proceed.

It would be a mistake to see either the benzene or the alkene behaving as a nucleophile. It is better to see the reaction as a coupling between two equal components with the transition metal acting as a control centre to ensure the carbon–carbon bond formation can occur.

The fact that these reactions do occur doesn't mean that all we have been discussing is wrong; it is the presence of transition metals that change the reactivity profile of the functional groups and enable these reactions to occur. Reagents incorporating transition metals add to and extend the scope and type of transformations available to the synthetic chemist. The key step in the syntheses of many drug molecules often involves the use of a transition metal catalyst in the formation of a carbon–carbon bond. Metals such as copper, zinc, cobalt and nickel have been used and it is beyond the scope of this module to cover them all in detail. However, the principles behind each are quite similar and will be illustrated using reactions involving palladium. Palladium is by far the most commonly employed metal catalyst and works for both minute and large-scale reactions. The variety and scope of these reactions together with their good chemo- and regioselectivity makes this an active and growing area of research.

4.2.2   The Stille reaction

The Stille reaction is a means of joining together aromatic and vinylic carbon centres, a process known as a cross-coupling. That is to say it forms a new C–C bond between alkene and/or aromatic carbons. It represents over half of all the carbon–carbon cross-coupling reactions carried out in total syntheses.

$$R^1-X \ + \ RSnBu_3 \ \xrightarrow{\text{Pd/catalyst}} \ R^1-R \ + \ XSnBu_3$$

The Stille coupling is a versatile C–C bond-forming reaction between organo tin compounds called stannanes, and vinyl or aromatic compounds with halides or other good leaving groups. Well-elaborated methods allow the preparation of different products from all of the combinations of halides and stannanes shown in Figure 4.1. Although stannanes are stable, their main drawback is the toxicity of the tin compounds used, and their low polarity makes them poorly soluble in water.

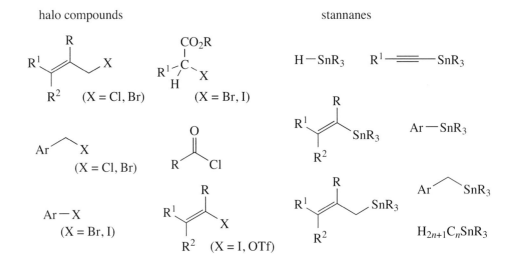

Figure 4.1   Types of halo compounds and stannanes as reactants in the Stille reaction.

The Stille reaction can often be employed near the end of a complex multistep syntheses without undue risk to the functionalities in the molecule's structure that are already in place.

During the catalysis, the palladium metal alternates or cycles between the 0 and II oxidation states, consequently the mechanism is often represented in a cyclic style focusing on the changes occurring at the palladium metal centre (Scheme 4.1).

Each arrow within the cycle represents a step in the reaction pathway. Compounds such as the stannane (R^1SnR_3) or the organic halide (RX) are shown joining and leaving the cycle using curved arrows. The catalyst is

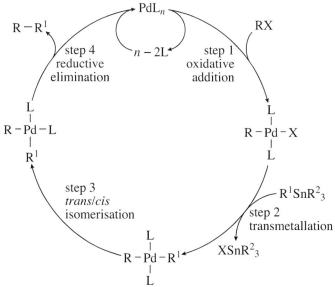

Scheme 4.1

shown at the top and the reactions are connected in a cyclic way such that one clockwise rotation from this point gives the sequence of reactions in the mechanism. The cycle contains steps that are given names such as oxidative addition, transmetallation and reductive elimination and all are key to the reaction. **Oxidative addition** is a process by which organic compounds are able to bond to a transition metal complex by breaking a C–X bond. The formal oxidation state of the metal is raised by two as a result of the two extra species, R and X, bonding to the metal – since the oxidation state of the metal increases, the metal is oxidised, hence the name.

■ Give an example of an oxidative addition that you have encountered previously in this module.

☐ The formation of Grignard reagents can be considered to involve oxidative addition, the magnesium being oxidised from $Mg(0)$ to $Mg(II)$.

$$R-X + Mg \longrightarrow R-Mg-Br$$
$$\quad\quad Mg(0) \quad\quad\quad\quad Mg(II)$$

For the purposes of the mechanism being discussed here, transmetallation can be considered a process by which an organic R group bonded to one metal is transferred to another metal centre.

$$R^1-Sn-R^2 + PdX \longrightarrow R^1-Sn-X + Pd-R^2$$

Thus, in the Stille reaction, transmetallation occurs in step 2 (in Scheme 4.1) and is used to introduce the second R group (R^1) into the cycle so that it can be coupled to the first R group. Specifically the R^1 group attached to the tin (Sn) of the stannane becomes attached to the palladium. It is essential that the organic compounds can be removed from the palladium in order to reform the transition metal catalyst so it can be used to make new carbon–carbon bonds. This process is called a **reductive elimination** and is the reverse of oxidative addition. The oxidation state of the palladium is reduced by two back to zero, so the metal is reduced, and a new C–C bond is formed between the two eliminated R groups (step 4).

$$R^1-M(II)-R^2 \longrightarrow M(0) + R^1-R^2$$

Overall the Stille reaction can be described as follows. Starting at the top of the cycle (in Scheme 4.1) with the catalyst, palladium(0) (PdL$_n$, where L is a ligand complexed to palladium and $n \geq 1$), the Stille reaction involves the oxidative addition of the organic halide R–X.

Note both the R group and the leaving group X are added to the palladium to give a palladium intermediate in the +2 oxidation state. This intermediate undergoes the transmetallation step with the stannane $R^1-SnR_3^2$ in which the R^1 group is transferred from the tin to the palladium and the group X moves in the opposite direction to form a tin salt. The two R groups on the palladium(II) (R and R^1) are initially on opposite sides of the palladium square-planar complex in a *trans* relationship. This complex isomerises to place the two R groups next to each other in a *cis* relationship in step 3. This isomerisation is necessary to enable the final step (step 4), the reductive elimination, to occur. This returns the palladium to the zero oxidation state at the top of the cycle and the product that is eliminated consists of the two R groups joined together by a new carbon–carbon bond.

The precise details of the mechanism are beyond the scope of our discussion but it is useful to think of the palladium metal as acting as a centre around which the starting materials can reorganise their atoms and then the electrons can move to create a new carbon–carbon bond.

■ What organic halide would you use with the stannane **4.2** to produce **4.3** using a Stille reaction?

CH$_3$ CH$_3$

CH$_3$CH$_2$ SnR$_3$

4.2

CH$_3$

—CH$_3$

CH$_2$CH$_3$

4.3

☐ *p-tert*-Butylbromobenzene **4.4** would be a suitable electrophilic partner in the Stille reaction.

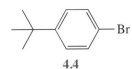

4.4

4.2.3 The Suzuki reaction

The Suzuki reaction is a palladium-catalysed coupling between an organoboronic acid, $R^1-B(OH)_2$, and a halide, R^2-X, analogous to the Stille reaction.

$$R^1-B(OH)_2 + R^2-X \xrightarrow[\text{base}]{\text{Pd catalyst}} R^1-R^2$$

This again forms a new carbon–carbon bond between the R^1 and R^2 groups. Initially it was restricted to couplings between aryl groups, that is both R^1 and R^2 had to be aromatic rings. Although this can be useful for the pharmaceutical chemist, the focus on preparing molecules incorporating new bonds between aromatic rings is limiting. Subsequently, the scope of the reaction has been extended to include vinyl boronates and vinyl halides.

The mechanism is broadly similar to that of the Stille reaction and again, it is best viewed from the perspective of the palladium metal centre.

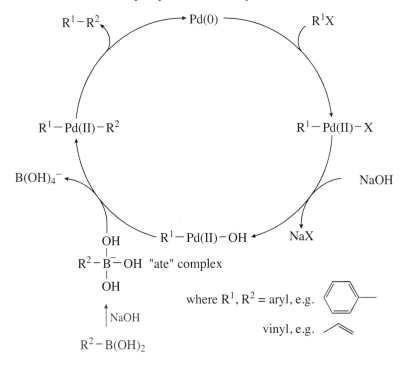

Scheme 4.2

The first step (top right) is the oxidative addition of the halide RX to the palladium(0) which generates the palladium(II) intermediate. The next step involves the exchange of the halide ligand on the palladium for hydroxide, OH. The intermediate R^1–Pd(II)–OH reacts with the boronic acid R^2–B(OH)$_3$ in a transmetallation step which transfers the second R group (R^2) to the palladium(II) centre. The product with a new carbon–carbon bond between the two R groups is expelled from the palladium intermediate in the final reductive elimination step to give back the Pd(0) catalyst. One difference between the Suzuki mechanism and that of the Stille coupling is that the boronic acid must be activated, for example, with base, before it reacts with the palladium (in red in Scheme 4.2). Treatment of the boronic acid with base, usually hydroxide, is thought to convert the boronic acid into a more nucleophillic 'ate' complex. This 'ate' complex is more reactive towards the palladium intermediate in the transmetallation step than the boronic acid.

In part due to the stability, ease of preparation and low toxicity of the boronic acid compounds, there is currently a widespread interest in applications of the Suzuki coupling.

■ What would be the product of a Suzuki coupling reaction between the boronic acid **4.5** and the vinyl bromide **4.6**?

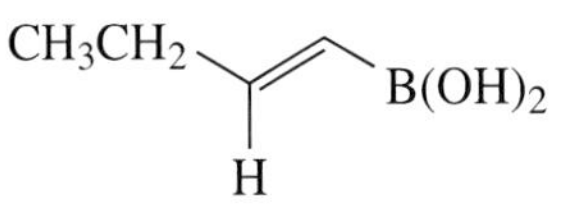

4.5

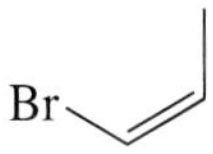

4.6

□ The product is a diene, **4.7**, and these find application as synthetic intermediates that will be discussed in more detail in Unit 8. For the moment, it is worth noting that the *E* and *Z* stereochemistry or the starting materials are preserved in the product.

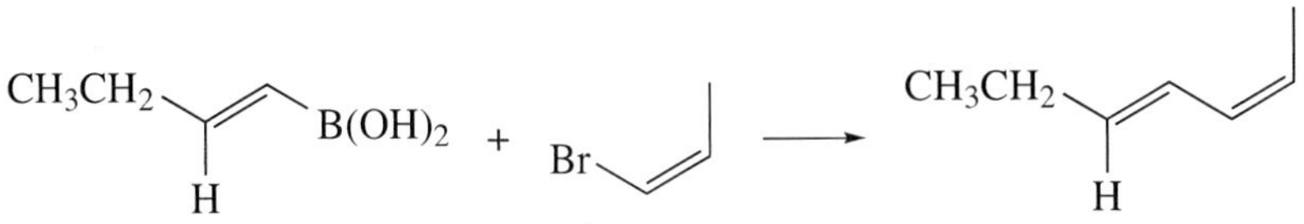

4.5 (*E*) 4.6 (*Z*) 4.7 (*E*,*Z*)

Sterically demanding substrates are accommodated by the Suzuki coupling and aryl–aryl couplings between aromatic rings with other substituents are possible.

Study note

Before moving on to the next unit you should produce your own summary of this section and then compare it with ours. Go to Unit 7 summaries in Unit 7 resources.

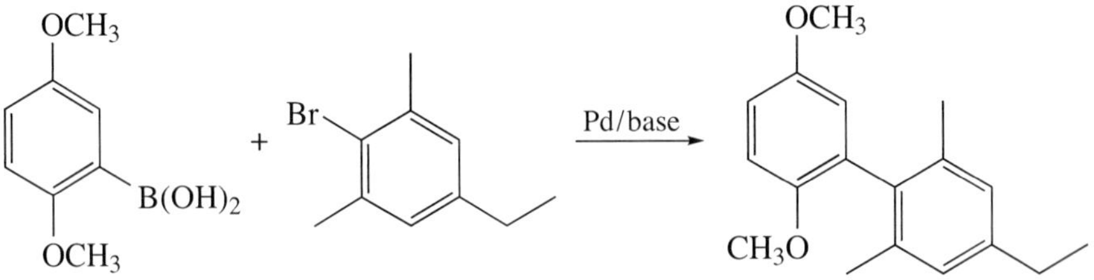

1   Introduction

In the module so far you have been introduced to a wide variety of functional group interconversions, and perhaps more importantly, a good selection of carbon–carbon bond-forming reactions. You may be wondering what is left to consider in a module focused on organic synthesis. Just think back over the molecules that have been mentioned so far during the module – you may have been surprised how many times cyclic structures have appeared. So, in this unit we are going to spend some time looking at the synthesis of such cyclic molecules.

Although for the most part, we have introduced the reactions discussed in this module using non-cyclic ('acyclic' or 'open chain') examples, cyclic molecules are extremely important as targets for organic chemists, and the need to synthesise cyclic molecules sets some particular challenges. In this unit we shall show how organic chemists have overcome many of these challenges, and how, in so doing, they have extended both the methodology and the underlying theory of organic chemistry.

Cyclic compounds are often referred to as being either **carbocyclic** or **heterocyclic**. Carbocyclic compounds have skeletal structures whose rings are composed entirely of carbon atoms. The structure of heterocyclic compounds involves a ring containing one or more atoms of elements other than carbon.

Carbocyclic compounds are subdivided into *alicyclic* and *aromatic* compounds. **Alicyclic** compounds are non-benzenoid carbocyclic systems. They make up perhaps the least extensive of the classes of cyclic organic molecules, but nevertheless include a range of useful plant and animal products such as the terpenes and the steroids, and some valuable pharmaceuticals, including the prostaglandins. Some alicyclic compounds with 6-membered rings are prepared by the partial or complete hydrogenation of benzene rings, but most of them are assembled by ring-forming reactions.

The only aromatic carbocycles we shall consider are compounds that have at least one benzene ring as part of their structure. Benzene rings occur widely in both natural products and synthetic compounds, and form part of many common bicyclic (that is, containing two rings) heterocyclic systems. They are rarely synthesised, but are frequently found in precursor molecules from which more complex structures are developed.

Many heterocycles are also described as being aromatic (this will be discussed further in this unit). The range and function of heterocyclic compounds is enormous, embracing whole classes of important compounds such as the alkaloids, the nucleic acids, and the majority of sugars, drugs and vitamins. Most dyestuffs, and agricultural and industrial chemicals, are also heterocycles. A great many of these compounds are found to contain nitrogen as a heteroatom, but oxygen and sulfur are also common. Both aromatic and non-aromatic heterocyclic rings are usually synthesised from acyclic molecules.

1.1   Synthetic strategies

When examining the synthesis of cyclic compounds, we find that nearly all of them are made from acyclic precursors. These precursor molecules all have at least two reactive centres, and the number of atoms that separates these centres when bond formation takes place will determine the size of the ring produced.

We can draw a distinction (Figure 1.1) between two types of ring formation. If there are two reactive centres of opposite polarity (that is, one nucleophilic, one electrophilic) in a single acyclic molecule, the reaction type is *intramolecular ring formation* or *cyclisation*. Alternatively, in *intermolecular ring formation* or *cycloaddition*, pairs of centres in two molecules interact to give the ring system. If both bonds form simultaneously in the intermolecular process, the reaction is described as a **concerted cycloaddition**. A variant of intermolecular ring formation is also possible, in which both bonds are formed to a single atomic centre.

intermolecular   intramolecular   intramolecular
ring formation   ring formation   ring formation
(cycloaddition)   (cyclisation)   (to a single centre)

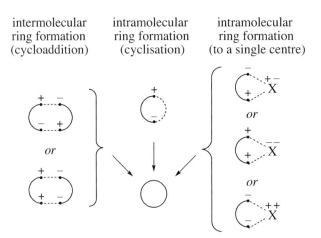

Figure 1.1   Classification of ring synthesis, showing alternative synthon polarities.

There are examples of all of these types of synthesis for both carbocyclic and heterocyclic compounds. In terms of the retrosynthetic analysis that you may have met if you studied the Level 2 module and that you will meet again in Unit 9, in the retrosynthetic direction the cyclisation approach corresponds to a one-bond disconnection, whereas the cycloaddition approach corresponds to disconnection of a pair of bonds.

In the synthesis of a cyclic molecule there will be three distinct stages:

i   the choice or preparation of acyclic reagents

ii   the construction of the ring

iii   the modification of the side chains resulting from stages (i) and (ii).

Of these, the stage (ii) ring-forming reaction is often the most significant, but, depending on the stability of the ring system under investigation, more effort may need to be expended on stage (i) or stage (iii). For a cyclic system that is susceptible to ring opening under reaction conditions, ring formation should ideally be the *final* step, where the target molecule is formed. This means that the side chains required at the end must be built into the acyclic precursors or develop as the synthesis proceeds, before cyclisation. However, if a cyclic molecule is stable, involving an aromatic or polycyclic system for example, both introduction and considerable modification of side chains may be possible after ring formation.

A stable cyclic molecule is particularly important when the target is a more complex bicyclic molecule such as the tranquiliser diazepam (**1.1**). A synthesis starting from acyclic compounds would require the construction of two rings. This is a longer, possibly more expensive process than starting the synthesis with one ring already intact.

If the benzene ring in diazepam (**1.1**) is intact, the synthesis is simplified to the synthesis of a single 7-membered heterocyclic ring. There are a range of benzene derivatives with functional groups such as carbonyl and amino groups that are ideal starting compounds for the synthesis of a bicyclic compound such as diazepam (**1.1**).

In this case the preferred route to compounds like **1.1** would be the reaction of a 2-aminobenzophenone (**1.2**) with an α-amino acid derivative (**1.3**). It turns out that many compounds of both types are readily available, and the reactions to form amide and imine bonds are reliable and high yielding. These factors will influence the choice of route.

1.1
Ar = phenyl

1.2   **1.3**

This is just one example of a general approach to the synthesis of bicyclic heterocycles in which a benzene ring is one of the rings required: a 1,2-disubstituted benzene is more usually selected as precursor rather than trying to form bonds to the ring directly.

Before we can begin the synthesis of cyclic compounds, we need to know:

- what factors affect ring formation
- what reactions and bifunctional precursors are available for our use
- whether the products from ring formation can be modified as necessary to yield our target molecules.

1.2 Factors affecting ring formation

Cyclic compounds have appeared frequently throughout this module, and so far in this unit we have approached the synthesis of ring systems in a straightforward fashion. So a reasonable question to ask is, why does ring synthesis seem so easy to accomplish? Here are some other questions to consider: do rings of all sizes form equally well? Also, why does the intermolecular reaction of bifunctional reagents (leading ultimately to polymerisation) not seem to be a problem when we are attempting cyclisations? We should now tackle these questions, and will deal first with the ring size issue.

If we examine accumulated data from the chemical literature on both the yields and rates of formation of rings of various sizes from a variety of cyclisation reactions, certain trends are regularly observed from which the following generalisations can be made:

- From accumulated yield data, it appears that rings with 5, 6 or 7 members, and large rings (13–20 membered) are more readily obtainable than rings of intermediate size.

- The accumulated data on the rates of cyclisation can be summarised as follows. Five-membered rings form most quickly, and 6-membered ring formation is also reasonably fast. Three- and 4-membered rings both form much more slowly than 5- or 6-membered rings with 3-membered rings forming faster than 4-membered rings. As the number of ring atoms increases above 6, it first becomes more difficult to achieve cyclisation, with a minimum rate of cyclisation seemingly between 8- and 12-membered rings (so-called 'medium rings'). After that, rates appear to increase towards an approximately steady value.

It is found that the yield and rate data for ring formation appear to run approximately parallel, but the picture is complicated because each is the result of contributions from two separate, important factors; thermodynamic and kinetic.

Thermodynamic factors include the relative stability of the ring system, and the position of equilibrium in the cyclisation reaction. However, even if these factors are favourable, cyclisation may be very slow, and the rate may then be reflected in a low yield. In addition, there may be alternative reactions that compete for starting material or product, thereby also reducing the net yield.

Kinetic factors control how fast cyclisation takes place. However, if the product is unstable or very reactive, rapid formation of the product may not guarantee an effective synthesis.

We shall now look in more detail at the factors affecting yields and rates.

1.2.1 Energy considerations

Ring size: thermodynamic criteria

You may recall from Unit 3 that there is a relationship between the Gibbs energy change for a reaction ($\Delta G^{\ominus}$, the difference in Gibbs energy between product and reactant) and the equilibrium constant:

$$\Delta G^{\ominus} = -RT \ln K$$

and that the Gibbs energy is made up of enthalpy ($\Delta H^{\ominus}$) and entropy ($\Delta S^{\ominus}$) components, as expressed in the equation

$$\Delta G^{\ominus} = \Delta H^{\ominus} - T\Delta S^{\ominus}$$

We'll look first at the entropy component. The entropy change, $\Delta S^{\ominus}$, can be considered as:

'overall change in freedom of motion or 'disorder' resulting from reaction'.

Thus, the greater the 'freedom' or 'disorder' in a system, the greater its entropy.

Converting an open-chain compound into a ring inevitably reduces the entropy, by limiting the freedom of the product molecule to undergo conformational change. So $\Delta S^{\ominus}$ for cyclisation is negative and the $-T\Delta S^{\ominus}$ term will be positive, making $\Delta G^{\ominus}$ less negative. This means that (other things being equal) the forward reaction will be less favourable, so the greater the loss of entropy on cyclisation, the less favoured will be the cyclisation equilibrium and thus the lower the proportion of product.

■   Is the reduction in entropy on cyclisation more or less significant for 3-, 4- and 5-membered rings than it is for the larger rings? (Think about the conformational freedom in the various rings that was discussed in Unit 4, Section 2.2.)

☐   In Unit 4, Section 2.2 we saw that cyclopropane, cyclobutane and cyclopentane had fairly rigid conformations and thus the loss in entropy is greater for cyclisation to the rigid 3-, 4- or 5-membered rings than for the more flexible larger rings.

Now consider the enthalpy component – that is, all other contributions to internal energy. In a series of cyclisations to form different ring sizes (for example, the series of reactions shown as Equation 1.1), you would be correct to conclude that the chemical bonds being made and broken are the same for all ring sizes. The part of the enthalpy change, $\Delta H^{\ominus}$, that is due to the making and breaking of bonds is therefore largely independent of the ring size.

$$(1.1)$$

However, there is *another* component of the enthalpy that is highly significant in small rings.

■   Think about forming a ring with three carbon atoms. What do you think this other enthalpy component might be? (It was discussed in Unit 3, Section 5.2.)

☐   It is angle strain. Compressing bond angles below the normal angle (for example, the tetrahedral angle of 109.5° for single bonds) requires an input of energy, increasing the enthalpy of the product and thus making

$\Delta G^{\ominus}$ significantly less favourable in the formation of 3- and 4-membered rings.

It is found that a heteroatom in the ring reduces the angle strain, and so does changing the hybridisation of ring atoms from sp^2 ('ideal' angle 120°) to sp^3 (ideal angle 109.5°) in small rings.

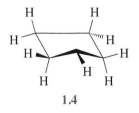

1.4

In addition to angle strain there is also strain of the type you first encountered with the ethane molecule, which is due to the non-bonded interaction of hydrogen atoms, or other groups, attached to adjacent ring atoms, especially when fixed in eclipsed positions. Saturated 5-membered rings, despite having ring-plane angles very close to the tetrahedral value, still prefer to adopt a slightly puckered conformation (**1.4**, also shown as a ball-and-stick diagram in Unit 8 iFigure 1.1) in order to avoid this strain. It also accounts for an enhancement of strain by 25–30% in 3- and 4-membered rings, and explains why the chair form of cyclohexane, with all bonds staggered, is thermodynamically the most favourable conformation for this system.

Strain can also arise from non-bonded interactions between substituents on non-adjacent ring atoms (transannular interactions). The 1,3-interactions of axial groups on a cyclohexane ring are a good example of this.

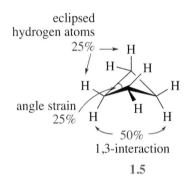

1.5

In fact, this 1,3-interaction in the non-planar cyclobutane molecule (**1.5**, also shown as a ball-and-stick diagram Unit 8 iFigure 1.2) is estimated to account for 50% of the ring strain, with angle strain and strain due to eclipsed hydrogen atoms making up the remainder.

So thermodynamic arguments support the generalisations in relation to 3- and 4-membered rings. Rings with 6 or more members, however, can adopt conformations that are virtually strain-free, so an explanation for the low yields and rates for the medium-sized rings must be sought elsewhere. Transannular non-bonded interactions are certainly a contributory factor, but this is not the whole story, as we shall see. An interesting example showing the delicate balance between ring strain and non-bonded interactions is offered by the following equilibria.

1.6a	1.6b	1.7a	1.7b
		norcaradiene	

An equilibrium mixture of **1.6a** and **1.6b** contains almost equal amounts of mono- and bicyclic hydrocarbon. By contrast, the ring strain in norcaradiene (**1.7a**) more than offsets the minimal amount of non-bonded interaction, driving equilibrium **1.7a/1.7b** far to the right. (Unit 8 iFigure 1.3 highlights the nature and severity of the non-bonded interactions in **1.6b**.)

Often each of the steps in a mechanistic sequence to form a ring should be considered as an equilibrium. Many cyclic products are more stable (have a much lower Gibbs energy) than the reactants and thus equilibrium often favours the forward reaction. This increased stability can derive from a variety of reasons, for example through increased resonance stabilisation or electron delocalisation (conjugation). The loss of small molecules (water, alcohols, hydrogen halides, ammonia) – a characteristic feature of condensation reactions – is essentially irreversible and can act as a 'driving force' for ring formation. Five- and 6-membered rings may also be able to achieve an aromatic system, with considerable stabilisation energy.

Ring size: kinetic criteria

As well as the position of equilibrium, we must also consider the rate of a cyclisation reaction, which is governed by the activation energy (E_a) (Figure 1.2).

This also has both an enthalpy term (ΔH), dependent on the nature of the transition state, and an entropy term (ΔS), related to the probability of the two reactive centres in a cyclisation getting close to each other. This probability decreases as the separation of these centres increases, due to the increase in rotational freedom with chain length.

The enthalpy term is affected by angle strain in small rings; and also by eclipsing and transannular strain due to the non-bonded interaction of hydrogen atoms, or of other groups attached to the chain, during the formation of the cyclisation transition state. This last factor becomes more unfavourable from 7-membered rings until about 11-membered rings, when its effect begins to decrease again.

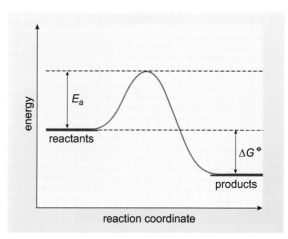

Figure 1.2 Reaction profile illustrating the distinction between Gibbs energy change, $\Delta G^\ominus$, and activation energy, E_a, for a reaction step.

For the formation of 3-membered rings the two reactive centres are always close to each other, giving an extremely favourable entropy term. For 5-membered rings, natural thermal motion brings the reactive centres within optimum bonding distance. But with 6-membered rings, the ends of the chain come too close together in a planar structure, and so the chain must be folded into the chair shape before reaction can take place. With larger rings the need for folding is even more pronounced.

■ Why do you think the formation of 4-membered rings is kinetically less favourable than that of 3-membered rings?

☐ It must be because the normal preferred conformation is the extended chain (**1.8**), and the probability of the molecule adopting the folded conformation (**1.9**) is low. Atoms 1 and 4 in **1.9** are about the same distance apart (*a*) as atoms 1 and 3 (*b*) (see also Unit 8 iFigure 1.4). So, as the bond begins to form, the enthalpy terms will be similar. It is only quite close to the point of closure that strain energy in the 4-membered ring transition state is exceeded by that for the 3-membered ring cyclisation.

1.8

1.9

Next we must consider the question of why intramolecular cyclisations compete well with intermolecular reactions that would lead to chain extension and, ultimately, to polymerisation.

Cyclisation versus chain extension

The cyclisation of a bifunctional compound (an **intra**molecular reaction) is usually favoured kinetically over the competing **inter**molecular reaction that would lead to chain extension/polymerisation. Since two groups attached to the same (short) carbon chain must be close to each other, an intramolecular reaction usually has an entropy advantage over a bimolecular reaction of the same two groups, unless the steric structure of the molecule holds them apart. A simple way of viewing this effect is that the 'effective concentration' of one functional group 'seen' by its reaction partner is artificially increased in the intramolecular situation, leading to increased probability (and hence rate of reaction) of the groups coming close enough to react.

By comparing the reaction rates of cyclisations with the corresponding bimolecular reactions of model monofunctional compounds, it is possible to estimate the size of this intrinsic advantage of intramolecular reactions. The 'intramolecular advantage' is low in the strained small rings, high in the common rings (that is, 5–7 members), dropping to very low values in the medium-sized rings, before rising to a standard value for large rings, irrespective of the reaction involved in ring closure.

It appears that the proximity of the reactive centres is not the only factor in the competition between intramolecular and intermolecular reaction. It turns out that achieving the correct orientation of the two reactive centres for intramolecular reaction becomes a problem for the formation of small rings.

1.3   Ways to favour ring synthesis

1.3.1   Rigidity elements and annulation

For the formation of 5–8 membered rings, the advantage of having reactive centres close together may be further enhanced by the incorporation of *rigidity elements* into the synthetic design. These are preformed sections of the cyclic system in which the reactive groups are constrained to a particularly favourable orientation. This approach is especially valuable in the synthesis of benzo derivatives, for example:

1.10

(1.2)

1.11

It seems inherently more likely that the intermediate **1.10**, once formed, would undergo cyclisation to give the benzodiazepine **1.11** rather than further chain extension; the probability of the two reactive groups meeting will be high. The following carbocyclic example (an intramolecular Friedel–Crafts reaction) illustrates the same tendency:

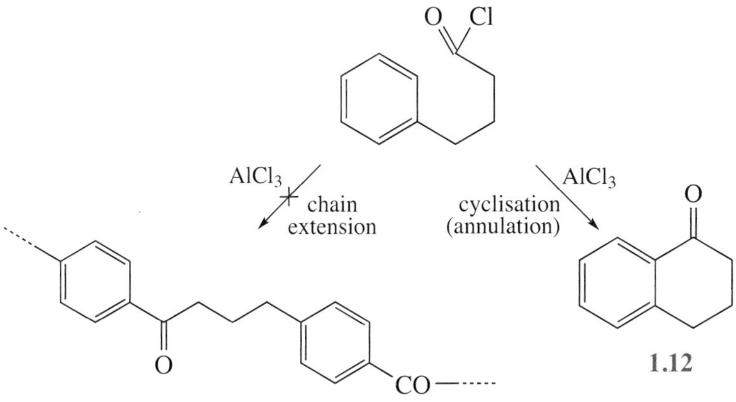

(1.3)

The syntheses of **1.11** and **1.12** are examples of annulation, that is, the building of a new ring onto an existing one.

Other rigidity elements are reactive functional groups on the same side of a saturated carbocyclic ring, and groups in *cis* positions on a carbon–carbon double bond, as in the formation of maleimide (**1.14**) and maleic anhydride (**1.15**) from maleic acid (**1.13**):

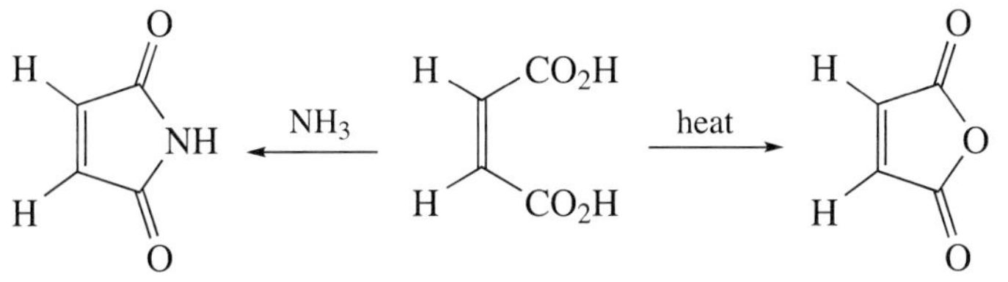

(1.4)

1.14   **1.13**   **1.15**

The value of rigidity elements in ring synthesis is demonstrated by comparison of the rate constants for the formation of the cyclic anhydrides of maleic acid and the much more rotationally flexible succinic acid (**1.16**); the rate constant for the former is about 100 times that of the latter.

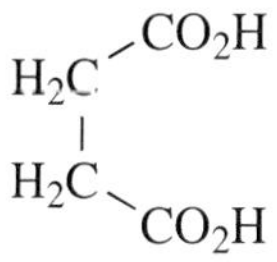

1.16

1.3.2   High-dilution techniques

A simple approach to increasing the relative probability of intramolecular reaction is to decrease the probability of intermolecular reaction by using the *high-dilution technique*, that is, having a very dilute solution of the bifunctional precursor in an inert solvent. This long-established strategy met with a fair amount of success in the synthesis of the useful C_{15} and C_{17} perfume bases exaltone (**1.17**; 60% yield) and dihydrocivetone (**1.18**; 70% yield), respectively. Other cyclic ketones up to C_{25} have been obtained this way, but, surprisingly, only negligible yields of the C_3 to C_{13} rings could be isolated.

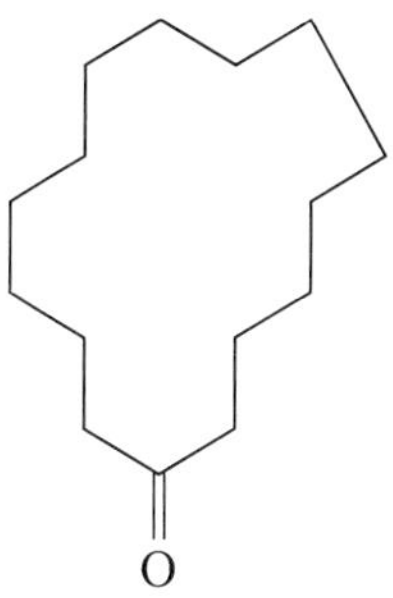

1.17

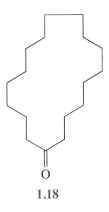

1.18

Lactone is a name used for cyclic esters; the corresponding cyclic amide is a 'lactam'.

If rate constant information is available both for a cyclisation and for the corresponding chain extension, it is possible to estimate the degree of dilution necessary to promote cyclisation. If we determine the concentration at which the rate of cyclisation equals the rate of chain extension, then at any lower concentration the intramolecular reaction will be favoured.

For the bromocarboxylates in Equation 1.1, for example, it can be shown that a dilution well below 10^{-4} mol dm^{-3} would be needed to improve the chances of obtaining the 8-membered lactone, whereas the 6-membered lactone should form readily in a 0.11 mol dm^{-3} solution.

1.3.3 Reactions at surfaces

A reaction that is found to give much higher yields of medium-sized rings than many others, is the acyloin cyclisation procedure that you may have encountered if you studied the Level 2 odule (Equation 1.5). It is also found to be very effective for very large rings.

$$\begin{array}{c} CO_2Et \\ | \\ (CH_2)_{n-2} \\ | \\ CO_2Et \end{array} \xrightarrow[\text{ii, HOAc}]{\text{i, Na}} (CH_2)_{n-2} \begin{array}{c} C=O \\ | \\ CHOH \end{array} \qquad (1.5)$$

The acyloin reaction takes place on the clean surface of finely divided metallic sodium suspended in a suitable solvent. Even with long chains, the terminal ester group can never be far removed from the first ester group that becomes attached to the surface. Competition from the chain-extension reaction will be further reduced if the rate of cyclisation is faster than the rate of desorption from the surface. A possible mechanism for acyloin cyclisation is given in Figure 1.3. Don't worry about the details, just notice how the groups become attached to the metal surface.

This technique may be thought of as a specialised variation of the high-dilution approach, since individual molecules are isolated from each other (in effect form a very dilute solution!) on the surface of the metal.

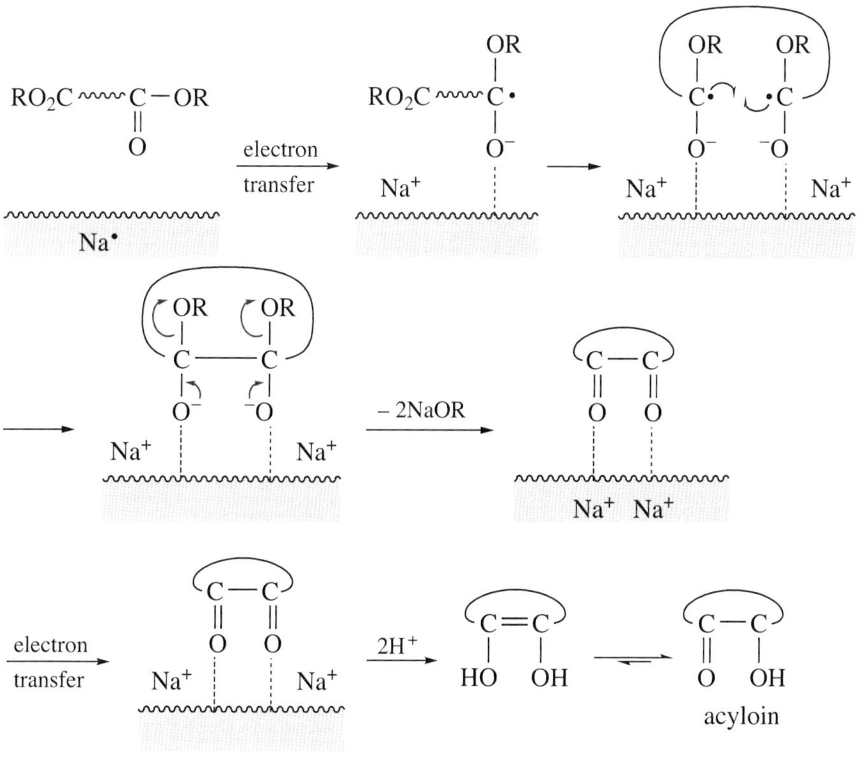

Figure 1.3   The acyloin reaction. (As you may have seen if you have studied the Level 2 module, a 'fishhook' arrow indicates the movement of a single electron.)

1.3.4   Template synthesis

Another method for overcoming large negative entropies of cyclisation is *template synthesis*, in which a chemical reagent is used to 'tie' the two reactive centres together before reaction. Nickel carbonyl has been used this way to bring about cyclisation of α,ω-dibromoalkadienes such as **1.19**, possibly via the **bis**-nickel complex **1.20**. You do not need to understand the nature of the bonding to appreciate the principle behind this technique.

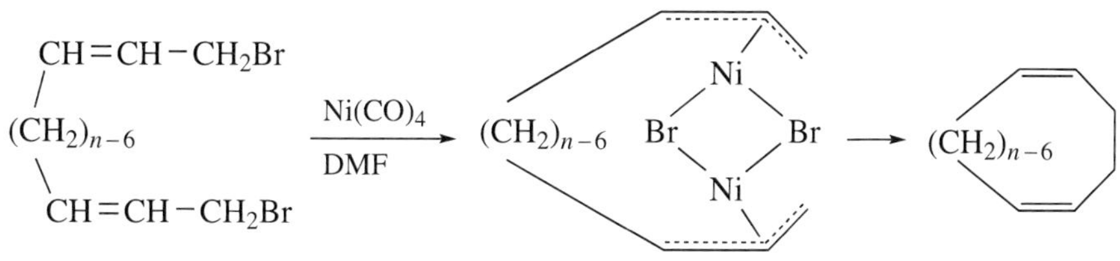

Yields are good for $n = 12$ (59%), 14 (70%) and 18 (84%), but with $n = 8$ or 10, monovinylcyclohexene or divinylcyclohexane, respectively, predominate.

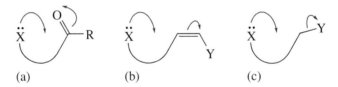

$n = 8$

$n = 10$

1.4 Selecting reactions and precursors for ring synthesis

Having examined the factors affecting ring formation we can now move on to look at how to select precursors for a particular target molecule. The examples given in Sections 1.2 and 1.3 should have demonstrated to you that a wide range of reactions familiar from open-chain organic chemistry may be utilised in the construction of both carbocyclic and heterocyclic molecules. Frequently encountered ring-synthesis reaction types are the attack of a carbon or heteroatom nucleophile at: (a) the carbon atom of a carbonyl group; (b) a carbon–carbon multiple bond conjugated with an electron-withdrawing group; and (c) a carbon atom activated by inductive withdrawal.

(a)   (b)   (c)

So what factors do we need to consider to enable us to select specific precursors for a particular target molecule? Before we can identify the necessary starting materials and reagents, a number of questions must be addressed:

- What polarity is required at the reactive centres of the reagent molecules to achieve the cyclisation? In other words, which should be electrophilic and which nucleophilic?

If the target compound is heterocyclic, we should note that most common heteroatoms are nucleophiles. Appropriate electrophilic carbon functions must then be selected to facilitate the required reaction. For carbocyclic targets, the chief criterion is the availability, or ease of synthesis, of precursors having the appropriate carbon polarities, such as carbanionic centres.

- What side chains or functional groups are required in the target molecule, and in what positions?

Many simple substituents and functions can be introduced directly in the course of ring formation. If not, a suitable 'handle' needs to be left on the ring so that the required functionality can be developed later.

- What is the unsaturation level required in the final product? In other words, how many double bonds are there in the target molecule and where are they placed?

It is often difficult to change the unsaturation level after ring synthesis, so provision for achieving the level of unsaturation required, must be built into the synthetic scheme. Fortunately, there is generally a wide choice of reactive functions available for any bond-forming reaction needed at any unsaturation level required.

The key factors to be considered are therefore heterocyclicity, substituents and side-chain development, and product unsaturation. We shall now examine each of these three factors in turn.

1.4.1 Heterocyclic systems: the synthesis of imidazoles and thiazoles

To illustrate appropriate polarity in heterocyclic synthesis we shall investigate the preparation of the 5-membered rings that include nitrogen and one other heteroatom, X (e.g. **1.21**). Where X is also nitrogen (–NH–), the parent heterocycle is imidazole, which is present in the amino acid histidine, its better-known decarboxylation product, histamine, and the drug used for treating gastric ulcers, cimetidine (Tagamet[®], **1.22**). If X is sulfur, the parent heterocycle is thiazole. This is present, at various levels of unsaturation, in such diverse compounds as penicillins, vitamin B_1 (thiamine), sulfathiazole (**1.23**) and luciferin (**1.24**), the chemiluminescent compound of the firefly.

1.21

1.22

1.23

1.24

Both parent heterocycles (**1.21**; X = NH or S) are aromatic ring systems, as will be explained for imidazole later in Section 1.6.

When synthesising heterocyclic compounds from acyclic components it is often useful to focus on making the cyclic structure by forming the carbon–heteroatom bonds that make up the ring. This approach is illustrated in Figure 1.4 and is part of the technique of **retrosynthetic analysis** that will be dealt with in detail in Unit 9. For now it is sufficient to see that working backwards from the cyclic system, it can be broken up into a range of molecular fragments as shown in Routes A–F and W–Z in Figure 1.4. This can help to identify possible combinations of acyclic reagents.

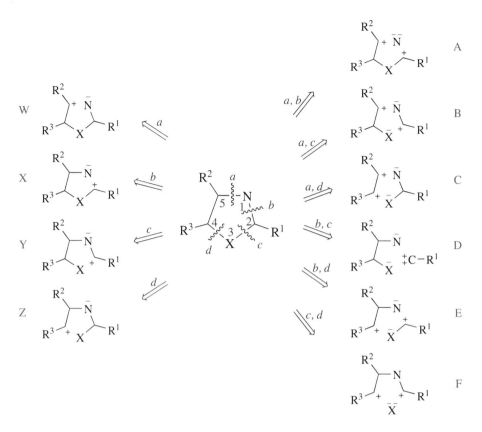

Figure 1.4 Disconnection chart for 5-membered nitrogen heterocycles with a second heteroatom at position 3. By focusing on the formation of carbon–heteroatom bonds we can identify molecular fragments required in the starting molecules and their polarity (minus for nucleophiles and plus for electrophiles). Two measures (plusses or minuses) suggest it needs to act as a nucleophile or electrophile in two bond-forming reactions.

These heterocycles often demand a wide range of bifunctional reagents with two nucleophilic centres, two electrophilic centres, or one of each for their synthesis. You will see how these are arrived at when we look at retrosynthetic analysis in Unit 9. Fortunately, the list of reagents available for heterocyclic syntheses is enormous, and is constantly increasing. Some of the more common reagents are listed in Data Table 11.1.

A *one-carbon fragment* is nearly always a molecule that can act as a dielectrophile – that is, one that can react with two nucleophilic centres in two successive bond-forming reactions. The bifunctional nature of these reagents usually results either from the survival of an electrophilic functional group after the first reaction is complete, or from the generation of a second electrophilic group after that first reaction.

■   How can methanal, or another aldehyde, behave a second time as an electrophile, after first reacting with a primary amino group?

☐   The first-formed product loses water, generating an imine (C=N−), which is polarised in the same way as the original carbonyl group.

You can see an illustration of this approach to route D (Equation 1.6) the reaction of 2-aminoethanethiol with methanal to yield the fully reduced thiazole (**1.25**) as product.

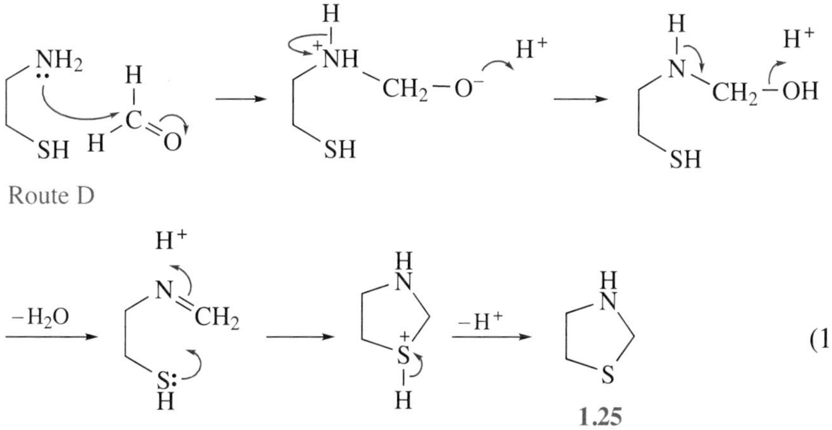

Route D

$$(1.6)$$

1.25

Reagents that introduce a *single nitrogen atom* usually behave as dinucleophiles. The ready loss of H^+ from a protonated nitrogen (R_3NH^+) regenerates the lone pair to act as a nucleophile for a second time. A dielectrophilic reagent partner is therefore required. Oxygen and sulfur may be introduced as HO^- and HS^- anions; the hydroxyl and thiol groups so generated can then act as nucleophilic centres a second time, especially if deprotonated.

Carbon–heteroatom fragments such as those required in routes B and E in Figure 1.4 have electrophilic carbon and nucleophilic heteroatom 'ends'. The reaction of an aminoketone with cyanamide fulfils this requirement (Equation 1.7). The polarised nitrile group acts like a carbonyl group in offering a carbon centre for attack by the nucleophilic amino group of the aminoketone:

You may wonder how it is that the aminoketone in Equation 1.7, which contains both a nucleophilic and an electrophilic centre, does not react with another molecule of itself to form a 6-membered ring. In practice, tricks do have to be used to avoid this 'dimerisation', for example by masking the nucleophilic amino group as a salt until it is needed for the reaction.

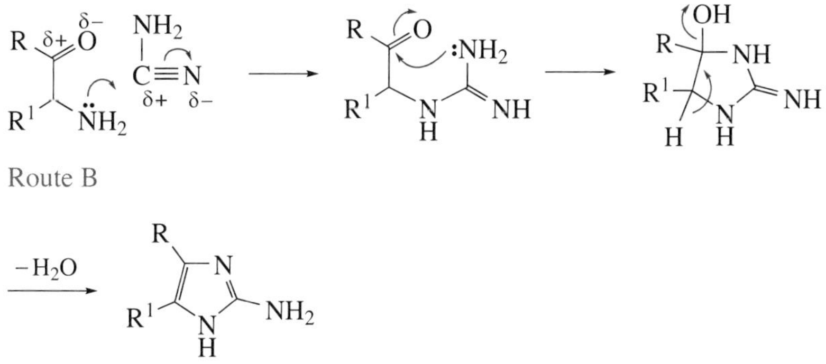

Route B

$$(1.7)$$

1.26

Many *two-carbon fragments* also show this alternate polarity ($-C^+-C^--$), but in route C a dielectrophile, ($-C^+-C^+-$), is clearly needed to react with the 3-atom fragment, $^-N–C–X^-$, with its two nucleophilic heteroatom ends. For the target molecule 2,4-diphenylthiazole (**1.27**), the precursors of choice are the dielectrophile, bromoacetophenone, and the dinucleophile, thiobenzamide (Equation 1.8).

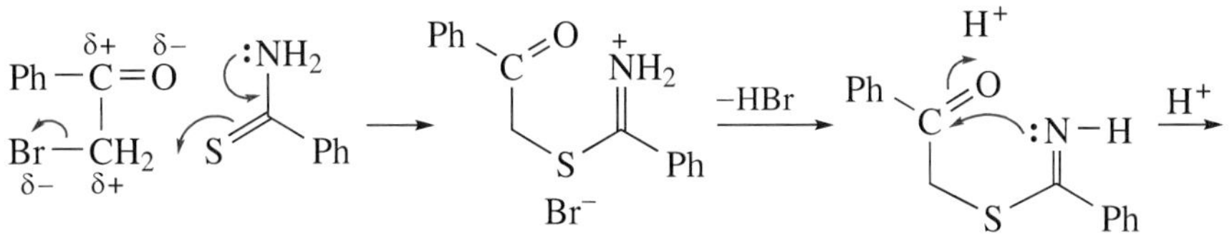

Route C

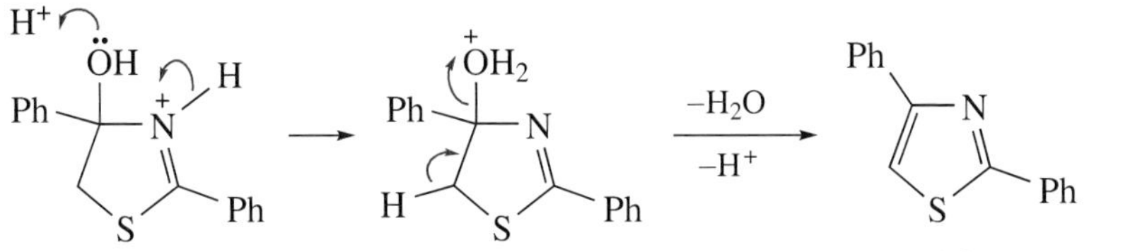

$$(1.8)$$

1.27

1.4.2 Substituents and side-chain development

The art of synthesising cyclic compounds is not limited to constructing the ring system. Equal attention must be paid to getting the correct substituents in position on the ring. There are four ways of introducing a side chain:

- Method A: *it may already be present in the linear precursor.* Examples in the previous section have shown how alkyl and aryl groups are usually unaffected by reaction conditions, and persist from reactant to product. Aryl groups may also have an important role in facilitating the development of double bonds in the new ring by coming into conjugation with them.

- Method B: *it may develop as the reaction proceeds.* The formation of the 2-amino group in imidazole **1.26** from the cyano group in the precursor is an example of this approach (Equation 1.7).

- Method C: *it may be introduced directly*, after cyclisation is complete.

- Method D: *it may be built up from a group already attached to the ring.*

As a general principle, if side-chain functions introduced during ring synthesis are not required intact, they should be readily transformable into the appropriate group. However, we must be careful to ensure that the conditions used for side-chain modification do not inadvertently affect any other group, or disrupt the ring. For a complex side chain we may need to override the retrosynthetic principle of making disconnections adjacent to the ring. It might be more effective, through judicious choice of starting material, to attach a short side chain to the ring, which allows the possibility of chain extension by further bond formation.

We shall now illustrate the four methods by considering the synthesis of vitamin B_1 (thiamine; **1.28**).

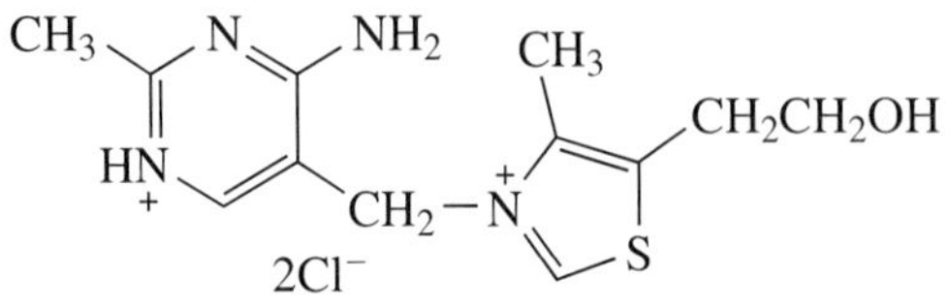

1.28

By focusing on the formation of the CH_2–N linkage we can identify two heterocyclic precursors, **1.29** and **1.30**.

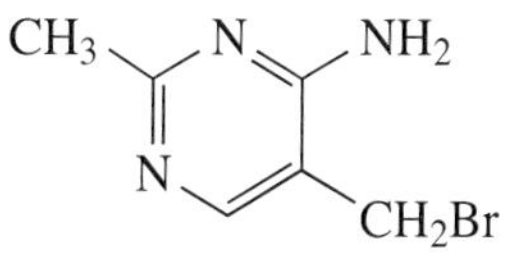

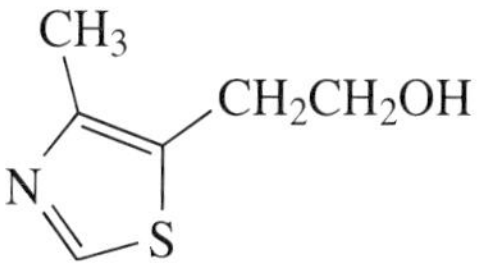

It turns out that the pyrimidine **1.31** can be readily synthesised as shown in Equation 1.9.

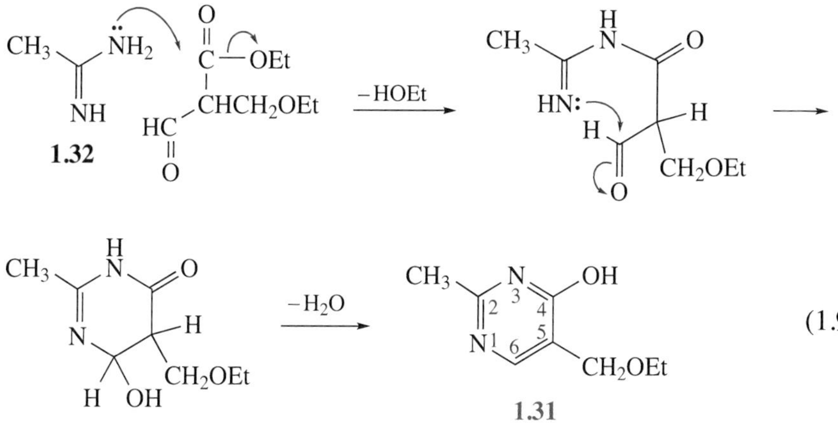

(1.9)

Notice that the hydroxyl group at position 4 develops during the ring formation (Method B); following elimination of water, the amide group generated during ring formation undergoes tautomerism to the hydroxyimine, forming an aromatic ring (discussed in Section 1.4.3). The ethoxymethyl group at position 5 was present in the acyclic precursor and persists through to the product (Method A).

hydroxyimine

The functional groups in pyrimidine **1.31** are not those required in the vitamin but they may easily be modified. The introduction of the amino group into the preformed ring of **1.31** takes advantage of the facile nucleophilic substitution that is found to be characteristic at carbon atoms adjacent to nitrogen in a fully unsaturated 6-membered heterocycle.

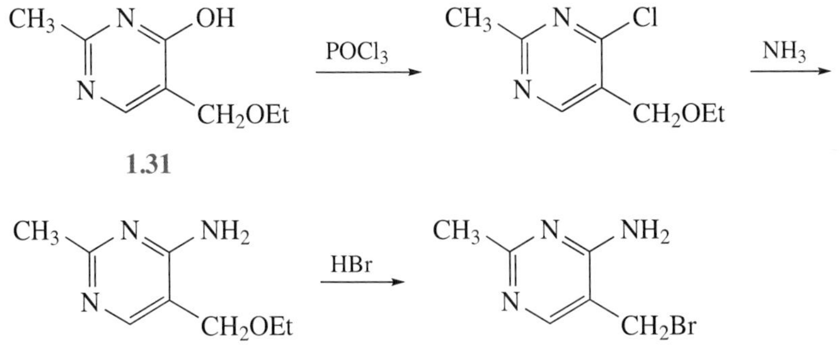

(1.10)

The transformation is carried out in two steps: first to 4-chloro with phosphoryl chloride, and then to 4-amino with ammonia. The ethoxymethyl group at position 5 may be converted into the required 5-bromomethyl substituent by cleavage of the carbon–oxygen bond with HBr.

■ To which of the methods, A to D, do the introduction of the 4-amino group and generation of the 5-bromomethyl substituents correspond?

☐ The amino group is introduced directly onto the ring (Method C). On the other hand, the bromomethyl group is built up from a group already attached to the ring, the ethoxymethyl group at position 5 (Method D). A bromomethyl group could not have been present initially, since it would have given the amino group of acetamidine (**1.32**) an alternative site for attack.

Now look back at Equation 1.8 and suggest appropriate precursors of thiazole (**1.30**).

Since neither methyl nor 2-hydroxyethyl groups will be altered by or interfere with ring formation, they may be built into the precursor **1.34** (Method A), which reacts with the thioamide **1.35** to yield thiazole, **1.30**. You may have suggested a bromoketone instead of the chloroketone **1.34**; this is a perfectly acceptable alternative.

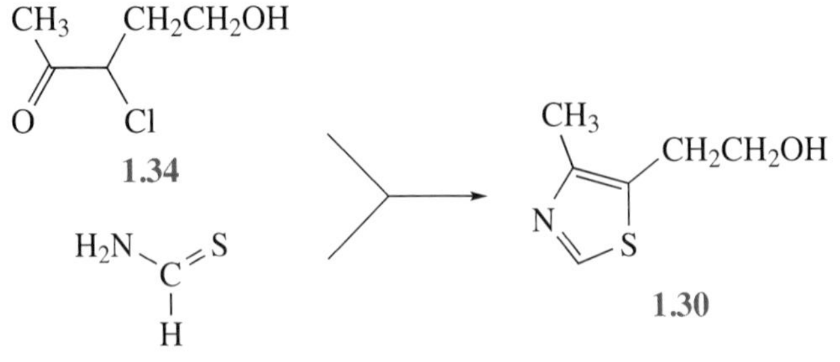

The two heterocycles can then react together to give thiamine bromide, isolated as its hydrobromide (**1.36**), in effect building the complex thiazolo side chain from the short bromomethyl chain already in position on pyrimidine (**1.33**) (Method D).

1.33 + **1.30** → **1.36**

2Br⁻

1.4.3   Unsaturation level of the product

Aromaticity in heterocyclic molecules

A discussion of **unsaturation level** in cyclic compounds must begin with a
look at the concept of aromaticity. The idea that a benzene ring, a carbocyclic
aromatic system, is unusually stable because of cyclic delocalisation of six
electrons in the π orbital system (Figure 1.5) should be reasonably familiar;
the delocalisation is conventionally denoted by the use of two resonance
forms. The extra stability gained by achieving aromaticity can help to favour a
ring synthesis.

Figure 1.5   The π orbital structure of benzene, and its resonance forms.

It is useful to know that aromaticity also occurs in heterocyclic systems that
comply with certain conditions.

The key to a generalised criterion for aromaticity is that a molecule must have
a planar monocyclic system of conjugation with a p orbital on each atom, and
that the π orbital system contains $4n + 2$ electrons, where n is a whole number
(0, 1, 2, 3...). Benzene fits this description with $n = 1$, and a total of six
π electrons.

Just as the only aromatic carbocycles considered in this unit are based on
benzene, we shall restrict the aromatic heterocyclic systems to those that can
be related to benzene. There are two main types to consider, and the first of
these is exemplified by pyridine, **1.37**.

1.37

Pyridine is much like benzene in its π electron structure (Figure 1.6). Each of
the five sp^2-hybridised carbons contributes one p orbital and one electron; the
nitrogen is also sp^2-hybridised and has one electron in a p orbital, completing
the cyclic conjugated p orbital system of six π electrons. It is worth noting
that the nitrogen non-bonded pair of electrons is located in an sp^2 orbital in

the plane of the ring, perpendicular to the π orbital system and therefore taking no part in it. Pyridines are consequently still able to function as bases.

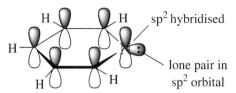

Figure 1.6 Pyridine and its aromatic π electron structure.

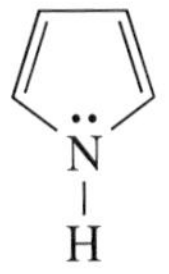

The second type of aromatic heterocycle is exemplified by pyrrole (**1.38**). Figure 1.7 shows this 5-membered ring has four sp^2-hybridised carbons, each contributing one p orbital and one electron. The π orbital set is completed by the sp^2-hybridised nitrogen, in this case contributing two electrons (its lone pair) in a p orbital to make up the six π electrons required for aromaticity. In contrast to the situation with pyridine, the 'non-bonded' pair is therefore fully involved in the aromatic delocalisation, and is consequently not available to be donated, such that pyrrole is only very slightly basic.

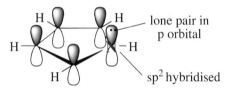

Figure 1.7 Pyrrole and its aromatic π electron structure.

The situations of the nitrogen atoms in pyridine and pyrrole are thus very distinct. In pyridine the nitrogen is part of a double bond and contributes one electron to the π system (as in benzene), whereas in pyrrole the nitrogen is not formally part of a double bond and supplies two electrons to the π system. In any case, both rings gain stabilisation energy from aromaticity, and this can favour ring formation.

These ideas can be readily extended to heterocycles containing other heteroatoms, or more than one heteroatom.

■   As you saw in Unit 3, the 5-membered heterocycle imidazole (**1.21**, X = NH) is aromatic; one of its nitrogens is pyridine-like, whereas the other is pyrrole-like.

Draw an orbital picture (based on Figures 1.6 and 1.7) to account for the aromaticity, and use it to decide which nitrogen is which.

☐   An orbital picture of imidazole is shown in Figure 1.8. There are five p orbitals, three on carbon atoms and two on nitrogen atoms. Each carbon p orbital contributes one electron. The nitrogen on the left is pyridine-like, it contributes one p electron and has a non-bonded pair orthogonal to the ring system. The nitrogen on the right with a hydrogen attached is pyrrole-like, it supplies two electrons in its p orbital making a total of six π electrons.

1.38

1.21

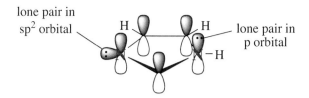

lone pair in sp² orbital

lone pair in p orbital

Figure 1.8   The aromatic p orbital structure of imidazole.

Introduction of unsaturation in heterocyclic compounds

Many of the cyclic compounds we have encountered so far have been either fully unsaturated (usually aromatic) or fully saturated, but an intermediate unsaturation level may be required. As with side chains, unsaturation may be present in precursors, develop during the ring formation process, or be introduced or removed once ring formation is complete, though this final method is often difficult to achieve.

In general, further unsaturation is only easy to introduce if the first-formed compound features groups capable of being removed in an elimination reaction, and especially if this introduces conjugation or generates an aromatic system. The tetrahydroquinoline **1.39** (Equation 1.11) qualifies on both counts.

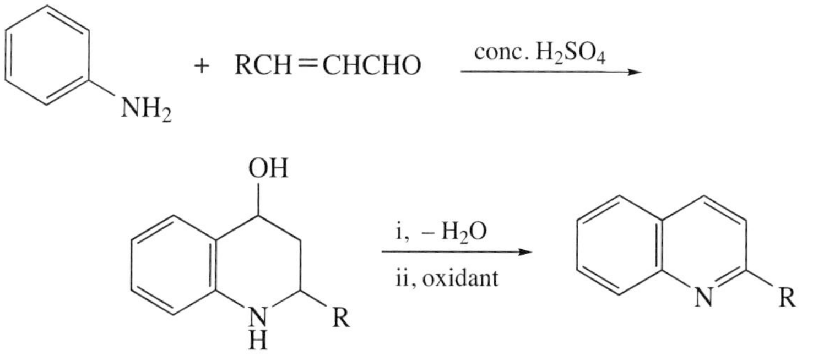

$$+ \quad RCH{=}CHCHO \quad \xrightarrow{\text{conc. } H_2SO_4}$$

$$\xrightarrow[\text{ii, oxidant}]{\text{i, } -H_2O} \tag{1.11}$$

1.39

Isolated double bonds in ring systems may often be saturated by catalytic hydrogenation, but care is sometimes needed with heterocyclic molecules to avoid ring opening. It is always easier to fully reduce or oxidise both carbocycles and heterocycles rather than to partially reduce these compounds.

A careful selection of the starting materials is the most satisfactory way to control the unsaturation level of the product. Table 1.1 shows the reaction of different 3-carbon units with hydrazine (H_2NNH_2). It is clear that the level of unsaturation in the heterocyclic product can easily be varied, depending on the choice of dielectrophile. Importantly, there is also often a choice of precursors from which to prepare the heterocycle at a specified unsaturation level.

■   Look at Reactions B and F, in Table 1.1, and, in each case, compare how many π bonds are present in the precursors and the products.

☐   For Reaction B, the precursors contain two π bonds and the cyclic products only one. In Reaction E, both precursors and product contain two π bonds.

Table 1.1 Effect of the choice of starting material on the unsaturation level of pyrazoles formed from hydrazine (X represents halogen, OH, OR other leaving group).

Dielectrophile	Unsaturation level	Product	Reaction
X–C–C–C–X	tetrahydro	tetrahydropyrazole (NH, N–H)	A
C=C–C— (with O) and —C–C–C–X (with O)	dihydro	dihydropyrazole (N, N–H)	B, C
—C≡C–C— (with O), X–C=C–C— (with O), —C–C–C— (with O, O)	aromatic	pyrazole (N, N–H)	D, E, F

It is possible to make the generalisation for these and other ring syntheses, that if ring formation includes an addition reaction (Reactions B and D), the unsaturation level in the product is reduced by the equivalent of one π bond in comparison with the starting molecules. By contrast, ring formation by substitution (Reaction A) or condensation (addition–elimination; Reaction F) retains the same levels of unsaturation in the cyclic product as in the linear precursors. You should check that this applies to the other examples in Table 1.1.

1.5   Cycloaddition reactions

1.5.1   The Diels–Alder reaction

The reaction is named after the German chemists Otto Diels and Kurt Alder, who received the Nobel Prize for Chemistry in 1950 for this contribution to organic synthesis.

The ring syntheses discussed so far in this unit have relied on reactions familiar from aliphatic and aromatic chemistry. In this section we shall look at a series of reactions used exclusively for the formation of cyclic systems. Of these, the most important is the Diels–Alder reaction.

The Diels–Alder reaction is the cycloaddition of a conjugated diene with an alkene (the dienophile, or 'diene lover') to produce a substituted cyclohexene product **1.41**; the simplest Diels–Alder reaction would be between buta-1,3-diene and ethene (Equation 1.12, X = H). In fact this particular example is not efficient, and the reaction is much better if X is an electron-withdrawing group. We shall consider in more detail the factors that promote a fast high-yielding reaction. For now, we shall use this simplest reaction to describe the reaction mechanism.

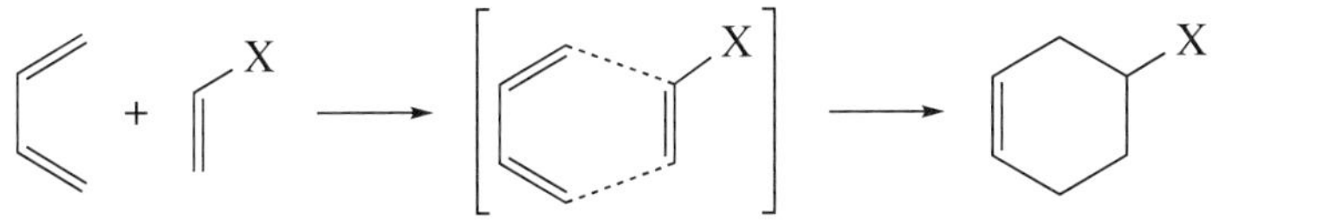

$$(1.12)$$

1.40
cyclic transition state

1.41

The mechanism of the Diels–Alder reaction is different from reactions studied up to now in the module, since it is neither polar (nucleophile–electrophile) nor radical. Rather, it is a concerted process in which both new carbon–carbon bonds form at the same time, through a cyclic transition state, in which a cyclic redistribution of bonding electrons takes place. (Sometimes, for convenience, the bond making and breaking is expressed using curly arrows, but they do not have their usual significance for direction of electron-flow, and can be written equally validly in either sense, **1.42** or **1.43**.) (It can even be represented as a radical process using fishhook arrows.)

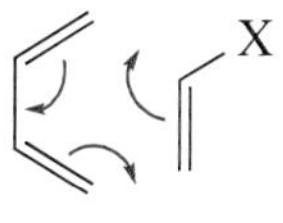

1.42

The cycloaddition can be pictured as occurring by end-on overlap of the two alkene p orbitals with the two p orbitals on carbons 1 and 4 of the diene (Figure 1.9).

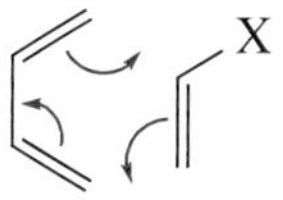

1.43

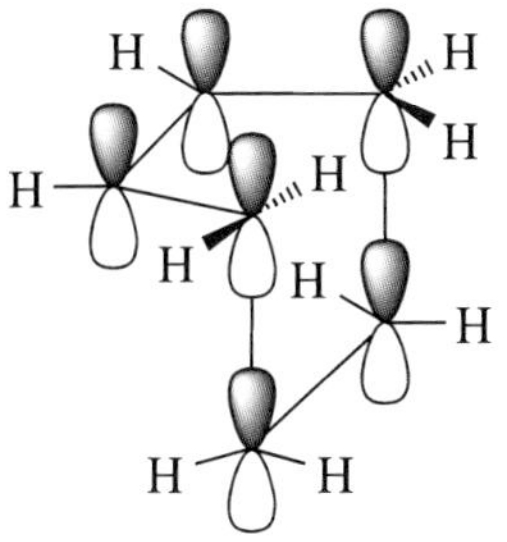

Figure 1.9   The bonding overlaps in the transition state of a Diels–Alder reaction.

The Diels–Alder reaction is so versatile, so easy to carry out and so high-yielding, that planning the synthesis of any molecule containing a 6-membered alicyclic ring should explore its possibilities, whether or not the target obviously includes the structure **1.41**.

So what is needed for an effective Diels–Alder reaction?

1.5.2   Characteristics of the Diels–Alder reaction

Diels–Alder reactions occur most rapidly and in highest yield if the dienophile is electron deficient (that is, it has an electron-withdrawing substituent). Thus, whereas ethene reacts only sluggishly, ethyl propenoate (**1.44**), propenenitrile (**1.45**), and maleic anhydride (**1.46**) are examples of highly reactive dienophiles; note also that alkynes, such as **1.47**, can act as dienophiles.

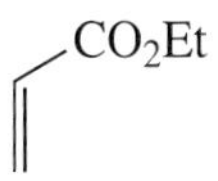

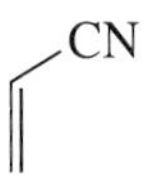

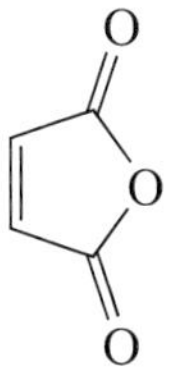

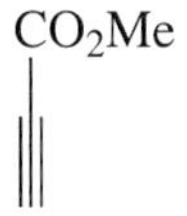

| 1.44 | 1.45 | 1.46 | 1.47 |

The reaction is also favoured if the diene component is electron-rich, so it should carry electron-releasing substituent(s); often alkyl groups are sufficient. In addition, it must be able to adopt what is known as an *s-cis* conformation (*cis*-like around the central single bond), that is, **1.48** rather than **1.49**. Only in the *s-cis* arrangement are the carbons 1 and 4 close enough to take part in the cyclic transition state; the *s-trans* conformation has the lowest energy, but would not allow the cyclic transition state.

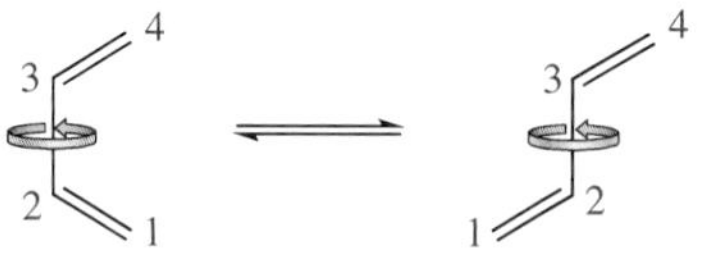

1.48 *s-cis*   **1.49** *s-trans*

Cyclopentadiene (**1.50**), in which the diene is locked into *s-cis* geometry, is so reactive that it reacts with itself at room temperature, one molecule acting as diene and another as dienophile, to form dicyclopentadiene, as shown in Equation 1.13:

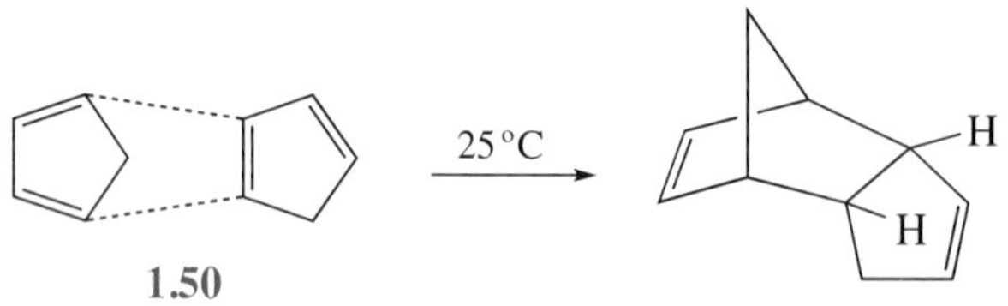

(1.13)

On the other hand, (2Z,4Z)-hexa-2,4-diene is very unreactive because severe steric strain prevents it from adopting the *s-cis* conformation **1.51**.

1.51

Many Diels–Alder reactions take place at room temperature or just above, which is fortunate since the Diels–Alder is a reversible reaction, and the products of kinetic and thermodynamic control are often different. Lewis acids (especially $AlCl_3$, BF_3 and $SnCl_4$) have been found to be very effective catalysts, reducing both reaction times and temperatures; they enable the kinetically controlled products to be formed, rather than the thermodynamic ones that would be formed if equilibration were allowed to occur.

The Diels–Alder reaction is regioselective (Unit 3), as exemplified by the data in Figure 1.10. Irrespective of whether the diene R group is electron-

withdrawing or electron-releasing, l-substituted butadienes give predominantly
3,4-disubstituted cyclohexenes, and 2-substituted butadienes give mainly
1,4-products. A Lewis acid catalyst tends to enhance the selectivity.

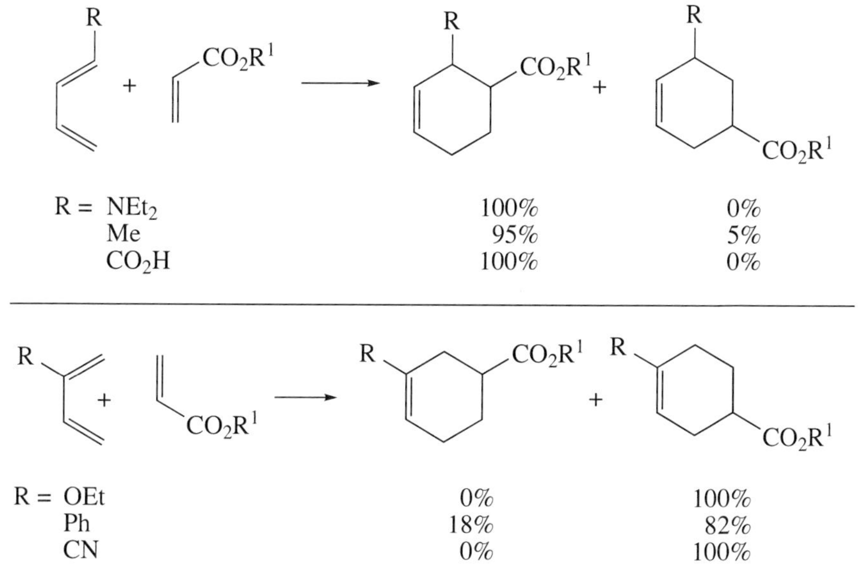

R =		
NEt$_2$	100%	0%
Me	95%	5%
CO$_2$H	100%	0%

R =		
OEt	0%	100%
Ph	18%	82%
CN	0%	100%

Figure 1.10 Regioselectivity in Diels–Alder reactions.

However, the great strength of the Diels–Alder reaction is its stereoselectivity.
Cis or *trans* relationships in the dienophile are maintained in the product, and
the geometry of diene substituents is conserved through the well-defined
transition state (Figure 1.9). In this respect the geometry of ring formation is
fixed, since the relative orientation of substituents on the product cyclohexene
ring of Figure 1.11 is solely determined by their configuration in the starting
materials.

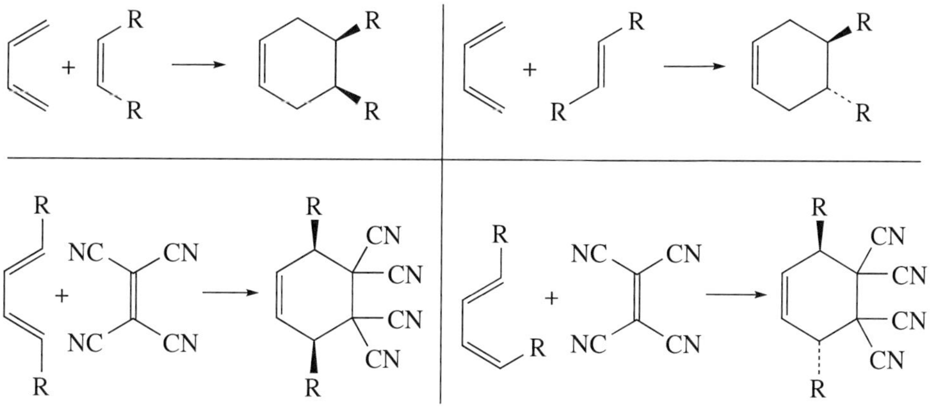

Figure 1.11 Stereoselectivity in the Diels–Alder reaction: the effect of diene and
dienophile stereochemistry.

If the ring formation were to take place in steps, there might be an
opportunity for bond rotation after formation of the first bond, leading to a
diastereomeric mixture. The fact that isomers have not been observed provides

strong evidence for a mechanism in which both new ring bonds form simultaneously.

Tetracyanoethene was deliberately chosen in Figure 1.11 because it is symmetrically substituted, which results in the formation of only one diastereoisomer of the product. However, if the dienophile is not symmetrically substituted, more than one diastereoisomer is possible.

In contrast, now consider the reaction between (2*E*,4*E*)-hexa-2,4-diene and maleic anhydride (Figure 1.12). The two reagents could approach in two different ways, which could give rise to two alternative products via overlapping (*endo*) or extended (*exo*) transition states respectively).

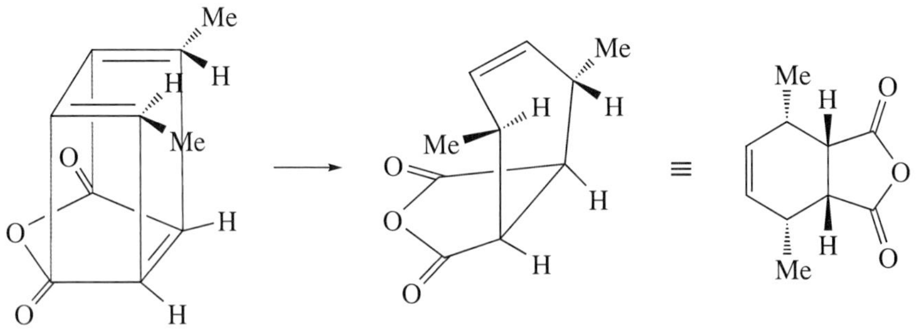

Figure 1.12 Stereoselecting in the Diels–Alder reaction: orientation of approach of the reactants. The red band represents the principal orbital interaction, and the purple band shows the secondary orbital interaction.

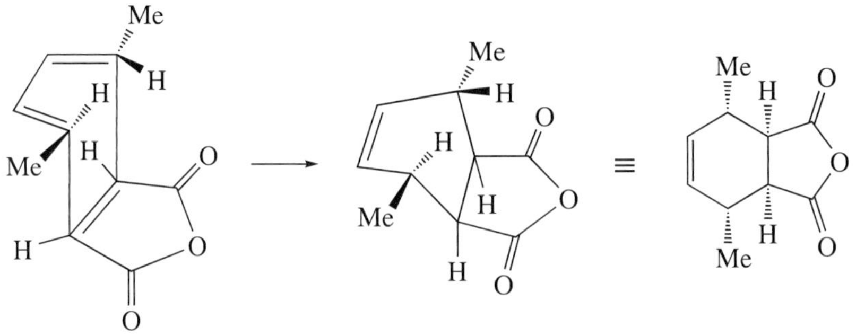

Perhaps surprisingly, in view of our earlier emphasis on the importance of steric hindrance, the **endo** adduct **1.52**, is kinetically preferred, and is the product usually isolated from low-temperature reactions. This is because, in addition to the orbital interactions between the bonding centres, shown in red in Figure 1.12, in the endo adduct there is a small stabilising orbital interaction (known as 'secondary orbital interaction', shown in purple) between the π orbitals of the diene and those of the π-bonded groups attached to the dienophile (Figure 1.12). Endo stereoselectivity is explained by invoking these secondary orbital interactions, which help to stabilise endo transition states like **1.52**, but are not possible in **exo** transition states like **1.53**. The exo form is the thermodynamically more stable product, and is formed under equilibrating conditions. Although most pronounced with cyclic dienes or dienophiles, and in intramolecular Diels–Alder reactions (Equation 1.14), a preference for endo adduct formation is also shown by many acyclic reagents (Equation 1.15).

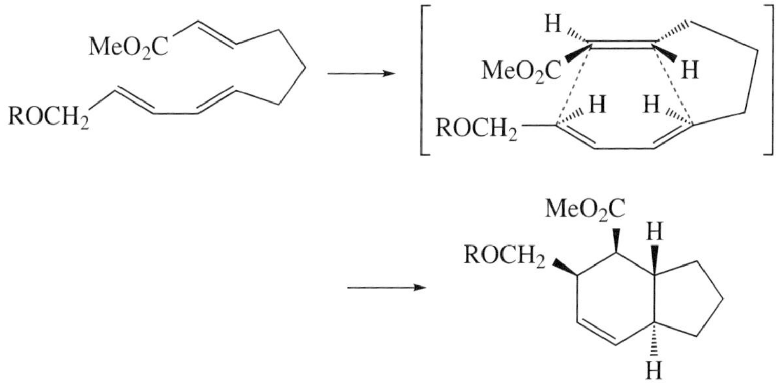

$$(1.14)$$

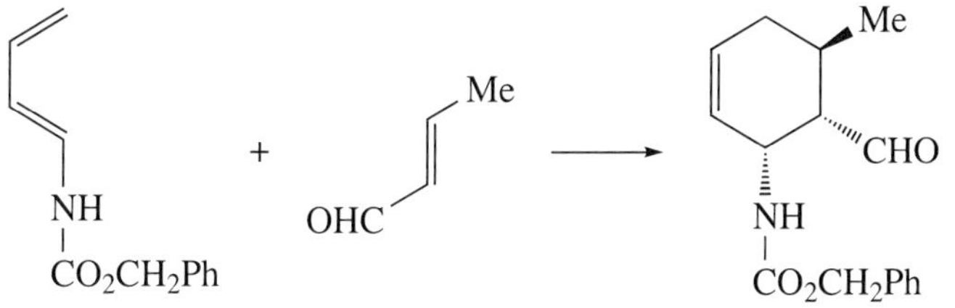

$$(1.15)$$

■ Draw the transition state that leads to the observed product stereochemistry for Equation 1.15.

☐ The required transition state is **1.56**. Since the electron-withdrawing group on the dienophile lies underneath the diene, this is called the *endo* approach.

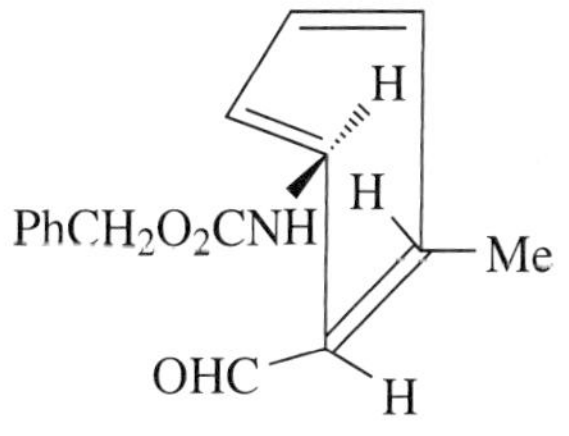

1.56

1.5.3 Hetero Diels–Alder reactions

It is possible to incorporate one or more heteroatoms into the diene and/or the dienophile. We shall look here at just a couple of examples of such hetero Diels–Alder reactions.

The incorporation of an electron-attracting heteroatom into a dienophile will make it more electron-deficient than an alkene, and so it should react with electron-rich dienes. The example in Equation 1.16 shows an aldehyde carbonyl group as the dienophile with the very electron-rich diene, **1.57**, (known as the 'Danishefsky diene').

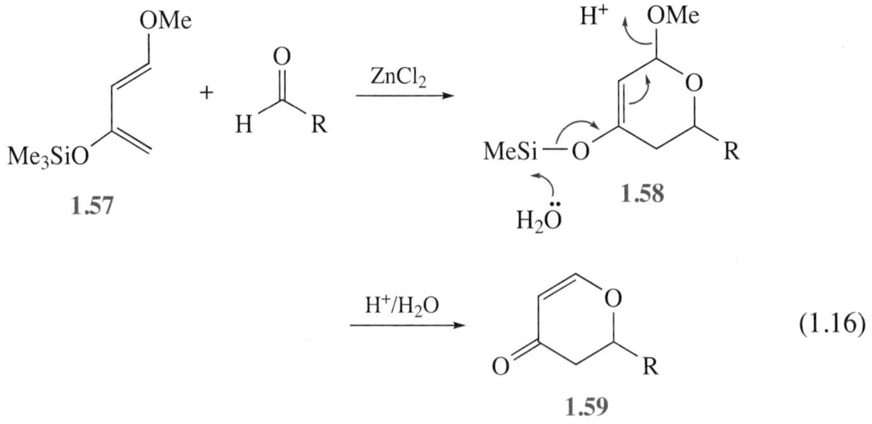

$$(1.16)$$

This gives the initial cycloadduct, **1.58**, which is converted to the dihydropyranone, **1.59**, on acid hydrolysis. As with carbocyclic Diels–Alder reactions, the presence of a Lewis acid catalyst ($ZnCl_2$ in this example) is advantageous, since, by coordinating to the dienophile, it further reduces the electron density in its reactive π bond.

If the heteroatom is in the diene, making it electron-deficient, an electron-rich dienophile may be needed for cycloaddition to succeed. These *inverse electron demand* Diels–Alder reactions have analogues in the carbocyclic series but are much more useful in heterocyclic synthesis.

■ Suggest what types of functional group might make an alkene into an electron-rich dienophile.

☐ Phenoxy, alkoxy and amino groups make enol ethers and enamines into effective dienophiles in inverse electron demand Diels–Alder reactions.

An example is shown in the dihydropyran synthesis in Equation 1.17:

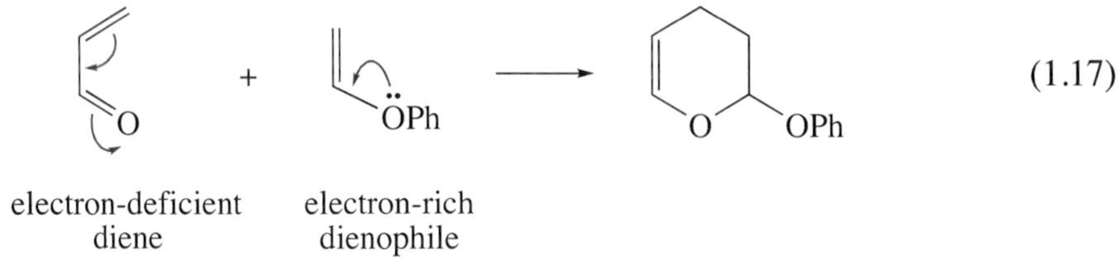

$$(1.17)$$

electron-deficient   electron-rich
diene   dienophile

However, increasing the electron supply to a heterodiene can compensate for the electronegativity of the heteroatom, and allow satisfactory reaction with normal dienophiles, as in the following example:

$$(1.18)$$

The methyl ($-CH_3$) and dimethylamine ($-N(CH_3)_2$) groups donate electrons to the alkene double bond and compensate for the electron withdrawing effects of the nitrogen.

Note that in this case the expected dihydropyridine product (shown in square brackets in Equation 1.18) is not observed, because it readily undergoes aromatisation to a pyridine.

1.6   Other rings formed by cycloaddition reactions

So far, when looking at cycloaddition reactions, we have restricted our discussion to the Diels–Alder reaction, to form 6-membered rings from a diene (4 atoms) and a dienophile (2 atoms) – that is, [4+2]-cycloadditions. You may have wondered whether other types of cycloaddition can be used in ring synthesis, and the answer is that they certainly can! There is indeed a whole family of concerted [3+2]-cycloadditions, to make 5-membered rings, that we do not have space to deal with in this module.

We shall, however, look briefly at cycloadditions that make 4-membered rings. Concerted thermal reactions in which two molecules, each containing a double bond, undergo cycloaddition to yield 4-membered rings (that is, [2+2]-cycloadditions) are difficult to achieve.

However, the ionic, stepwise cycloaddition of **cumulenes,** to a variety of doubly bonded compounds is a major route to 4-membered heterocyclic rings. Cumulenes are molecules in which two double bonds terminate on the same carbon atom, as in **ketenes (1.60).**

These reactions are regioselective, and many products show retention of stereochemistry because of the rapid ring closure after the initial bond formation. Advantage is taken of this regioselectivity in the reaction shown in Equation 1.19. The orientation of the reactive molecules follows from their normally expected direction of polarisation.

This does not mean that these cycloadditions are more important or widely used than the [3+2]-cycloadditions mentioned above (indeed, many would argue that the reverse is true!)

$$R_2C{=}C{=}O$$

1.60

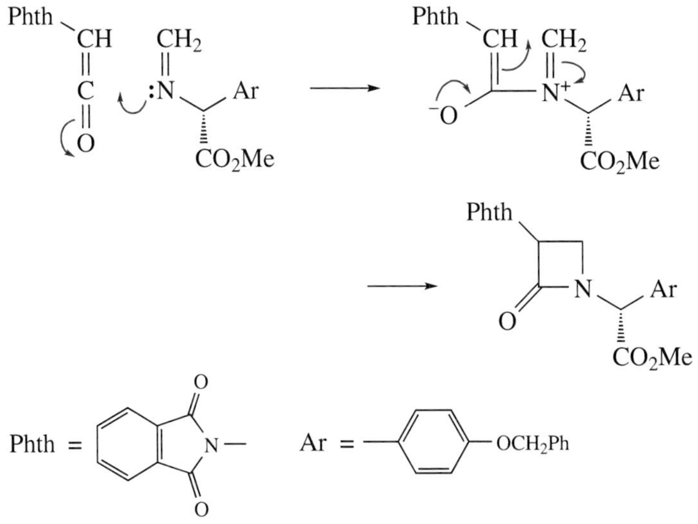

$$(1.19)$$

Phth =   Ar =

Study note

Before moving on to Section 2, try to write a summary of this section and then compare it with ours. Go to Unit 8 summaries in Unit 8 resources.

2 Solid-phase synthesis of peptides and other molecules

The preparation of organic molecules has become a well-defined process over the last 50 years. Chemists have discovered a great deal about producing molecules in a chemo-, regio- and stereoselective manner (Figure 2.1), as well as being able to predict what sort of molecule it might be desirable to prepare.

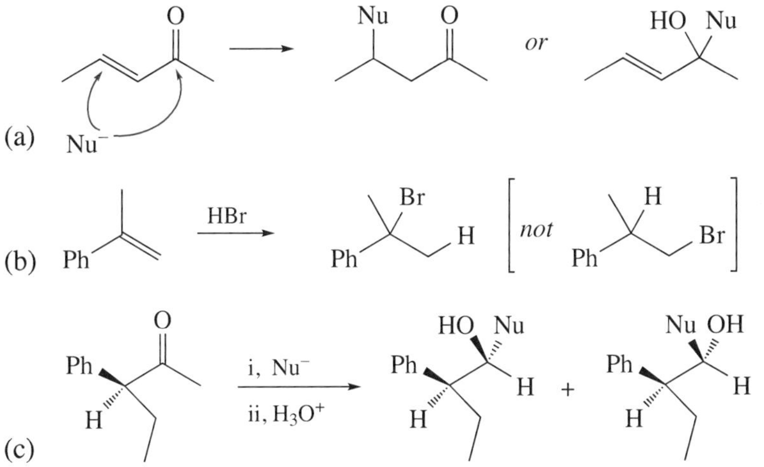

(a)

(b)

(c)

Figure 2.1 The preparation of organic compounds.

As you saw in Unit 1, the use of molecular modelling with computer software has given a greater understanding of the interactions required when a potential drug molecule binds to an enzyme or a receptor (Figure 2.2).

In the pharmaceutical industry, potential drug candidates can fail at any stage, so in crude terms, the larger the supply of potential target molecules, the greater the chances of a successful drug candidate making it to market. It follows, therefore, that as new therapeutic areas emerge, many more drug candidate molecules are required for biological screening in an ever shorter time frame. This in turn requires the turn-around time for synthesis to be shortened, with ever-lower levels of impurities and, increasingly, a requirement for synthetic routes to adhere to the principles of green chemistry. These promote the use of less toxic reagents and solvents. Processes should, where possible, be catalytic, not stoichiometric; use renewable raw materials; and occur with high atom economy and with minimal pollutive effects.

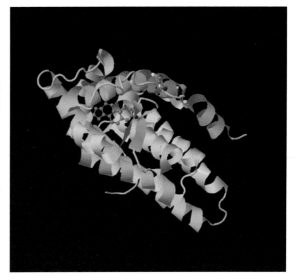

Figure 2.2 A steroid receptor. The four fused rings of the steroid skeleton are shown in grey. (Based on pdb file 2am9 (Pereira de Jesus-Tran et al., 2006).)

2.1   The development of solid-phase synthesis

The traditional route to an organic compound involves the mixing of carefully controlled amounts of reagents, usually in a solvent. This is called a **solution-phase synthesis**. The reaction must then be allowed sufficient time to take place (reaction rates can vary from virtually instantaneous at a low temperature to several days' reflux in a high-boiling solvent). Purification is then effected, often by a combination of filtration, aqueous work-up, solvent extraction and solvent evaporation, followed by chromatography, crystallisation or distillation. The final part of the 'chemical processing' involves the gathering of data (for purity and identity) on the target compound. Most chemists would agree that carrying out the reaction and subsequent spectroscopic analysis (for example, mass spectrometry, ^{1}H and ^{13}C NMR, infrared spectroscopy) are by far the most interesting aspects of any synthetic preparation. The isolation and purification of a substance can be time-consuming and tedious, though it is absolutely central to target molecule synthesis.

Ideally, a reaction should be carried out with minimum purification. Optimisation of a reaction to give maximum yield and purity is important in industry. The Process Research and Development arm (PR&D) of a company is charged with this responsibility. The goal, ideally, is no purification other than removal of the reaction solvent, but if there are by-products or excess reagents, they must be removed.

At this point, we will begin to consider the application of a **solid phase** to help attain our synthetic goals. A solid phase is advantageous for the following three reasons:

1   *It acts as a tether for a substrate undergoing functionalisation*

The substrate remains covalently bound to a highly visible solid (typically a hydrocarbon-derived polymer), via a linker molecule, whilst synthetic manipulations are carried out. The product can therefore be easily removed from a reaction by filtration and then the target molecule cleaved from the polymer to give a pure substance.

This is illustrated in Figure 2.3 where a reactant (R_1) is covalently attached to the solid support (S) using a linking group (L). The linking group contains a functional group, for example an alcohol, amine or carboxylic acid, that can form a covalent bond with the reactant to fix it to the support. The reactant, once immobilised on the support can be reached with the second reactant (R_2) with an excess of reagents. Any unreacted reactant (R_2) and excess reagents can be washed away. The product is then cleaved from the linker group to remove the product from the solid support.

The main advantages of this approach are increased product yield and ease of purification. To ensure maximum yields in reactions, large excesses of reagent can be used. Whatever is left in solution is simply rinsed away afterwards with a solvent. This chemistry was developed originally for peptide synthesis, where more complete reactions and purer products were required. If the product is attached to an insoluble polymer, it can be more readily isolated after a reaction.

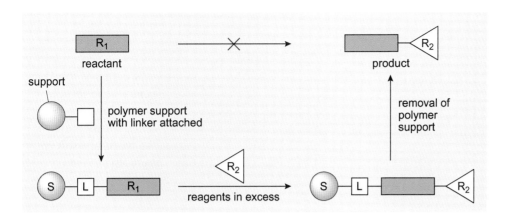

Figure 2.3 A schematic representation of the role of the solid support (S) and a linker (L) as a means of tethering a reactant.

2 To support a reagent to make it more efficient or convenient to use

For example, an oxidising or reducing reagent or a carbon–carbon coupling reagent can be attached to a solid support. The phenylchlorosulfonium chloride (**2.1**) in Scheme 2.1 is a mild oxidant used to oxidise the primary alcohol in **2.2** to an aldehyde in **2.3**. Untethered, the reagent (**2.1**) is both 'sticky' and produces an unpleasant smelling by-product in the reaction. By immobilising it on a solid support (represented by S in a grey sphere) it can be more easily handled and the by-product can be readily removed.

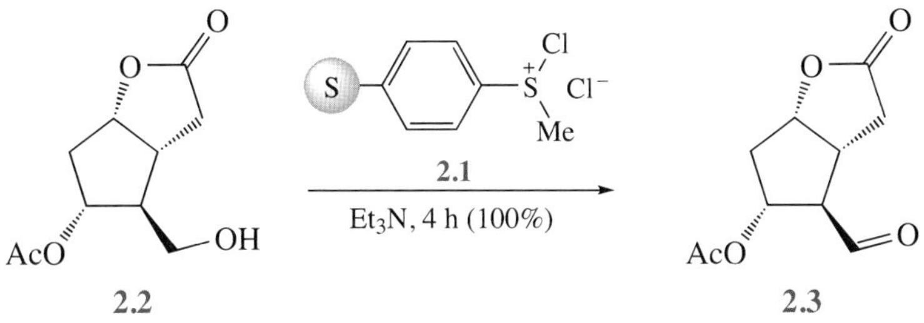

Scheme 2.1

3 To act as a tether for a 'scavenger'

A substrate which is present to bind unwanted byproducts of a reaction, for example attaching nitrogen-containing ligands to a solid support, these molecules are present to bind to unwanted by-products of a reaction. Specifically, they will aid removal of metal ions, for example, Cu^{2+}, from solution, even when other amine compounds are present.

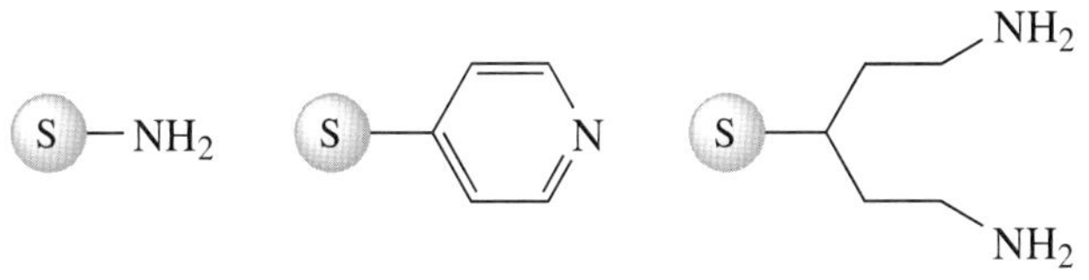

Thus, the use of a solid support has wide-reaching advantages in organic synthesis.

Parallel synthesis is the generation, simultaneously, of a number of analogous compounds, where each has perhaps one structural difference.

Table 2.1   A five-compound library.

	A	B	C	D	E
C	AC	BC	CC	DC	EC

Table 2.1 shows five different compounds, A, B, C, D and E being treated with compound C in one operation. The result is a small 'library' and each component could be screened individually for biological activity – let us assume that BC is the compound that shows the most promising activity. This approach might be adopted when it becomes fairly certain that the active compounds most likely terminate in a C moiety.

Combinatorial chemistry is the generation of libraries of compounds by synthesising all possible combinations from a set of smaller chemical structures or building blocks as shown in Table 2.2. These may be small organic molecules with a variety of functional groups, peptides or nucleic acids. The libraries so generated are mixtures containing many structures, one or more of which may have desirable biological activity.

Table 2.2   A compound library derived from all possible combinations of five compounds.

	A	B	C	D	E
A	AA	BA	CA	DA	EA
B	AB	BB	CB	DB	EB
C	AC	BC*	CC	DC	EC
D	AD	BD	CD	DD	ED
E	AE	BE	CE	DE	EE

* Assume BC is the compound that shows most promising activity.

The repetitive nature of the synthetic processes involved in most combinatorial applications lends itself to automation. This allows a chemist to prepare thousands of compounds of known structure in the time that it would take to prepare only a few pure substances in the usual manner. An obvious drawback is that the observation of biological activity within a mixture may be due to an individual substance or the mixture itself. Further work is thus required to purify any library that looks promising, as well as the scaling up of the synthesis from what might at most be only a few milligrams of a compound during the initial preparation of a library.

2.2 Peptides and their synthesis: general principles

Peptides as a class of compounds were introduced in Unit 2 and they include examples such as enzymes and receptors that are immensely important to life in general and to human health in particular. There are many peptide hormones; the octapeptide Angiotensin II (**2.4**) is a hormone present in blood plasma that regulates blood pressure.

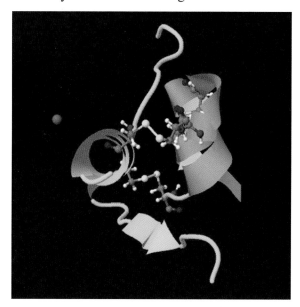

2.4

Insulin (Figure 2.4) is a peptide hormone of 51 amino acids which regulates the amount of glucose in the bloodstream. It consists of two peptide chains linked by two disulfide bridges.

Figure 2.4   Insulin: a peptide hormone. (Based on pdb 3ins (Wlodawer et al., 1989).)

Peptides are also found in nerve tissue. Endorphins are peptides produced by the pituitary gland and hypothalmus in vertebrates and are responsible for feelings of well-being and excitement. In addition, there are peptide antibiotics and peptides that are used by organisms as toxins for defence, for example, against insects. The amino acids that are 'sequenced' in a naturally occurring peptide are taken from the set of 20 amino acids, represented by **2.5**, introduced in Unit 2. Each has a three letter abbreviation, which helps simplify the notation for peptides, as shown in Data Table 4.1, and Figure 1.1 in Unit 2.

2.5

2.6   **2.7**

Proteins can comprise giant molecules made up of very long sequences of α-amino acids joined by amide (peptide) bonds, **2.6**, as we saw in Unit 2. At the other end of the spectrum, two amino acids joined by an amide bond forms a dipetide, **2.7**, three amino acids, a tripeptide, and so on.

The number of possible peptides that can be synthesised starting by combining the 20 naturally occurring amino acids in all possible ways is arrived at based on 20 raised to various powers:

monopeptide $20^1 = 20$

dipeptides $(20 \times 20) = 20^2 = 400$

tripeptides $(20 \times 20 \times 20) = 20^3 = 8000$

tetrapeptides $(20 \times 20 \times 20 \times 20) = 20^4 = 160\ 000$

pentapeptides $(20 \times 20 \times 20 \times 20 \times 20) = 20^5 = 3200\ 000$

hexapeptides $(20 \times 20 \times 20 \times 20 \times 20 \times 20) = 20^6 = 64\ 000\ 000$

heptapeptides $(20 \times 20 \times 20 \times 20 \times 20 \times 20 \times 20) = 20^7 = 1380\ 000\ 000$

- ■ For n residues there are 20^n possible combinations of amino acids. How many combinations could be assembled to make a peptide with 20 amino acids?

- ☐ $20^{20} = 1 \times 10^{26}$ peptides. Thus the scope for different types of proteins is vast and it is this huge diversity that allows for the high specificity in the actual peptide combination that is selected.

For proteins, the number of amino acid residues is even greater and it can be as high as 500 residues.

All that is needed to make a peptide is the formation of amide bonds between the carboxylic acid and amine groups of amino acids. Of course, both functional groups are present in each of the starting materials, amino acids, so the ability to control the way in which particular amino acids should be condensed together is crucial. The temporary masking of amino and carboxylic acid groups by 'protecting groups' allows the desired amide bonds to be made sequentially. Amino acids also need to be 'activated' to facilitate amide formation, as amines do not readily react with carboxylic acids. Fortunately there exist powerful methodologies which allow the rapid assembly of peptides. Protection, deprotection (i.e. the opposite of protection) and activation have now become very straightforward and routine procedures.

You can see from **2.6** that the functional group linking the two α-amino acid residues is an amide: the key bond, CO–NH, is known as a peptide bond. Peptides are conventionally represented with the terminal amino group (N-terminal end) on the left and the terminal carboxylic acid group (C-terminal end) on the right.

Peptide bonds are separated from each other, and from the end groups, by a single carbon atom, known as the α-carbon atom which, in all but one type of residue, bears a substituent on the side chain. Clearly, it is the selection and order of these side chains that gives a peptide its distinctive biological properties.

■   Anticipating that peptide synthesis will involve the formation of an amide from the carboxyl group of one amino acid and the amino group of another, which amino acids are likely to introduce chemical complications because of groups in their side chains?

□   Any amino acid that has an additional amino or carboxyl group in its side chain would be able to form alternative amides using that function. So aspartic acid, glutamic acid and lysine could present problems. But you may have also selected other cases where a functional group in the side chain could offer alternative chemistry under the conditions necessary to form peptide bonds. For instance, the OH groups of serine, threonine and tyrosine may interfere, as might the SH group of cysteine and the –NH–C(=NH)–NH$_2$ group of arginine. You are probably not yet in a position to comment on the amido groups of asparagine and glutamine, the aromatic amino functions of tryptophan and histidine and the sulfur atom in the thioether, methionine, but they are generally too unreactive to be troublesome. The remaining side chains are certainly unreactive.

■   Draw the two-dimensional molecular structures of the following peptides in the style of **2.7** (i.e. ignoring stereochemistry):

i   H–Ala–His–OH

ii   H–Phe-Ile-Gly-Met-Gly-Pro–OCH$_3$

☐ (i) Structure **2.8** is H–Ala-His–OH; (ii) **2.9** is H–Phe-Ile-Gly-Met-Gly-Pro–OCH$_3$:

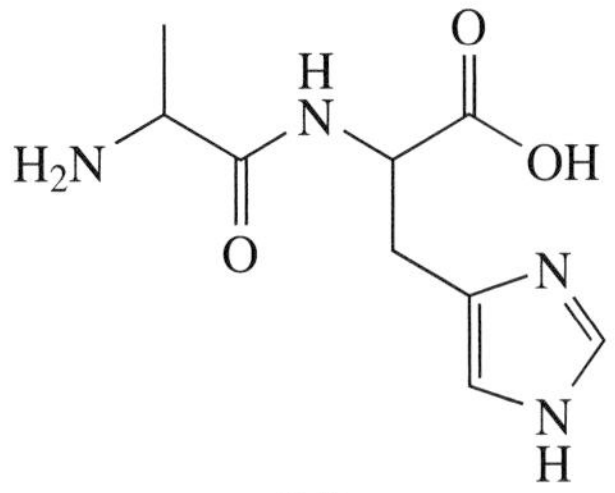

2.8

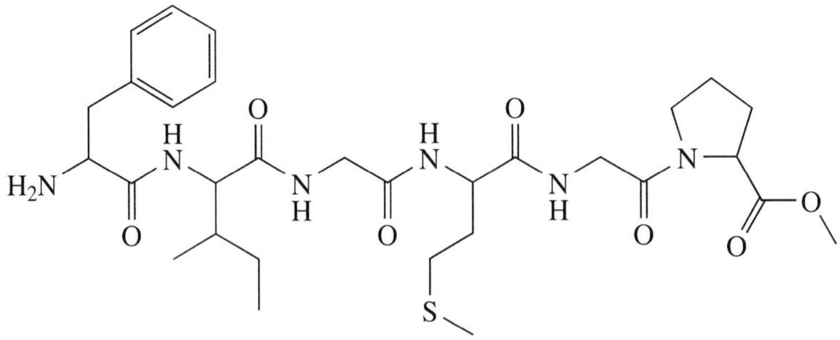

2.9

■ How many stereoisomers would you expect compound **2.5** to have if R = H, and if R ≠ H?

☐ If R = H, compound **2.5** is glycine and there are no stereoisomers; the structural formula describes just one compound. If R is not H, then the three-dimensional structure of **2.5** can be written two ways, related to each other as mirror images. In other words, **2.5** could exist as a pair of enantiomers because the α-carbon is chiral.

Except for glycine, all of the 20 natural amino acids are chiral. It turns out that, in proteins, these all have the same chirality, shown in Structure **2.10**.

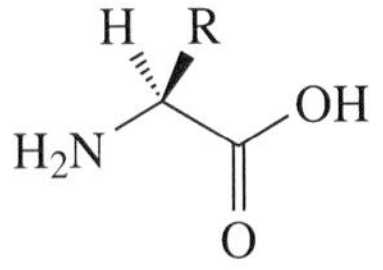

In summary, all the naturally occurring amino acids have the configuration **2.10** except for glycine (R = H) which is achiral. This turns out to be the S configuration (using the sequence rules for assigning absolute stereochemistry, as discussed in Unit 4 Section 4) for all the compounds except for cysteine, which is R (because of the high-priority sulfur atom in the side chain) and, of course, glycine.

2.10

■ Consider, for example, the ester **2.11** of an amino acid. What do you think might be the easiest type of process that would generate the mirror image amino acid ester, **2.12**? (*Hint*: recall the formation of enolates from Unit 6.)

2.11   **2.12**

☐ Removal of the α-hydrogen as a proton, leaving a negatively charged and resonance stabilised planar anion, and reprotonation on the other face of the molecule.

The conversion of an enantianerically pure sample of **2.11** into a sample in which **2.11** and **2.12** are both present is known as *racemisation*. Changing the configuration at a chiral carbon, usually by removal and replacement of a proton is known as *epimerisation*. As, with the exception of glycine, all proteinogenic amino acids are chiral, epimerisation must be avoided during peptide synthesis to avoid changes in configuration at the chiral centre.

Strategies for peptide synthesis will have to address:

(a) activating the carboxyl functional group for reaction with the amine group

(b) protecting the α-amino and α-carboxyl functions not involved in the peptide bond to be formed in the synthesis, to avoid both a mixture of linear peptides and the formation of cyclic dipeptides

(c) protecting the side-chain functionalities so that they do not interfere with the chemistry of peptide bond formation

(d) avoiding epimerisation at the α-carbon atom.

2.2.1   Protection: a simple illustration

As a starting point, consider the simplest possible synthesis of a peptide from two amino acids: the formation of H–Ala-Gly–OH from glycine and alanine. The methods for activation and protection selected need to be used in a way that avoids the other condensation products possible with these two amino acids, namely, H–Gly-Ala–OH, H–Gly-Gly–OH, H–Ala-Ala–OH and cyclic or extended chain alternatives. The way this is achieved is shown in Scheme 2.2.

In this example, we have avoided the complications of reactive side chains and assume our conditions throughout pose no risk of epimerisation at the alanine α-carbon atom. We have also left the activation and protection methods unspecified. Continuing in the same manner, we turn now to the synthesis of the tripeptide, H–Ala–Gly–Val–OH, from its constituent amino acids.

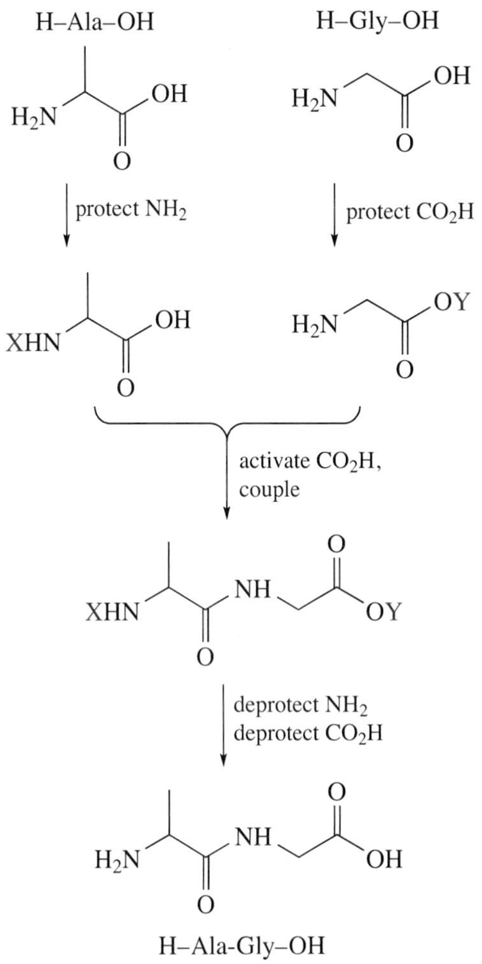

Scheme 2.2

There are two two-step options in assembling the tripeptide from its amino acids: one could prepare H–Ala-Gly–OH (as in Scheme 2.2) and extend at its carboxyl terminus with H–Val–OH; alternatively, preparing H–Gly-Val–OH and extend at its amino terminus with H–Ala–OH gives the same peptide. Throughout either route, we use protection to ensure that only the two amide (peptide) bonds we want to be formed are the ones formed, and we show how this can be done for the first option in Scheme 2.3.

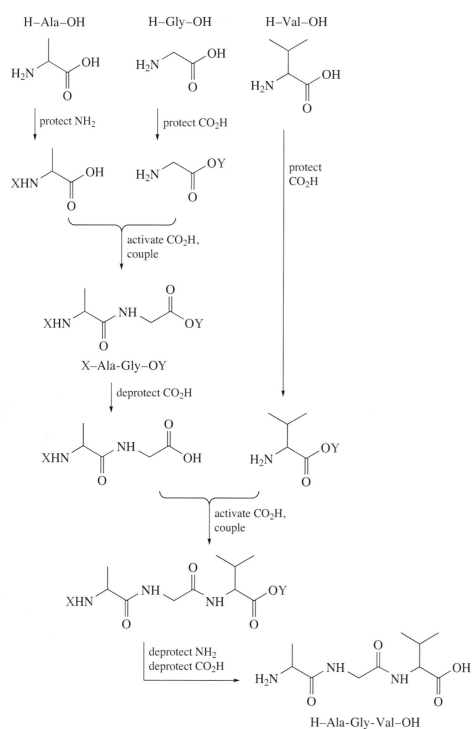

Scheme 2.3

■ Study Scheme 2.3 for a few minutes and, without further reference, see if you can complete the corresponding scheme for the second option.

□ The scheme is shown in Scheme 2.4.

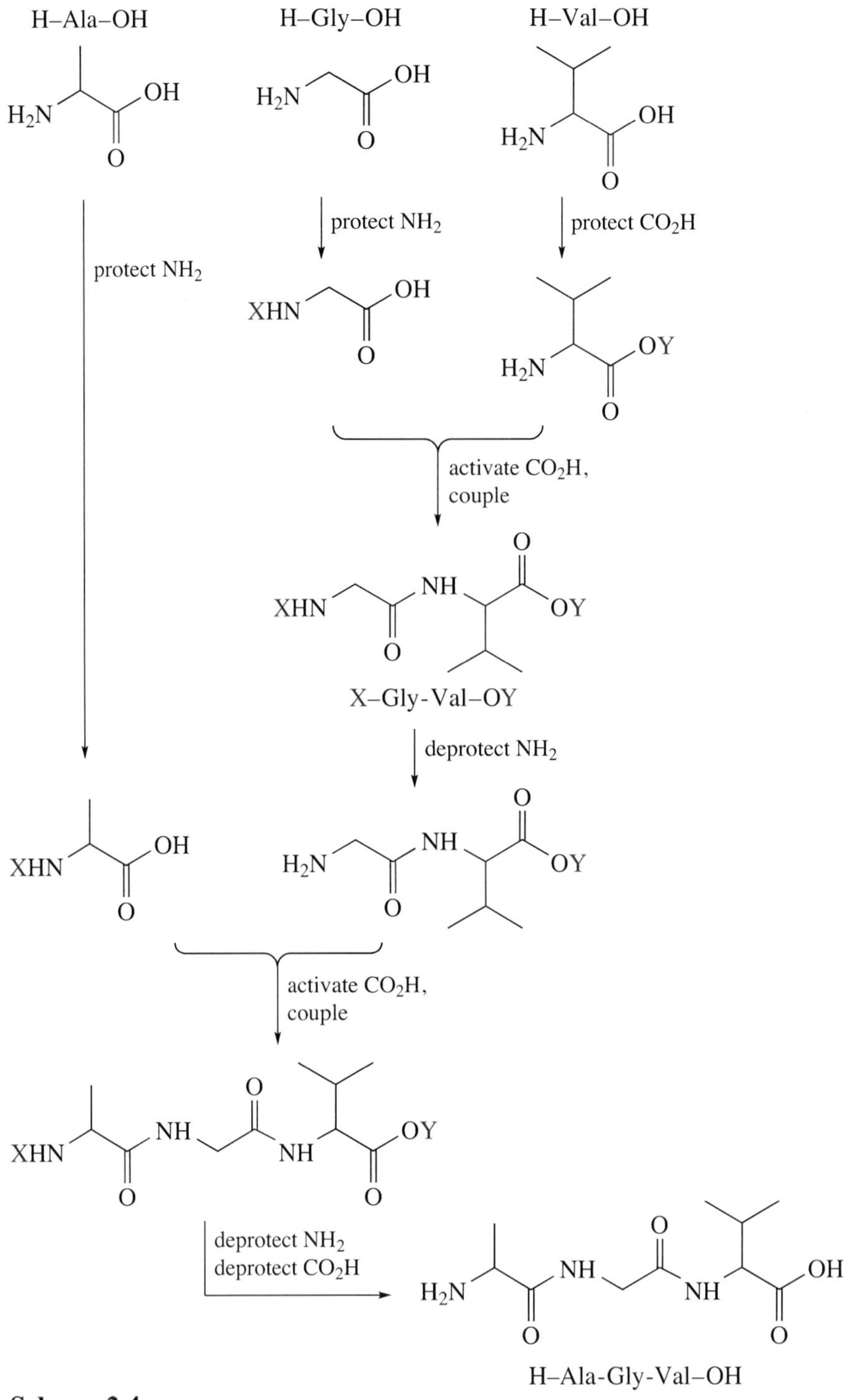

Scheme 2.4

■ Reflect on the use of the protecting groups X and Y and, given that they can be easily attached, state two other requirements of their chemistry: (a) one that applies to each of them separately; and (b) one that relates to differences in their chemical behaviour if they are to be used together in Scheme 2.3.

☐ An essential requirement of any protecting group is that it should be removable by a reaction that leaves the rest of the molecule unaffected. A more subtle requirement, evident in Schemes 2.3 and 2.4, is that there must be a reaction that removes X whilst leaving Y intact and vice versa. We say that the protection strategies using X and Y must be **orthogonal**.

2.2.2 Protecting α-amino and α-carboxyl groups

While it is necessary to mask these groups when they are not involved in the desired coupling, it is equally important that the protecting groups employed can be easily and selectively removed. This will then allow further step-wise elongation of the peptide by further condensation reactions at either end until the target compound is obtained.

The method of choice for α-amino groups is most frequently the temporary conversion to an oxycarbonyl (oc) or **urethane** derivative. For example, protecting glycine in this way would be illustrated as follows (where L is a good leaving group):

$$\tag{2.1}$$

The coupling reaction that forms a peptide bond at the other end will be a nucleophilic reaction at an activated carboxyl group. Being flanked on both sides by atoms with unshared electron pairs makes the carbonyl group of urethanes very unreactive towards nucleophiles, even more so than the amide carbonyl of a peptide bond. Yet the amino group can be recovered from the urethane under any one of a number of mild conditions, depending on the selection of R; see Table 2.3.

Perusal of the last column indicates already some mutual exclusivity that you will find useful later. Z-derivatives show the propensity for C–heteroatom cleavage of $PhCH_2$–heteroatom compounds by catalytic hydrogenation. While it also shares with Boc and Bpoc a cleavage reaction with acid, it survives the milder conditions that are effective in removing these two. Boc, but not Bpoc, is stable under catalytic hydrogenation and while Fmoc is also vulnerable under catalytic hydrogenation, it is stable in acid and cleaved by base, treatment that leaves the other three unaffected. There is also a potentially useful selection by degree in the acidolysis of Bpoc derivatives.

Table 2.3 Deprotection of the most commonly used urethane *N*-derivatives of amino acids.

R(OCO−)	Name	Abbreviation	Reaction and comment
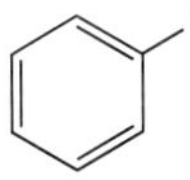 CH₂(OCO—) [benzyl structure]	benzyl-oxycarbonyl	Z	Reduction with H_2 over palladium-carbon catalyst (**hydrogenolysis**) OR acid catalysed cleavage (**acidolysis**) with AcOH
$(CH_3)_3C(OCO—)$	tertiary-butyl-oxycarbonyl	Boc	Acidolysis with trifluoroacetic acid (TFA), and also removed by stronger acid, e.g. HBr in acetic acid or HF
$(CH_3)_2C(OCO—)$ 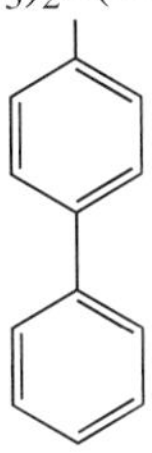 [biphenyl structure]	2-(4-biphenyl)-isopropyl-oxycarbonyl	Bpoc	Very mild acidolysis, e.g. chloroacetic acid in dichloromethane, that leaves Z- and Boc groups intact. Reacts under H_2/Pd–C conditions, however
[fluorenyl structure] —CH₂(OCO—)	fluorenylmethyl-oxycarbonyl	Fmoc	Mild base, e.g. 20% piperidine in dimethylformamide (DMF). Fmoc derivatives are stable in acid. Vulnerable to some reaction with H_2/Pd–C

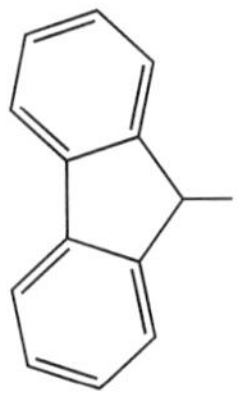

■ Consider the structures of the urethanes Z–NHR¹, Boc–NHR¹ and Bpoc–NHR¹. What ionic aspect of the group R in Table 2.3 that is common to all three do you think might be involved in explaining why they are easily cleaved by acid catalysis?

□ All three R groups correspond to relatively stable carbocations. The benzyl cation is stabilised by resonance with the aromatic ring, the *t*-butyl cation is stabilised by positive inductive effects of the methyl groups and the aryldimethyl cation has the advantage of both effects.

Acidolysis of urethanes involves the thermodynamically favourable release of carbon dioxide if, as above, the formation of R^+ is also favourable (Scheme 2.5).

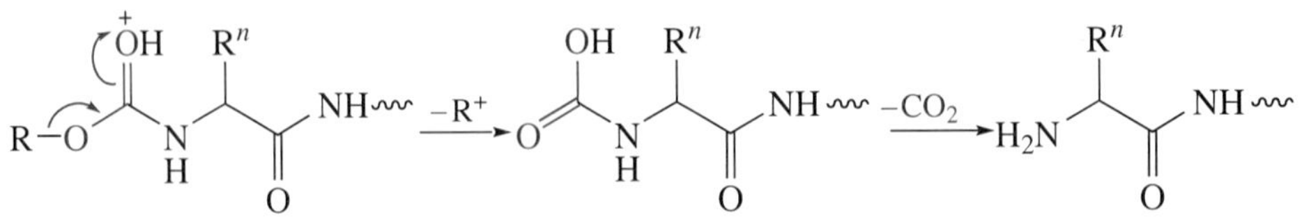

Scheme 2.5

The intermediate carbamic acid, $-NHCO_2H$ loses CO_2 readily under acid conditions. The benzyl cation ends up as benzyl bromide if HBr is the reagent, and the tertiary cations from Boc and Bpoc lose another proton to give the alkenes $R''(CH_3)C=CH_2$ or are otherwise 'scavenged' by compounds added for the purpose (e.g. water or thiophenol (PhSH)).

This leaves Fmoc to consider.

■ Consider why, on the above argument, Fmoc is comparatively stable in acid.

□ R'' would be a primary cation without resonance or inductive stabilisation and would therefore inhibit a reaction that required its formation.

But why should it react so easily in base? The explanation is to be found in the concept of aromaticity (that we discussed earlier in this unit) arising when $4n+2$ π-electrons are perfectly conjugated within a ring (Scheme 2.6). The 5-membered ring anion meets this criterion with four electrons from two double bonds and two electrons from the former C–H bond, making a total of 6 π electrons ($n = 1$).

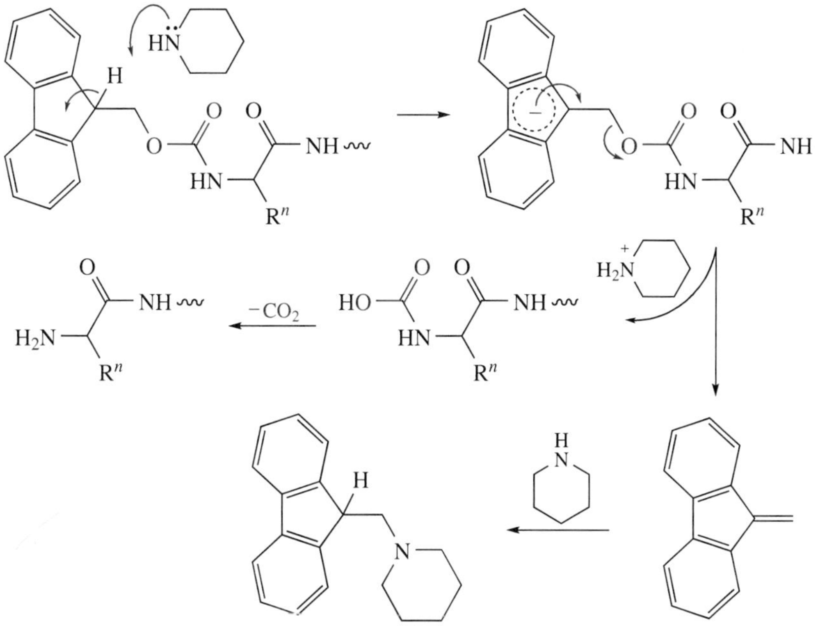

Scheme 2.6

We now turn to the other end of our amino acid or peptide reagents and look at protection of the carboxyl group. This would seem at first to be somewhat easier because most alkyl esters of carboxylic acids are quite stable under peptide coupling conditions. Moreover the carboxylic acid is regenerated by hydrolysis under basic conditions, suggesting deprotection could be carried out without disturbing the amino-protecting groups just described, the one exception being Fmoc. But many esters are a little too stable, the necessary treatment with alkali causing other problems elsewhere in the peptide structure.

■ Recall from Section 2.2 one aspect of peptide structure that could be vulnerable to alkali.

□ A base like OH⁻ may remove a proton from an α-carbon atom giving an enolate-like anion. Reprotonation would then result in some epimerisation, that is, an unwanted change of configuration at that atom.

■ Can we make use of the properties of particular groups you have studied in the context of α-amino protection? Try to suggest two simple types of esters that might be converted into the corresponding carboxylic acids by reagents that avoid basic conditions.

□ Benzyl esters are cleaved by hydrogenolysis (H_2/Pd–C) and *t*-butyl esters are cleaved by acidolysis.

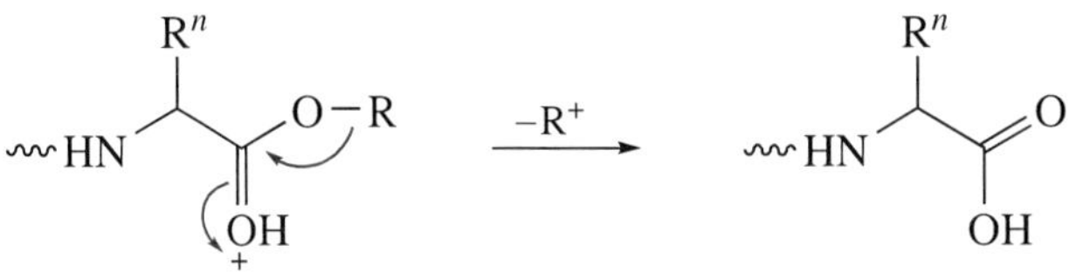

So by judicious choice of X and Y in Scheme 2.3 (or in Scheme 2.4) one can ensure deprotection at the intermediate stage is selective, and a similar strategy could be applied throughout all stages in the synthesis of a much longer peptide. Particular combinations of X and Y to ensure such orthogonality are known as protocols and two popular ones are illustrated in Table 2.4.

Table 2.4 The two common orthogonal pairs of protecting groups.

Functional group	Protecting group	Abbreviation	Protection conditions	Removal conditions
Protocol I				
—NH_2	—C—$OC(CH_3)_3$ ‖ O	Boc	$(Boc)_2O/OH^-$	trifluoroacetic acid (TFA)
—C—OH ‖ O	—CH_2Ph	Bn	$BnOH/H^+$	H_2/Pd–C
Protocol II				
—NH_2	—C—OCH_2Ph ‖ O	Z	ZCl/OH^-	H_2/Pd–C
—C—OH ‖ O	—$C(CH_3)_3$	Bu^t	$(CH_3)_2C{=}CH_2/$ H^+	trifluoroacetic acid (TFA)

- Illustrate the application of Protocol I on Scheme 2.3, and of Protocol II on Scheme 2.4, by:

  i   selecting appropriate conditions from Table 2.4 and inserting them in parentheses after each 'protect...' and 'deprotect...' entry;

  ii inserting, as appropriate, in a clear space on each scheme, the completed key: 'X = ; Y = '.

- Scheme 2.3 should display $(Boc_2O)/OH^-$, (BnOH), (BnOH), $(H_2/Pd–C)$, (TFA) and $(H_2/Pd–C)$ after 'protect NH_2', 'protect CO_2H', 'protect CO_2H', 'deprotect CO_2H', 'deprotect NH_2' and 'deprotect CO_2H', respectively. 'X = Boc; Y = Bn' should have been written in a clear space.

  Scheme 2.4 should display (ZCl/OH^-), (ZCl/OH^-), $((CH_3)_2C{=}CH_2/H^+)$, $(H_2/Pd–C)$, $(H_2/Pd–C)$ and (TFA) after 'protect NH_2', 'protect NH_2', 'protect CO_2H' 'deprotect NH_2', 'deprotect NH_2' and 'deprotect CO_2H', respectively. 'X = Z; Y = Bu^t' should have been written in a clear space.

We shall return to the use of the other protecting groups later, but for now let's move on to consider activation and coupling.

2.2.3   Forming the peptide bond

We said at the start of Section 2.2 that direct formation of the peptide bond from free amino and carboxyl groups does not occur under the mild reaction conditions required for a high yielding and widely applicable coupling method. The carbonyl group must be made more reactive; –CO OH must be converted into CO–L, where L is a good leaving group.

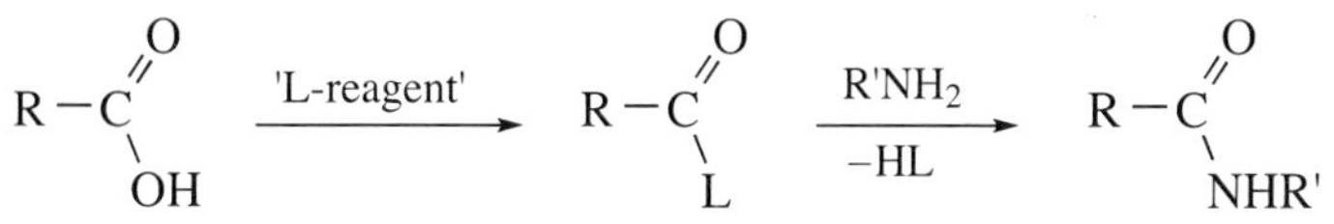

You might have thought the acid chloride (L = Cl), widely used in general organic chemistry, would have been suitable. Unfortunately, this derivative is a little too reactive and, without special precautions, leads to many wasteful side reactions when applied to amino acids and peptides.

A great many other 'L-reagents' have been used in the development of peptide coupling methods and, although a wide choice remains available, we have space to illustrate only one type and a few variations which are among the most popular. The type is based on the carbodiimide functional group –N=C=N– and exploits its highly electrophilic carbon atom. The dicyclohexyl-substituted derivative is the most commonly used example; **dic**yclohexyl**c**arbodiimide, DCC (Scheme 2.7).

The first step is the nucleophilic attack by the carboxylic acid on the highly electrophilic carbon atom of the carbodiimide group.

Reaction with $R'NH_2$ releases the thermodynamically stable **dic**yclohexyl**u**rea, DCU.

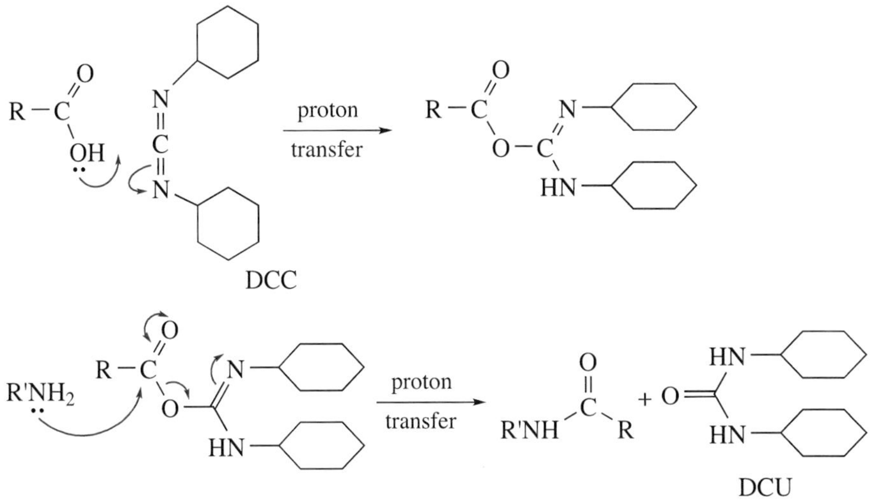

Scheme 2.7

But even this reagent is not without its problems, introducing side reactions in some cases, especially racemisation (see Section 2.2.4). So it is most commonly used as an intermediary, an agent to provide the cleanest activation *via* yet another group. We show just two of these in Scheme 2.8 and how the combination works to provide 'clean' and high-yielding coupling procedures.

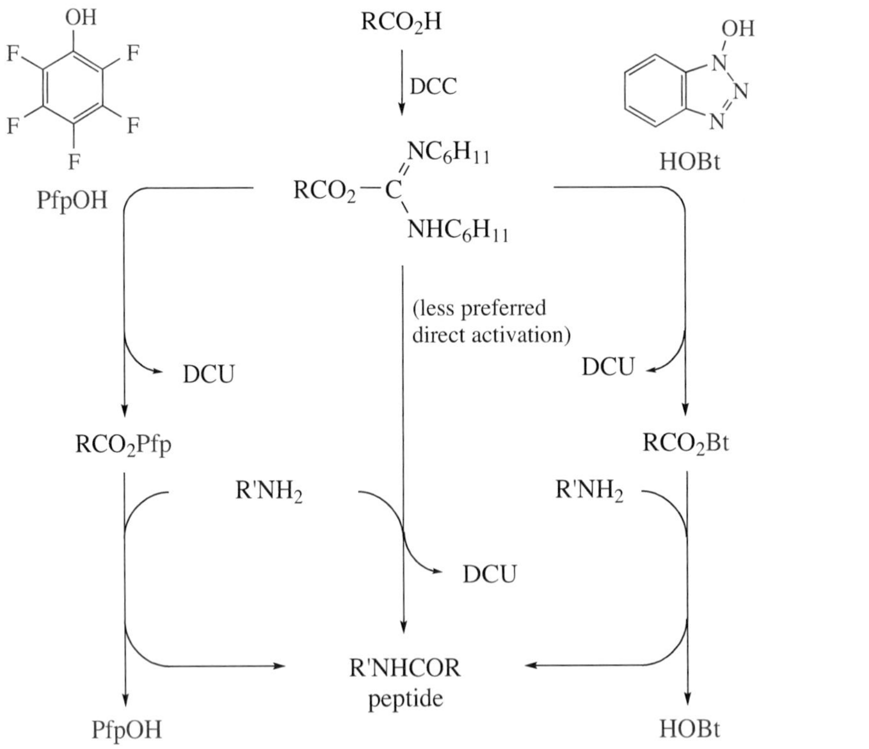

Scheme 2.8

Activation of a carboxyl via a pentafluorophenyl (Pfp) ester is shown down the left-hand side. DCC and PfpOH are added to the N-protected amino acid or small peptide (RCO_2H) and the Pfp ester can be isolated or allowed to react in situ with the carboxy-protected derivative of the second amino acid (or peptide), $R'NH_2$.

1-hydroxybenzotriazole (HOBt), shown on the right-hand side, can be used to the same effect and is one of the most widely used reagents for coupling. The insoluble DCU is a co-product in all three cases and you will notice the activating hydroxy compound is regenerated, making it truly catalytic.

■ Complete your illustrative versions of Schemes 2.3 and 2.4 by placing, as examples in parentheses after 'activate CO_2H' entries, the reagents for Pfp-activation in the first scheme and for HOBt-catalysed activation in the second.

☐ You should have written '(e.g. DCC/PfpOH)' and '(e.g. DCC/HOBt)' in the appropriate places.

2.2.4 The risk of epimerisation ('racemisation') in coupling: oxazolones

We have said that epimerisation could occur, in principle, whenever basic reagents are present, and you may have wondered how we could justify basic conditions for some of the protection and deprotection reactions described above. The answer is that conditions are sufficiently mild, with relatively weak base or high dilution, to preclude the problem. But there is another stage at which epimerisation can occur, and for a rather subtle reason.

We have stressed the need for the reacting carboxyl function to be activated. If the amino group of the same amino acid has been acylated, then the reaction sequence in Scheme 2.9 may occur.

The first-formed five-membered ring derivative, **2.13**, is known as an **oxazolone**, and although this compound does react with a carboxy-protected amino acid $R''NH_2$ to give a peptide product, the bad news is that it can also equilibrate with an isomer, **2.14**, in which the α-H atom is relocated.

Having six π electrons like benzene, but where two are provided by an oxygen atom rather than C=C, the isomer enjoys the stabilisation of aromaticity. This is bad news because, as you can see, in the equilibrium back to the first isomer, the hydrogen can turn up on either side of the molecule, giving **2.13** or **2.15**, destroying the stereochemical integrity at that carbon atom.

The good news, however, is that when R' is an alkoxy group such as in the common urethane protecting groups Z, Boc, etc., oxazolones are not formed at all readily. But the problem remains when the activated carboxyl component in a coupling is the C-terminal part of a peptide. For example:

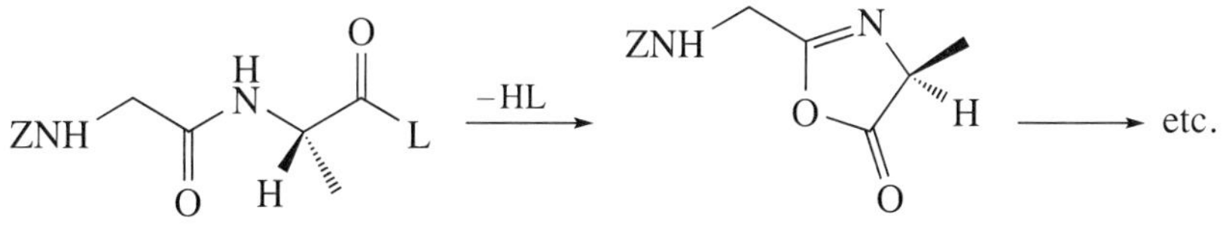

Z–Gly-Ala–L

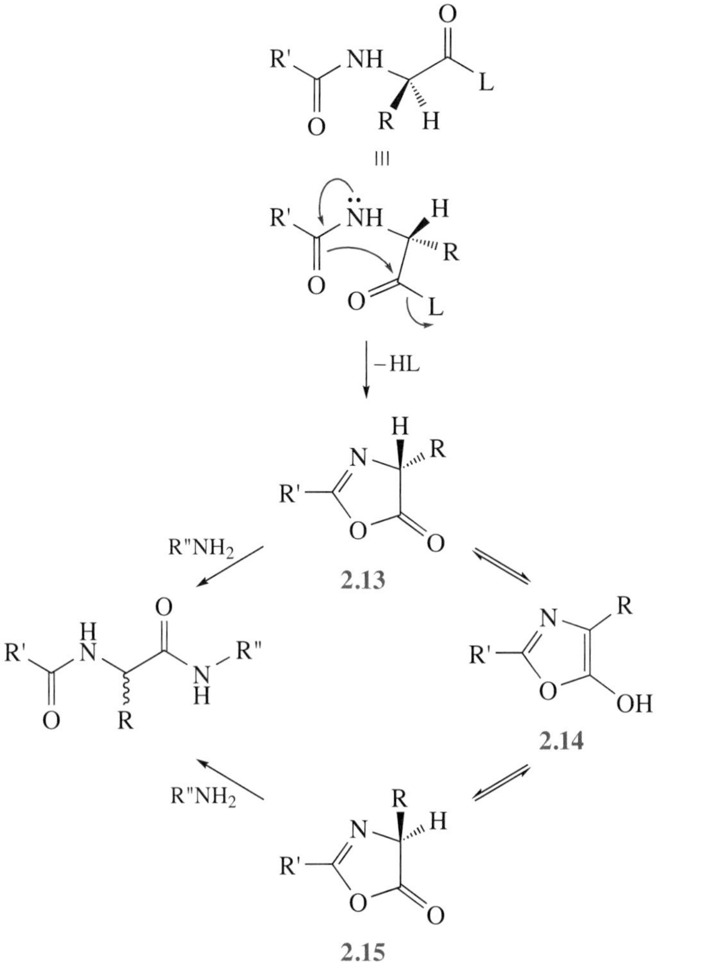

Scheme 2.9

Two strategies overcome the oxazolone problem. First, one may be able to avoid it by selecting a particular sequence of couplings, and second, one can select an activating/coupling reagent that is unlikely to provoke the reaction.

As an example of the first approach, consider the alternative strategies below for the final coupling in the synthesis of a protected tetrapeptide:

(i)   Z–Ala–OH + H–Gly-Phe-Ala–OBu^t $\longrightarrow$ ⎫
(ii) Z–Ala-Gly–OH + H–Phe-Ala–OBu^t $\longrightarrow$ ⎬ activate and couple
(iii) Z–Ala-Gly-Phe–OH + H–Ala–OBu^t $\longrightarrow$ ⎭

Which of these alternatives is least preferred?

Coupling (i) avoids the problem because the *N*-acyl derivative of the activated carboxyl component (Ala) is a urethane, Z–Ala–OH. In coupling (ii), the carboxyl component is glycyl, which has no chiral centre, so oxazolone formation has no stereochemical consequences. Coupling (iii) is vulnerable to epimerisation at the phenylalanyl centre, –Phe–OH, via oxazolone formation from the activated carboxyl group, so this is the least preferred alternative. Incidentally, apart from glycine, the cyclic amino acid proline is the only other amino acid that is free from problems of this sort. (The existing five-membered ring discourages formation of a second one fused to it.)

Oxazolone formation can also be minimised by selecting appropriate activation conditions. Thus, while DCC alone will often present problems, it turns out that DCC/HOBt coupling significantly reduces the risk of epimerisation. If, in a particular case, this reagent also leads to extensive epimerisation, then one other method of activation can be deployed that is even safer, but can introduce other side reactions. This is the azide method, summarised in Scheme 2.10, which can be particularly appropriate for the coupling of two peptide fragments with a vulnerable residue at the C-terminal end of the carboxy component.

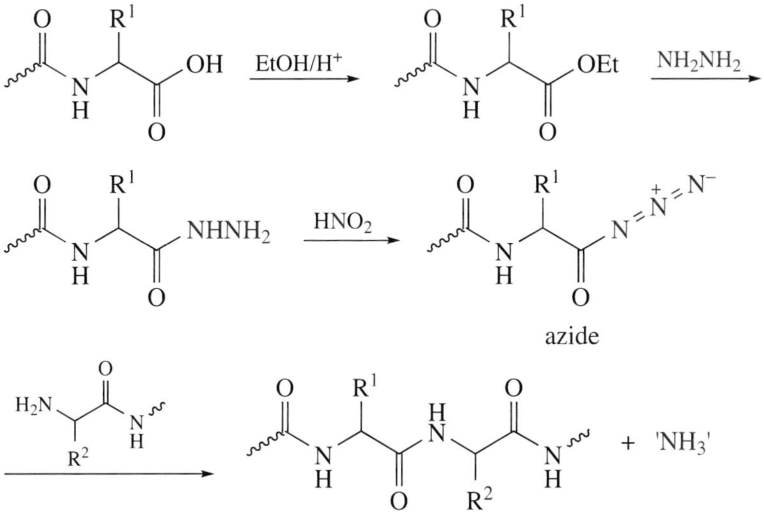

Scheme 2.10

Study note

Before moving on to Section 3, try to write a summary of Section 2 and then compare it with ours. Go to Unit 8 summaries in Unit 8 resources.

3 The nature of the solid support in organic synthesis

A solid support is the species to which the substrate or one of the reagents is bound. It must be inert, insoluble in the solvents commonly encountered in synthesis, be readily functionalised if it is an organic molecule, be capable of accepting a high loading of reactant molecules by having the ability to swell, and be removable in very high yield after use. Since the concept of Solid Phase Organic Synthesis (SPOS) was first proposed by Merrifield in 1963 (who was subsequently awarded the Nobel Prize for Chemistry, 1984), the solid support that bears his name, Merrifield resin, has remained in widespread use and is readily available. It consists of cross-linked polystyrene, formed by the radical-induced polymerisation of styrene (**3.1**) in the presence of a small quantity (1–2%) of 1,4-divinylbenzene (DVB, **3.2**). Functionalisation of the polymer in a Friedel–Crafts alkylation with chloromethyl methyl ether $ClCH_2OCH_3$ (**3.3**), and $SnCl_4$ (**3.4**), as Lewis acid catalyst is then effected to produce the Merrifield resin (Scheme 3.1). This undergoes smooth substitution with a range of molecules via the chloromethyl substituent, **3.5**.

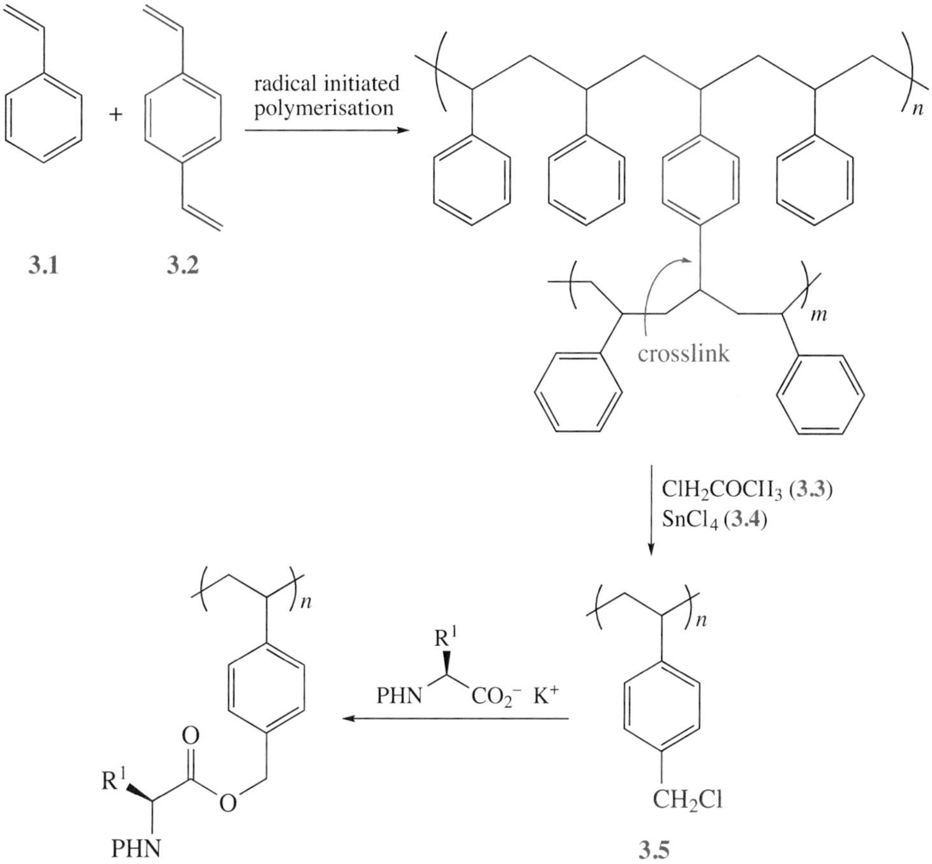

Scheme 3.1

It should be noted that the cross-linking is occasional, and that not every aromatic ring possesses the chloromethyl substituent. Carboxylic acids, amino acids, phenols, alcohols and amines are among a variety of compounds that can be substituted for the chlorine atom. If these molecules also contain groups that may be further functionalised (e.g. hydroxyl groups), they are termed linkers. **The Merrifield resin** was developed originally for **Solid Phase Peptide Synthesis (SPPS)**. The amino acid (**3.6**) is attached directly to the resin by first forming the potassium or caesium carboxylate salt of the amino acid (as in Scheme 3.2). The peptide is then synthesised by a series of condensation reactions with protected amino acids. One disadvantage is that the fairly harsh conditions required to remove the resultant peptide from the resin (typically HF) can lead to decomposition of a small amount of the peptide itself. It must be kept in mind that the resin is there to facilitate the expansion of the substrate attached to it, and/or simplify its purification. If there are difficulties in removing a resin after the important chemistry has been carried out, isolation of the final product may be jeopardised.

Adding a 4-hydroxybenzyl alcohol linker (**3.7**) to the Merrifield resin produces the **Wang resin** (**3.8**). It is prepared by treating the Merrifield resin with 4-hydroxybenzyl alcohol and sodium methoxide, which deprotonates the relatively acidic phenol.

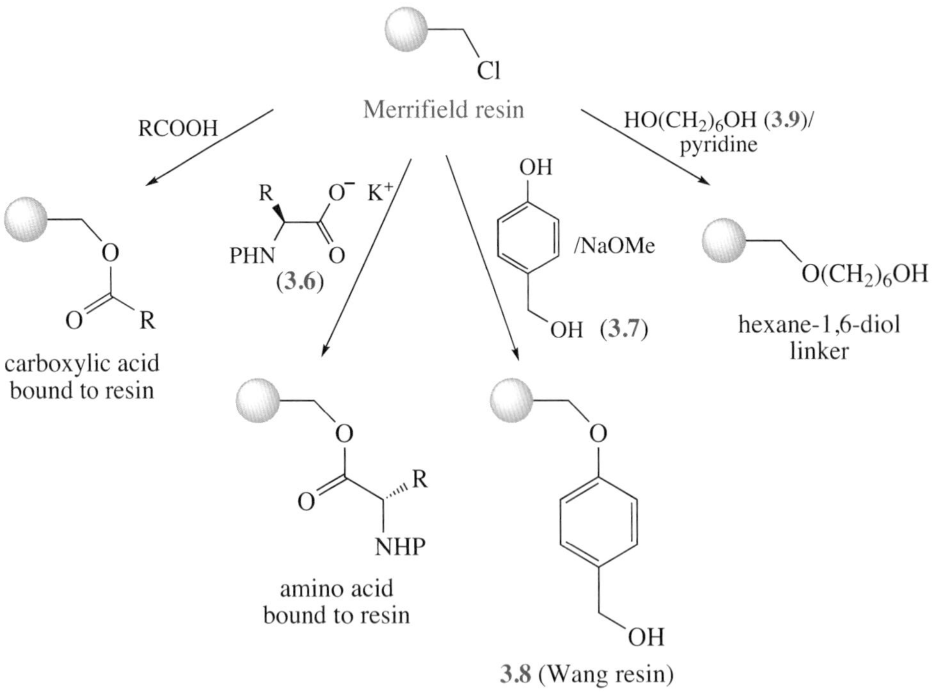

Scheme 3.2

The Wang resin has the advantage that trifluoroacetic acid, TFA, which is much milder than HF, can be used to effect cleavage from the substrate after use. Aliphatic diols, for example, hexane-1,6-diol (**3.9**) can also act as a linker.

Further developments have led to the **Rink amide linker** (**3.10**) with an amine functional group as the point of attachment for use in many solid phase applications, such as the synthesis of amides and peptides (Scheme 3.3). The presence of the two electron-donating methoxy groups on the aromatic ring serves to fine-tune the process of cleavage with TFA to ensure maximum yield of the substrate. Note that since the amine group from the linker is cleaved when the product is released, an amide, not a carboxylic acid, is produced when the substrate is removed.

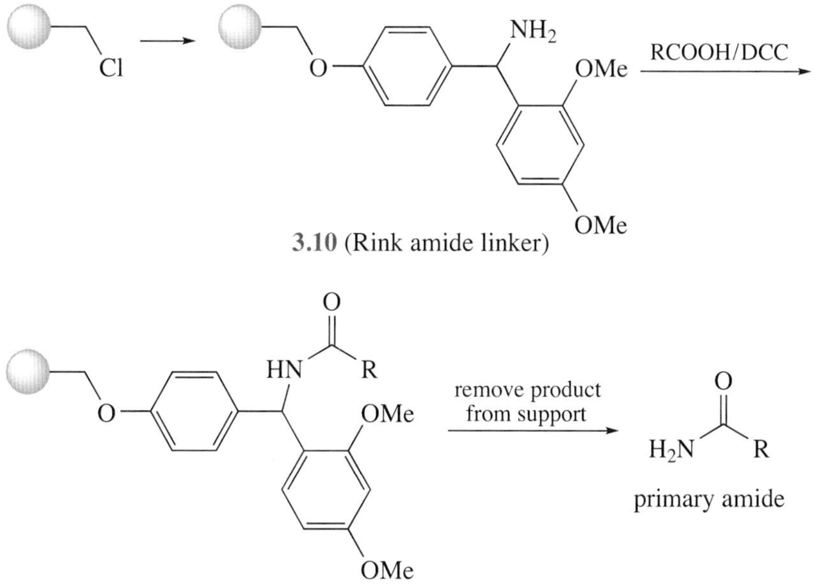

3.10 (Rink amide linker)

Scheme 3.3

3.1   Traceless linkers

As you are now aware, the starting materials for SPPS are loaded onto the resin via a linker that must be cleaved from the product molecule, involving an extra step and sometimes harsh, acidic conditions. **Traceless linkers** have been conceived to circumvent these potential disadvantages. The aim is to form the target molecule in the same step as the linker is removed, or to cleave it under mild conditions. A whole host of elements (Si, Ge, S, Se, N, P, Cr and others) can feature in traceless linkers, with Si and S being amongst the most widely used. For example, in the synthesis of a range of 1,4-benzodiazapines using a traceless linker strategy, an arylstannane (**3.11**) was coupled to an acid chloride under palladium catalysis (Scheme 3.4). By using different acyl chlorides (RCOCl), the range of different 1,4-benzodiazapines can be built up and tested for activity. The silicon linker was eventually removed on treatment with aqueous HF, the driving force being the strength of the Si–F bond. True to its name, there is no trace of where the linker was originally joined in the final product.

3.2   Swelling of the solid support

The most important factor on solid-phase synthesis is the structure of the solid support to which the substrate is attached. The introduction to this section briefly discussed the importance of chemical inertness of the support and the use of functional groups as points of substrate attachment. However another

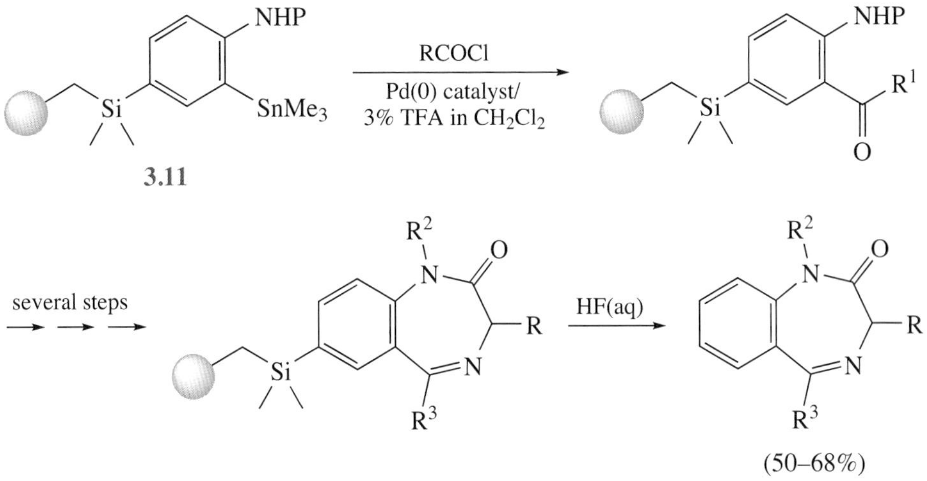

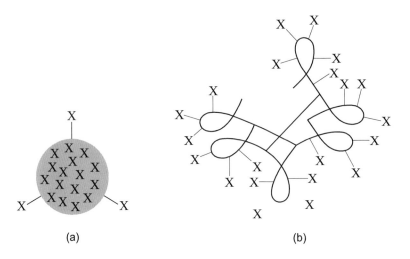

Scheme 3.4

crucial property of the support is that it must be **swellable**. For any solid particle most of the functional groups will be on the inside and not on the surface. In order for these groups to be accessible, the support must swell in a suitable solvent (Figure 3.1). This will maximise the contribution of the solid support medium. This involves a large increase in surface area when the resin is placed in a solvent, and exposes many more of the functional groups as points where substrates may be loaded.

(a)

(b)

Figure 3.1   Accessibility of the reactive X groups in a solid polymer (a) before and (b) after swelling of the polymer matrix by a suitable solvent.

3.3   Solid-phase peptide synthesis

We have seen that a peptide is a sequence of two or more amino acids and that there are 20 natural amino acids, differing by side chain (Unit 2). Activated amino acids are joined together in condensation reactions where amide bonds are formed and water is liberated, with a suitable protecting group strategy being employed. Solid-phase peptide synthesis has a number of advantages over solution-phase peptide synthesis. Principal amongst these is that the purification of the various intermediates in the synthesis can be achieved simply by washing away all impurities; the peptide is attached to an insoluble support which is in the form of small beads, whilst all other reagents and by-products are soluble. This allows the various reagents needed during the synthesis (activated amino acids, deprotection reagents, etc.) to be used in excess, which results in high chemical yields. The repetitive nature of solid-phase peptide synthesis means that it is also suitable for automation, and a number of companies now manufacture peptide synthesisers which are capable of automatically and rapidly synthesising any desired peptide sequence. The speed of automated solid-phase peptide synthesis is largely due to the fact that purification achieved by washing can be far more rapid than purification by chromatography or crystallisation. The traditional drawbacks of solid-phase peptide synthesis, particularly the small scale and high cost, are gradually being overcome. Since an excess of each reagent is used to try and ensure complete reaction, this is an expensive way of preparing peptides. In particular, an excess (typically 3 to 10 equivalents) of each activated and protected amino acid is required, and whilst these are commercially available, they tend to be very expensive.

Triostin A is a peptide antibiotic that binds to DNA via the aromatic groups.

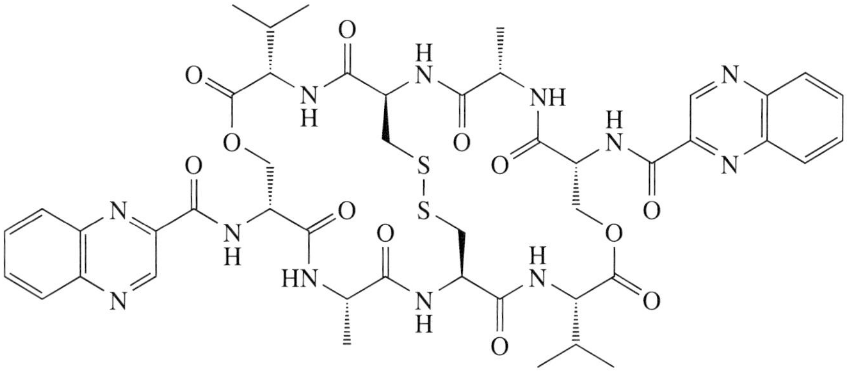

Key stages from the first solid-phase synthesis of the Triostin A illustrate how a protecting group strategy is deployed, such that selective deprotection is possible (Scheme 3.5). As you will discover, peptide coupling requires a plethora of reagents, though the principles in each enlargement of the chain remain the same.

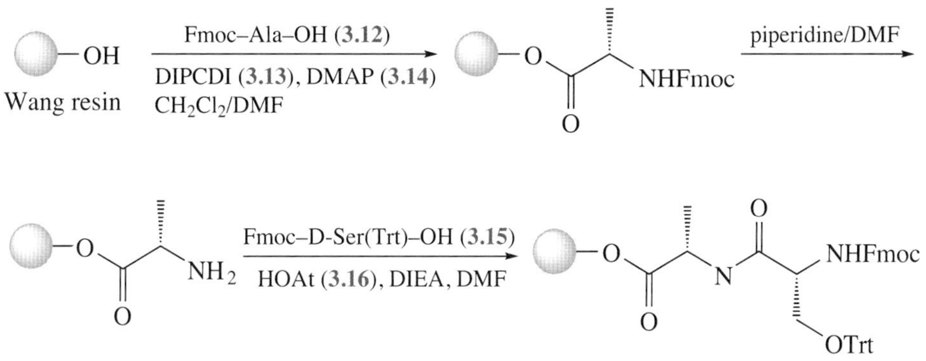

Scheme 3.5

The synthesis begins with the coupling of Fmoc-protected alanine, Fmoc–ala–OH (**3.12**), via the C-terminal end to the Wang resin. The free acid of the C-terminal end is used to form the ester linkage to the resin. Activation of the acid is effected with diisopropylcarbodiimde (DIPCDI, **3.13**) with *N,N*-dimethylaminopyridine (DMAP, **3.14**) as a catalyst. The Fmoc group must then be cleaved to produce the free amino group and for this standard, basic conditions are used (piperidine in DMF). To attach the next amino acid, D–Ser(Trt)–OH (**3.15**), HOAt (**3.16**, 1-hydroxy-7-azabenzotriazole) is used, rather than HOBt (**3.17**) or DCC as it reacts more rapidly, together with diisopropylethylamine (DIEA) in the polar, aprotic solvent, DMF.

3.13 (DIPCDI)   3.14 (DMAP)   3.16 (HOAt)   3.17 (HOBt)

3.4 Solid-phase organic synthesis (SPOS) of compounds other than peptides

As solid supports have revolutionised peptide synthesis, they also find many uses in the preparation of a variety of other organic compounds. The principles involved will be illustrated by examining two syntheses.

3.4.1 Synthesis of oxazolidinones from *N*-Boc-Tyr(OBn)

Chiral oxazolidinones are excellent compounds for directing enantioselective alkylation reactions. The oxazolidinone (**3.20**) is derived from a protected tyrosine derivative, **3.18** (Scheme 3.6). Selective removal of the Boc group using HCl is followed by formation of the oxazolidinone ring (**3.19**) using phosgene, $COCl_2$, and a base. Acylation on the nitrogen follows, using propanoic acid anhydride to give **3.20**. The substrate thus prepared can then be readily attached to a resin after removal of the benzyl group to give **3.21** under reductive conditions (H_2 with a Pd catalyst) followed by treatment with one of the common solid phase resins.

Treatment of the resin-bound oxazolidinone (**3.22**) with a hindered base gives the enolate ion, **3.23**, which is then alkylated with benzyl bromide to create a new chiral centre (Scheme 3.7). Treatment of the resulting compound **3.24** with $LiBH_4$ removes the chiral auxiliary to give an alcohol found to be predominantly the enantiomer (**3.25**) in 90% yield. The potential here for preparing compound libraries by combinatorial methods, for instance by varying the structure of the alkylating agent (benzyl bromide in this case) is substantial.

The Wang resin is the preferred solid support in this particular case, giving superior yields and enantiomeric excesses when compared to other resins. The reactions work best over short reaction times, because cleavage of the substrate from the solid support is a significant side reaction.

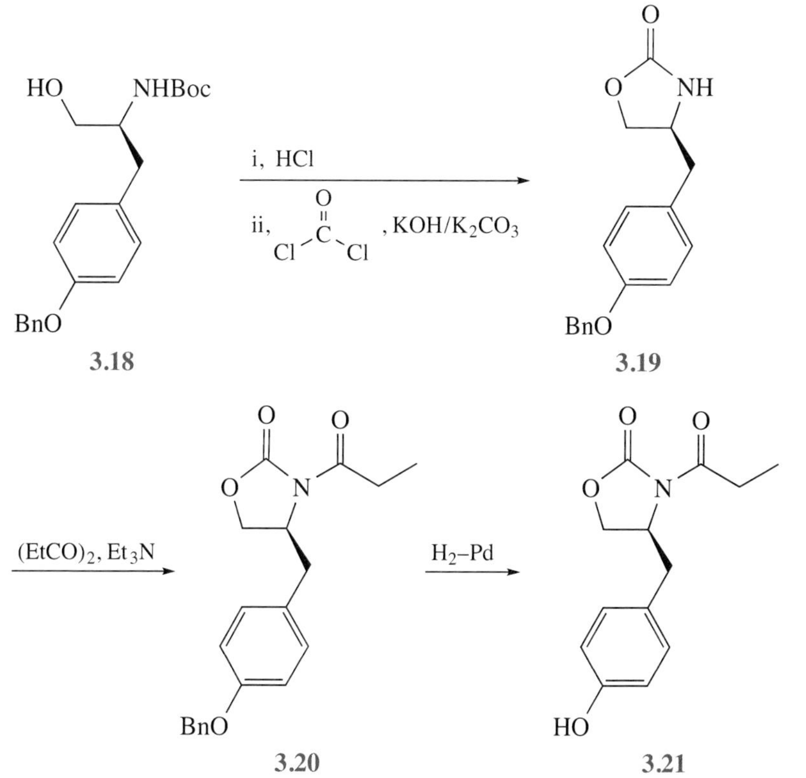

Scheme 3.6

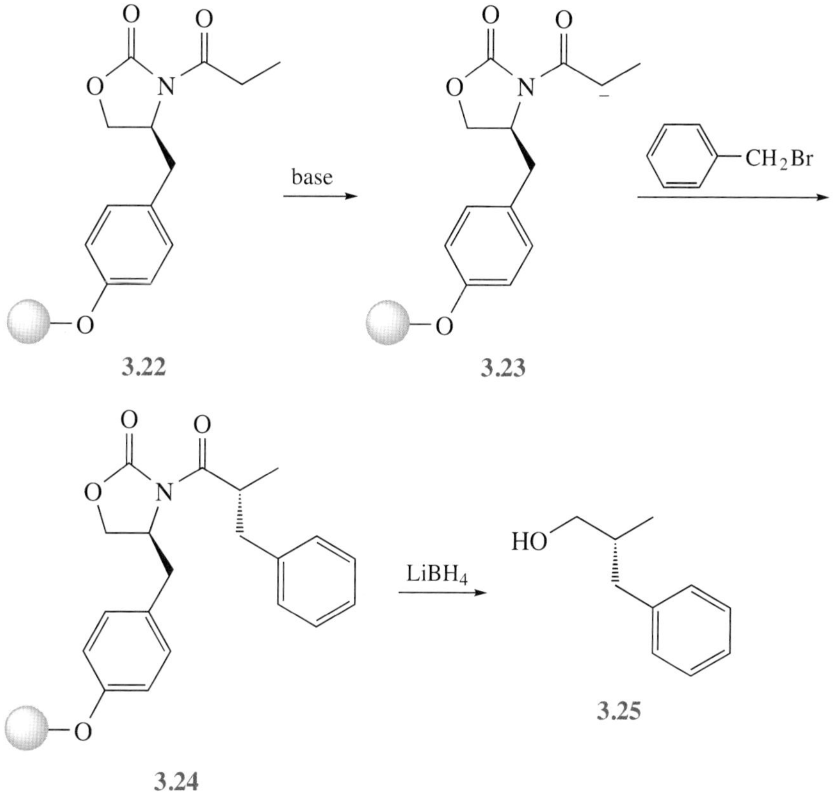

Scheme 3.7

3.4.2 Synthesis of thiomorpholin-3-ones using Merrifield resin

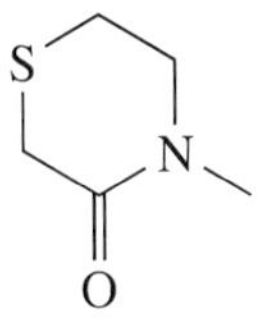

Compounds possessing a thiomorpholin-3-one skeleton (**3.26**) have been shown to possess interesting biological activity centered on brain function.

The synthesis of this compound uses a sulfur linkage in a SPOS methodology. The Merrifield resin is first treated with 2-sulfanylethanol (**3.27**) and further synthetic manipulation produces the key intermediate (**3.28**) which cyclises in the presence of caesium iodide to leave the target thiomorpholin-3-one (**3.29**), free of its solid-phase resin.

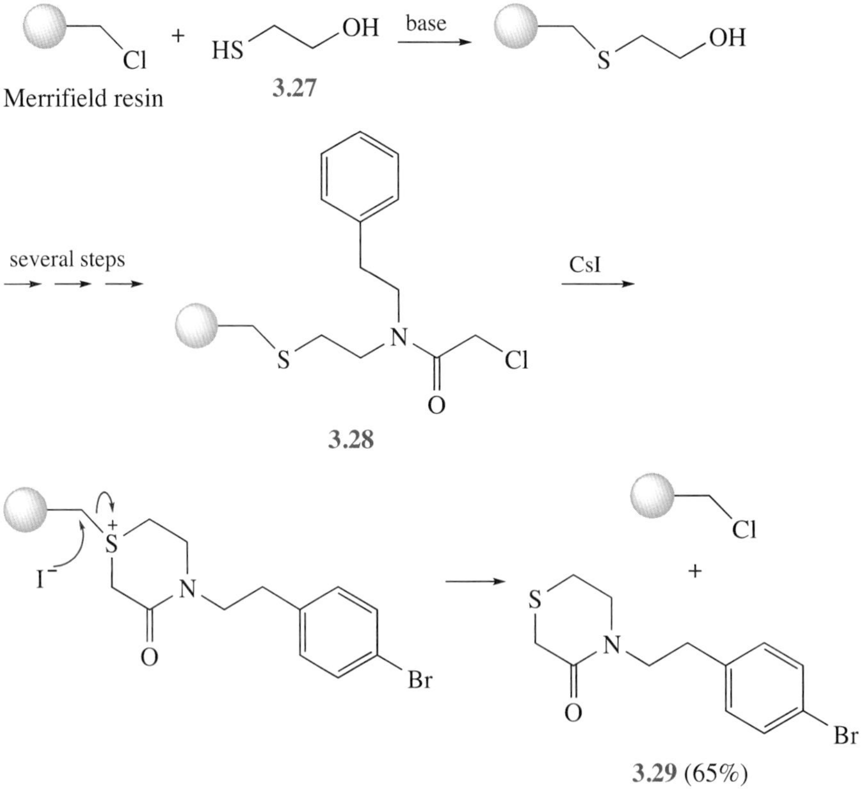

3.26

Scheme 3.8

3.4.3 Solid-supported reagents

Previously we considered the benefits of holding the substrate on a solid support, but there are many good and obvious reasons for anchoring a reagent in a similar manner. Remind yourself of these by reference to the introduction (Section 2.1). By way of example, consider the use of pyridinium chlorochromate (PCC) supported on alumina (Al_2O_3).

The use of chromium(VI) reagents for the oxidation of organic compounds, particularly alcohols, is one of the most well-known reactions in chemistry (discussed in Unit 6 Section 1). Chromium salts are toxic (suspected carcinogens) and product isolation can be difficult due to the formation of tar-like by-products, which tend to hold on to the desired organic product. PCC is a mild chromium oxidant (Unit 6 Section 1), in that it will oxidise primary

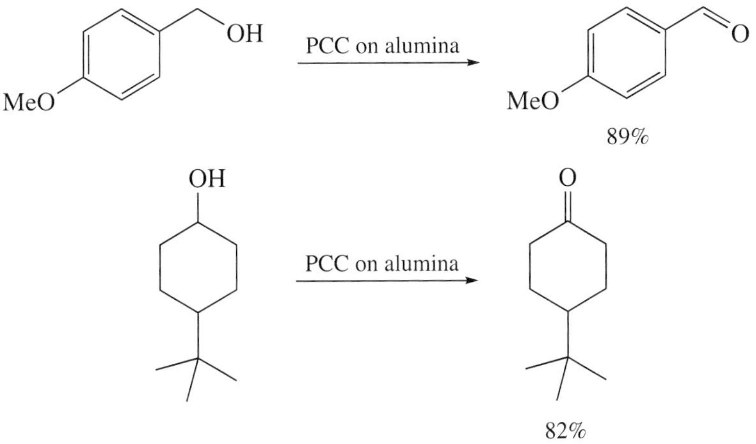

Scheme 3.9

and secondary alcohols to the corresponding aldehydes or ketones, without over-oxidation to the carboxylic acid or decomposition. PCC is more conveniently handled when supported on alumina (achieved simply by mixing PCC and alumina in an organic solvent and then evaporating the solvent) (Scheme 3.9). The compound to be oxidised is then added and the mixture stirred. After the reaction is judged to be complete it is filtered using thin-layer chromatography (TLC). The product is then isolated by further filtration and column chromatography on silica gel.

This approach could also be used for the purification of Wittig reaction products (Scheme 3.10).

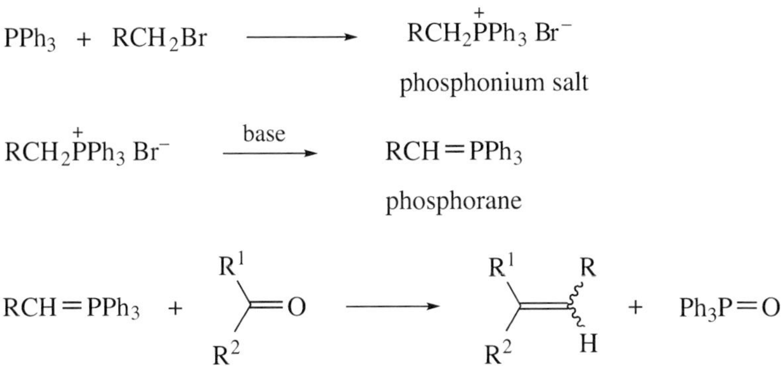

Scheme 3.10

The Wittig reaction is a tried and tested method of C=C bond formation. By careful choice of reagent and conditions, an aldehyde or a ketone can be transformed into an E or Z alkene (see Unit 7).

The downside can be the removal of triphenylphosphine oxide, formed as a by-product that is soluble in most organic solvents, and thus difficult to remove completely by precipitation.

■　Describe how solid phase immobilisation of a reagent could be of use in overcoming this problem.

▢ The supported phosphine, **3.30** is prepared, and treatment with base produces **3.31** the phosphorane. Reaction with the carbonyl compound gives the product and leaves phosphine oxide, **3.32**, supported on the resin which is then removed by filtration.

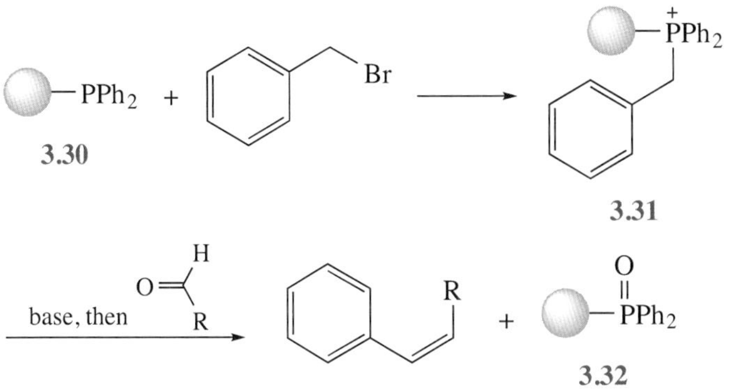

Scheme 3.11

■ What type of reagent would convert the phosphine oxide back to phosphine and recycle the reagent?

▢ A reducing agent would reduce the phosphine oxide to the phosphine, for example, $LiAlH_4$.

Schemes 3.12 and 3.13 show two occasions where a solid support can provide advantages in organic synthesis.

Swern-type oxidation: (mild oxidation of alcohols to aldehydes or ketones, involving non-volatile, non-odorous sulfur-containing by-product).

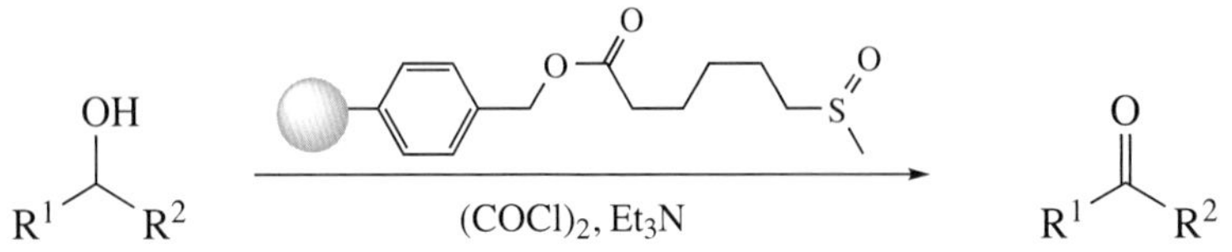

Scheme 3.12

Conversion of amides to thioamides (again involving non-volatile, non-odorous by-products):

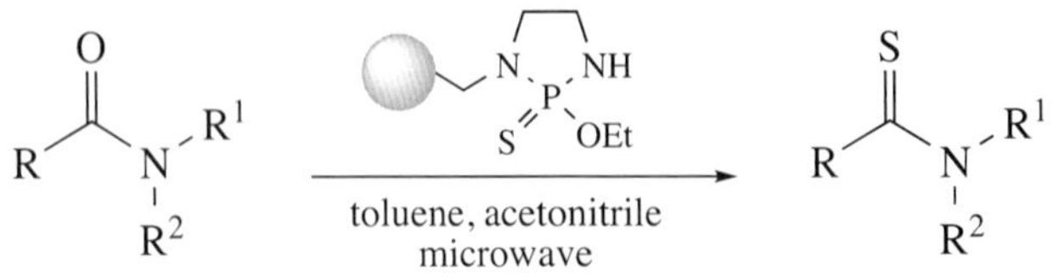

Scheme 3.13

3.5 Parallel synthesis

Parallel synthesis was briefly introduced in Section 2.1. During the process of seeking or developing a new chemical that will exhibit a desired effect (e.g. pharmaceutical action, catalysis, etc.), it is necessary to prepare a number of analogues of the initial (lead) compound in order to optimise the desired effect and minimise side effects. Traditionally, this process was carried out by synthesising and testing the compounds one after another. Recently however, an alternative approach called **parallel synthesis** has been developed, which substantially reduces the number of synthetic manipulations that need to be carried out. This takes advantage of the fact that all of the analogues tend to be prepared by the same synthetic approach, just varying one reagent to make changes to the final product. For example, if the synthesis of the initial compound uses ethanal, the preparation of analogues derived from propanal, butanal, benzaldehyde, etc. might be investigated.

To see how this methodology works, consider the synthesis of a series of pentapeptides of general formula H–Xxx-Gly-Ala-Leu-Phe–OH. In this sequence, Xxx represents the amino acid which needs to be optimised to maximise the activity of the compounds. In order to achieve this it is desirable to prepare the pentapeptides with each of the 20 naturally occurring amino acids at this position. The parallel synthesis of this series of compounds would be achieved as follows:

*   The polymer-supported tetrapeptide H–Gly-Ala-Leu-Phe–O–polymer would be constructed using standard solid-phase peptide synthesis methodology.

*   The resin would be divided into 20 equal portions, and each of these would be treated with a solution of a single activated amino acid derivative with suitably protected side chains to prepare one of the 20 desired pentapeptides.

*   Each of the 20 polymer-supported pentapeptides would be deprotected to give a single pentapeptide, the activity of which would then be determined after cleaving from the solid support.

This is a relatively simple example since the variation amongst the pentapeptides is in the final step of the synthesis, that is, at the N-terminal amino acid. Suppose however, that the pentapeptides had the general structure H–Gly-Ala-Xxx-Leu-Phe–OH. This is slightly more complicated since, if the above protocol was to be followed, it would be necessary to carry out the introduction of the last three amino acids 20 times. However, with suitably designed apparatus this can be avoided and the parallel synthesis of the pentapeptides can be achieved by the following protocol:

*   The polymer-supported dipeptide H–Leu-Phe–O–polymer would be constructed using standard solid-phase peptide synthesis methodology.

*   The resin would be divided into 20 equal portions, and each of these would be treated with a solution of a single activated amino acid derivative appropriately protected to prepare one of the 20 tripeptides of formula H–Xxx-Leu-Phe–O–polymer.

- The 20 different polymer-supported tripeptides would be recombined in such a way that chemistry can be simultaneously carried out on all of them, *but without allowing them to mix with one another.*
- The remaining two amino acids would be simultaneously introduced onto each of the tripeptides, thus generating the desired pentapeptides.
- The 20 pentapeptides would be reseparated from one another and cleaved from the solid support and deprotected for testing.

The challenge in this approach is to find a method which will allow the different polymer-supported tripeptides to be recombined into a single reaction vessel without allowing them to mix with one another. A number of ingenious solutions to this problem have been developed, probably the simplest of which is the use of so-called 'teabags'. In this approach, the beads of resin are held within perforated plastic bags analogous to teabags (Figure 3.2).

Thus reagents dissolved in the reaction solvent can pass through the perforations and react with the resin, and by-products can pass out of the teabag through the perforations. The perforations are however too small to allow the resin to escape from the teabag. Using this methodology for the above example, the synthesis would start with 20 teabags all containing a batch of resin. Initially, all 20 teabags would be placed in the same reaction vessel and the first two amino acids would be added. At this stage, the teabags would be separated and to each would be added a solution of a single activated amino acid. Following this, the teabags would be labelled (to specify which amino acid was added to which teabag), placed in a single reaction vessel and the remaining steps of the synthesis completed. Finally, the teabags would again be separated and the individual pentapeptides cleaved from the solid support.

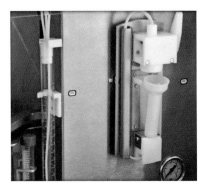

Figure 3.2 Plastic 'teabags' as reaction vessels in parallel synthesis.

A number of other methodologies have been developed for parallel synthesis, including the use of glass tubes with a piece of **sintered glass** at the bottom to allow solvent into and out of the glass tube which contains the resin. Alternatively, for very small-scale synthesis, cellulose can be used as the solid support and this allows the compounds to be constructed on paper disks or even at different positions on the same sheet of paper.

Parallel synthesis is not restricted to the synthesis of peptides, but can be used to rapidly synthesise families of any class of compound provided that the chemistry can be carried out on a solid support. Solid-phase parallel synthesis is also amenable to automation which further increases the rapidity with which the compounds can be synthesised (Figure 3.3).

3.6 Combinatorial chemistry and analysis

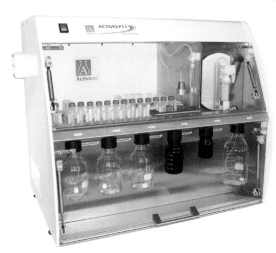

Figure 3.3 Automatic synthesiser for parallel synthesis.

In a parallel synthesis, a family of compounds is prepared simultaneously but individually, so that the result is a set of single pure compounds. **Combinatorial synthesis** takes this one stage further and produces the family of compounds all mixed together in the same flask. Such a mixture is commonly referred to as a **compound library**. The advantage of this approach is that a library consisting of a large number of compounds (millions in some cases) can rapidly be prepared. The mixture of compounds can then be tested for chemical or biological activity, and if no activity is observed then it is usually assumed that none of the compounds in the library possesses any activity.

This can only be an assumption, since the library may contain one or more active compounds, but their activity may be inhibited by another component of the library. However, this approach is very useful in the early stages of compound optimisation where large numbers of compounds can rapidly be prepared and rejected. The disadvantage of combinatorial synthesis is that if the library of compounds does show some activity, then it often takes a large amount of work to determine the structure of the individual compound (or compounds) which are responsible for the activity.

3.6.1 Split and mix synthesis

Combinatorial synthesis on solid phase can generate very large numbers of products, using a method described as a **split and mix synthesis**. For example, split and mix can be used for the generation of large libraries of peptides (Figure 3.4).

Consider the generation of a library of tripeptides. Three resin-bound amino acids are made in three separate pools, for example pool 1 Gly, pool 2 Ala, pool 3 Ser, as in stage 1 in Figure 3.4. The three pools are then thoroughly mixed and separated into three new pools. Each pool now contains equal portions of all three resin-bound amino acids. To each pool is then added another, different amino acid, for example Pro to pool 1, Val to pool 2, Thr to pool 3. After coupling, we obtain three dipeptides in each pool, hence 9 altogether as shown in stage 2. All three pools are mixed thoroughly once more and separated into three pools. Now each pool contains the 9 (3^2) new dipeptides. To each pool is then added another, different amino acid, for example Leu to pool 1, Ile to pool 2 and Asn to pool 3. After the amino acid coupling reaction, we have now generated 9 tripeptides in each pool as shown in stage 3 of Figure 3.4, a total of 27 (3^3) tripetides in our library. We could go on to generate (3^4) tetrapeptides, (3^5) pentapeptides, etc. If we began with all 20 natural amino acids and wanted to generate a library of pentapeptides in this way, we would be able to synthesise a maximum of 20^5 or 3200 000 compounds.

Thus, combinatorial chemistry was spawned from peptide chemistry and initially served the needs of biochemists and those medicinal chemists who specialised in peptide science. Its first decade or so concentrated on oligopeptides and related molecules. It has continued to evolve, however, and now permeates virtually every corner of medicinal chemistry. Efforts are underway to discover new, biologically active pharmaceuticals using these methods.

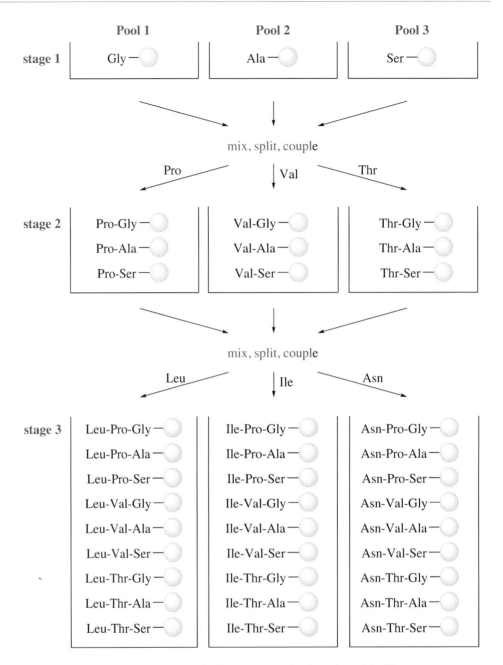

Figure 3.4 Split and mix synthesis scheme of a 27-tripeptide library.

3.6.2 The economics of combinatorial synthesis

One difficulty observed in combinatorial synthesis is that to achieve satisfactory reaction rates and conversion, the use of excess reagents and resins is important, which leads to cost implications. Another key point is the size of any potential library. Its ease of use will depend on the specific structures included and the purposes for which the library is to be tested. The relevance of speed to drug discovery is crucial. If it were known in advance the particular structure that would satisfy the perceived need, a successful compound library would only need to have one substance in it, that is, there would be no need for the library! If one has a general idea of the type of structure that would be useful, the library will have many promising compounds but still be relatively manageable in number. If the type of structure being aimed for is unknown, then a successful library must have a larger and more diverse number of compounds in it.

Given the high costs and complexities which dominate contemporary drug discovery and the time from initial synthesis to marketing (estimated to be on average between 10 and 15 years), ever more rapid preparation and evaluation of a few thousand analogues is essential to remain in a competitive position. From an economic standpoint, it is estimated that fewer than 10% of new therapies introduced repay their development costs. Those few that do must return a sufficient surplus to cover the costs of the rest and provide sufficient additional funds to cover the costs of future projects (as well as to satisfy the shareholders). These imperatives have placed a premium on speed of discovery and development. The portion of this time devoted to synthesis and screening in the drug-seeking campaign is usually about 3–5 years. The enhanced speed of construction through combinatorial methods can be expected to decrease the time to market by perhaps as much as one year in favourable cases. While this reduction is less than was originally hoped for when these methods were introduced, it is not trivial.

Year by year, many more libraries are reported, together with reports on the biological activity of their contents. Libraries are currently of primary value in seeking lead compounds or in basic studies on cellular processes. The means of delivering therapeutically significant blood levels of peptides through the oral route remain elusive. The several successes that have been achieved have been primarily the result of screening campaigns or serendipitous observations.

3.6.3   Active compound determination

If a library of chemicals has shown some desired activity, then the next step is to determine which component of the library is responsible for the activity. In some cases, it is possible to test the activity of the compounds whilst they are still attached to the polymeric support, and this allows the direct analysis of the active component. In particular, it is possible to design biological assays so that an active compound results in a colour change. If the active compound is still attached to a polymeric support, then the bead to which it is attached will appear to change colour. This bead can then easily be physically separated and the compound detached from the polymeric support before identification by standard spectroscopic techniques. In practice, mass spectrometry is usually the only technique which is sensitive enough to detect and provide information about the very small amount of material (a few nanograms or picograms) attached to a single bead.

Two key limitations of the above approach for active component determination are:

- that the compounds must be tested whilst they are still attached to the solid support

- that many components of the library may have the same molecular weight and so give indistinguishable molecular ions in their mass spectra.

The latter problem can be overcome by an approach called tagging. In parallel synthesis, each compound is synthesised in a separate tea bag reaction vessel. After cleavage from the solid support, one vessel gives one compound. These compounds are individually screened, and if one is active, the structure of a compound at a particular location is known and can be simply confirmed by analytical methods. For split and mix methods, even if one bead bears only one compound, many beads are usually being screened at the same time, each containing a different compound. To identify the structure of a hit, one solution is to code onto each bead some 'information' to identify one bead from another. This 'information' will enable the structure of the compound on the bead to be determined.

3.6.4   Encoding strategies: tagging

The basic idea behind encoding techniques is to record directly on the bead all the synthetic steps by introduction of a specific code for each step. After completion of the synthesis and detection of the active bead, the codes are read from the bead, enabling the identification of the 'history' of this active bead. In this way, the different chemical steps are known and the structure of the compound can be identified without having to analyse the compound structure.

In a tagged library, two different types of compound are constructed on each bead. One of the compounds is the structure whose activity is to be determined, and the other is present just as a unique marker to allow the structure of the compound to be determined. As an example, consider the synthesis of a library of a series of compounds known as benzodiazepines (**3.33**).

The target compounds vary in three places (R^x, R^y and R^z), and if ten variable components are used at each stage, there will be a total of 1000 compounds. A synthesis of this compound library can be carried out with tagging as shown in Scheme 3.14.

The synthesis starts with the attachment of ten different (various structures for R^x) ketoacids to ten different batches of a suitable polymer. After this, a specific amino acid is also attached to the polymer beads, with a different amino acid being used for each of the ten components. The side chain of the amino acid (shown in red) will provide the unique tag corresponding to the structure of R^x.

This generates the set of resins (**3.34**; Scheme 3.14(a)). At this stage, the ten batches of resin are combined, mixed, the Fmoc-protecting group removed by treatment with piperidine, and the resin then separated again into ten batches. Each batch is then allowed to react with one of ten different Fmoc-protected amino acid fluorides (a highly reactive amino acid derivative) to form an amide. The protecting group (P) is then removed from the tag, and a second protected amino acid is added to form a dipeptide. Once again, a different amino acid is used for each of the ten batches of resin. The ten batches of

3.33

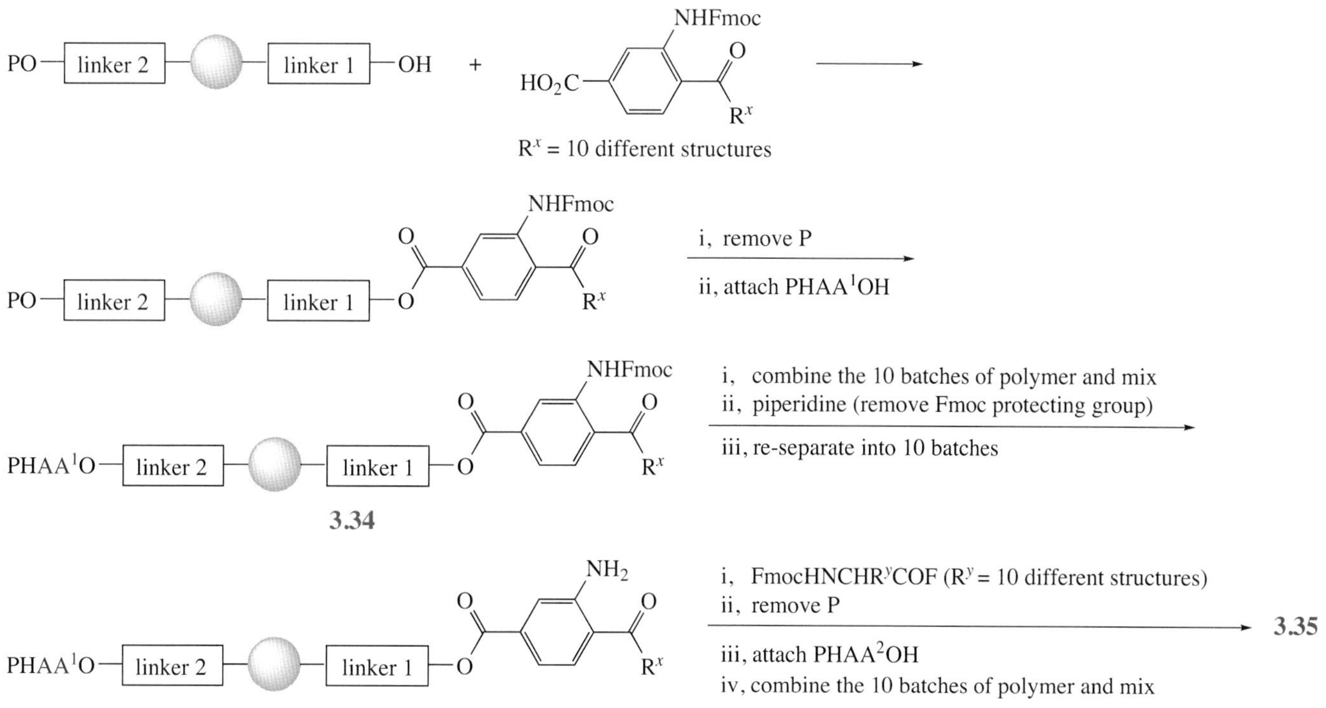

Scheme 3.14(a)

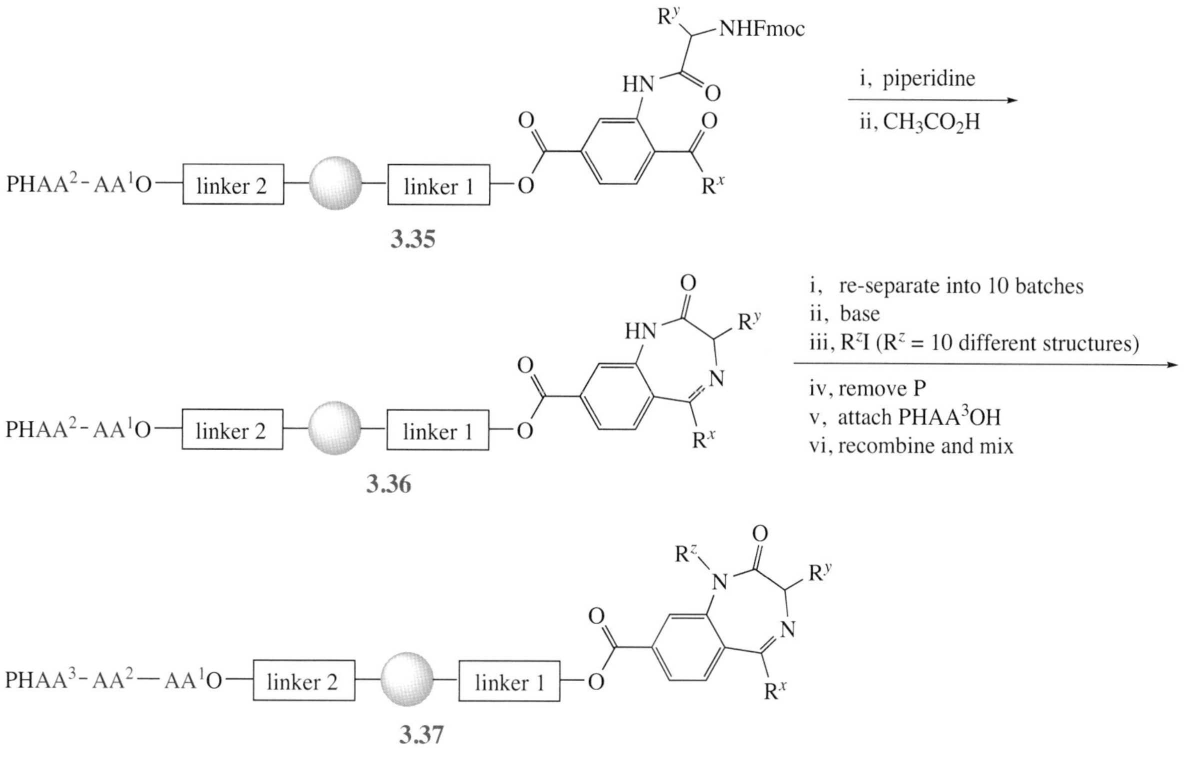

Scheme 3.14(b)

resin are again recombined and mixed to give polymer library **3.35**. Treatment of polymer **3.35** with piperidine again removes the Fmoc-protecting group, and subsequent treatment with mild acid results in cyclisation to form the benzodiazepine ring, giving polymer **3.36** (Scheme 3.14(b)).

These two steps are common to all of the compounds in the library, and so are carried out on the entire batch of polymer. At this stage, the polymer is again split into ten equal batches, and each batch is treated with a base (to remove the proton attached to the nitrogen atom within the benzodiazepine ring), and then each batch is allowed to react with one of ten iodoalkanes (R^zI). The protecting group (P) is again removed from the tag, and a third amino acid is added to the tag chain, with a different amino acid being used for each of the ten batches of resin. Recombination of the ten batches of resin then provides the entire library of polymer-linked benzodiazepines (**3.37**).

The library of benzodiazepines can now be tested for biological activity while still attached to the polymer. Should an active component be present then the peptide tag H–AA^3-AA^2-AA^1–OH can be cleaved from the bead bearing the active benzodiazepine and the structure of the peptide determined by mass spectrometry. This takes advantage of the fact that under appropriate conditions, the sequence of the fragment ions in the mass spectrum of a peptide allows the sequence of the amino acids to be determined, as described in Unit 2.

Since the synthesis was designed so that the structures of AA^1, AA^2 and AA^3 code for specific structures of R^x, R^y and R^z in the benzodiazepine, the sequence of the amino acids in the peptide tag can be correlated with the appropriate structures of R^x, R^y and R^z, thus allowing the structure of the benzodiazepine to be deduced.

If the activity of a library needs to be determined after the compounds have been cleaved from the solid support, then determination of the structure of the active component has to be done by resynthesis of individual components or sublibraries. For a small library, it may be feasible to individually synthesise and test each component of the library. For large libraries (which may contain millions of compounds), this approach is however impractical, and the solution is a process called **deconvolution** in which a series of sublibraries are prepared and tested. To illustrate how this works, consider a library of 160 000 tetrapeptides produced by a process similar to that shown in Figure 3.4 where we used 20 pools, one for each amino acid. Suppose that when tested, this library showed some biological activity. To determine which component of the library is responsible for the activity, a series of sublibraries are prepared and tested. Thus, the synthesis would be repeated but only 19 amino acids would be used at the first stage. The final library would again be tested for activity, and if no activity was present, then the active compound must contain the amino acid that was omitted.

This process is repeated, omitting each amino acid in turn at each stage of the synthesis. In this way, the structure of the active component can eventually be determined.

3.6.5 Analysis of compound libraries

In the mid-1990s, researchers began to move away from the split and mix combinatorial chemistry approach in favour of high-speed, automated parallel solid-phase and solution-phase synthesis of discrete compounds. Both solution-phase and solid-phase parallel synthesis permitted the production of large numbers of discrete pure compounds as well as large quantities of these discrete compounds, eliminating the need for extensive decoding of mixtures and re-synthesis following identification of 'active' compounds in high-throughput screening. Importantly, parallel syntheses could be performed readily on a 'plate' with many wells. Unlike the 'teabag' reaction vessels described earlier, these wells allow different reaction combinations to be tried simultaneously without the danger of mixing between combinations. The results of each reaction in each well can be screened for biological activity in situ, using automated plate readers. The relative ease of automation of parallel synthesis led to a tremendous influx of compounds for lead discovery and lead optimisation.

Almost all of the analytical characterisation tools (e.g. high-performance liquid chromatography (HPLC), NMR, Fourier transform infrared (FTIR), and liquid chromatography–mass spectrometry (LC–MS)) are series techniques, that is to say analysis of one compound after another is the norm. With the generation of compounds in parallel, this leads to bottlenecks in the drug discovery process as there are so many compounds that require analysis and purification. Parallel synthesis suffers from some of the same shortcomings of split and mix synthesis or indeed any synthesis (e.g. the expected compound may not be pure, or even synthesised in sufficient quantities). It turns out that mass spectrometry techniques, coupled with sophisticated chromatographic purification procedures allow the most rapid identification of active components of compound libraries. Fortunately, coincident with advances being made in mass spectrometric detection of parallel compound streams are the advances being made in parallel sampling and parallel chromatographic separations. Parallel chromatography-mass spectrometry systems now available consist of multiple HPLC pumps, multiprobe autosamplers, parallel UV detection, and parallel mass spectrometer ion source interfaces. Instrument manufacturers are continually being challenged to introduce more cost-effective and more compact systems.

3.7 Applications of SPOS to the synthesis of drug molecules and natural products

An illustrative example of the power of solid-phase synthesis is the resin-assisted synthesis of the adrenergic-blocking agent, propranolol. Allylisopropyl amine **3.38** is treated with a resin-bound trimethylammonium carbonate (a base) and iodine, which leads to the formation of oxazolidin-2-one (**3.39**; Scheme 3.15). The iodine is easily displaced by a reaction with a supported trimethylammonium acetate (**3.40**), to give **3.41** which is subsequently hydrolysed and converted into the mesylate **3.42** (a very good leaving group), which can then be displaced with a resin-bound trimethylammonium naphtholate. This affords the target compound (**3.43**) very cleanly.

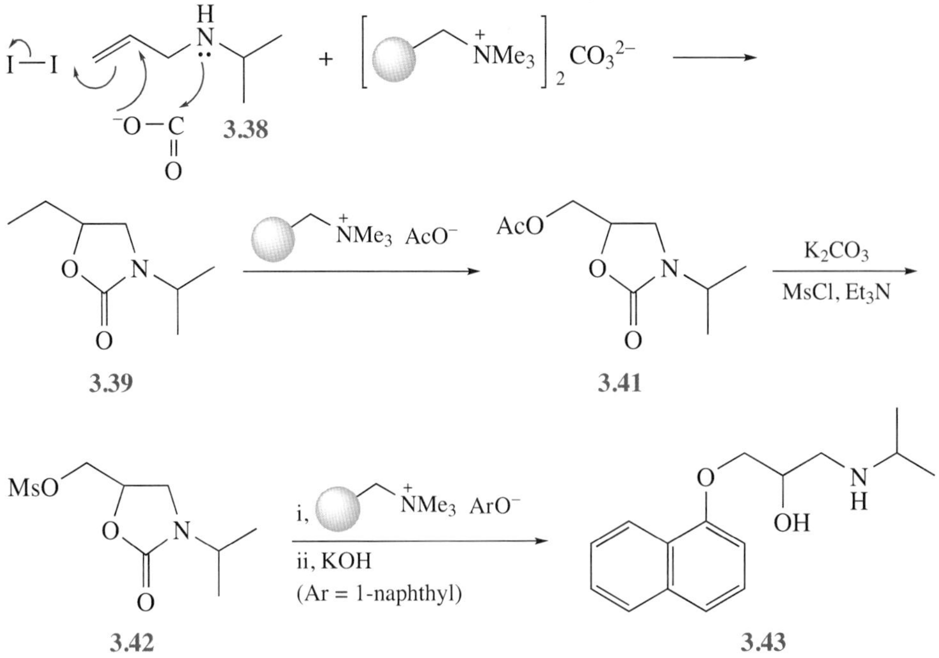

Scheme 3.15

In the six chemical steps required for this preparation, three involved the use of resin-based reagents. It should be the case that many possible variants leading to a library of related molecules could be prepared by simple modifications of the reagents and substrates.

■ Based on the route outlined in Figure 3.4 and Schemes 3.14a, 3.14b and 3.15, think of ways in which variations might be made to generate a compound library.

☐ Different amines could be used in the starting material. The isopropyl could be exchanged for a whole series of alkyl groups. Note that the allyl group must remain as it takes part in the cyclisation reaction. The other obvious substitution would be to vary the 1-naphthyl group with a range of aromatic or aliphatic hydrocarbon moieties.

3.8 The scale-up of solid-phase reactions

Solid-phase synthesis and combinatorial chemistry are not generally considered to be large-scale techniques. On the contrary, 20 mg may constitute the sum total of compounds present in one well of a 96-well plate! There are, however, examples of compounds that show promising biological activity having been first synthesised using solid-phase techniques. The role of the process chemist is to produce multigram quantities of such compounds for early preclinical studies. If the compounds were obtained using a solid-phase approach, solution-phase synthesis may not be immediately possible. Synthesis on the solid phase has the attractive feature of considerably simplified work up, a facet that is of particular appeal when scaling up a procedure. So often when scaling up a synthesis, the original choice of reagents and conditions may not be suitable for use on a large scale, due to cost, unmanageable quantities of by-product(s) where expensive purification is needed, or environmental considerations. A large-scale solid-phase synthesis has the advantage of staying more true to the original synthesis in which reagents and undesired products are simply washed away from the resin-bound final product. The principal disadvantage of solid-phase synthesis is the cost of the resin: it may simply prove too expensive to scale up in this way. Merrifield resins can be purchased most cheaply. If a resin is to be used in this way, it needs to be 'highly loaded' with as much substrate as possible; 4–5 mmol g^{-1} of resin might be considered a high load.

3.8.1   A β-lactam synthesis

β-lactams are extremely important compounds. The four-membered ring forms a key structural element in penicillins, cephalosporins and carbapenems (so-called β-lactam antibiotics discussed in Units 2, 3 and 4). In the SPOS (Scheme 3.16), a resin was prepared, to allow for a mild cleavage of the product from the solid support. High-load (4.4 mmol g^{-1}) Merrifield resin was treated with 2-methoxy-4-hydroxybenzaldehyde (**3.44**), potassium carbonate, and catalytic potassium iodide in DMF to yield the resin-bound aldehyde (**3.45**). The reduction of the aldehyde resin was performed with sodium borohydride to yield the high-load resin called Sasrin® (**3.46**).

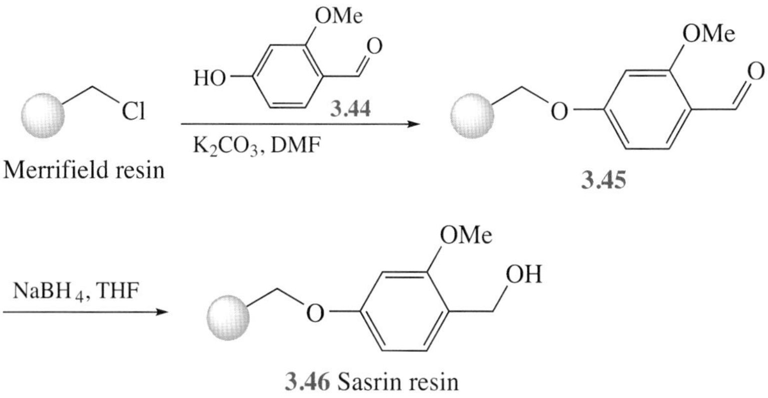

Scheme 3.16

The Sasrin® resin was then used to perform a β-lactam synthesis, first by coupling it with Fmoc-Val-OH. The Fmoc group was removed and the resin-bound amine, **3.47**, was then condensed with benzaldehyde to form an imine, **3.48** (Scheme 3.17). A [2+2] cycloaddition reaction was performed with phenoxyketene, **3.49**, formed by adding phenoxyacetyl chloride to the imine and triethylamine, and the product β-lactam, **3.50**, was cleaved under relatively mild conditions (TFA). From 169 g of Sasrin® resin 105 g of crude product was obtained with a purity of > 95%. After crystallisation with toluene, 100 g of **3.50** with a purity of > 99% was obtained as a 2 : 1 mixture of diastereomers.

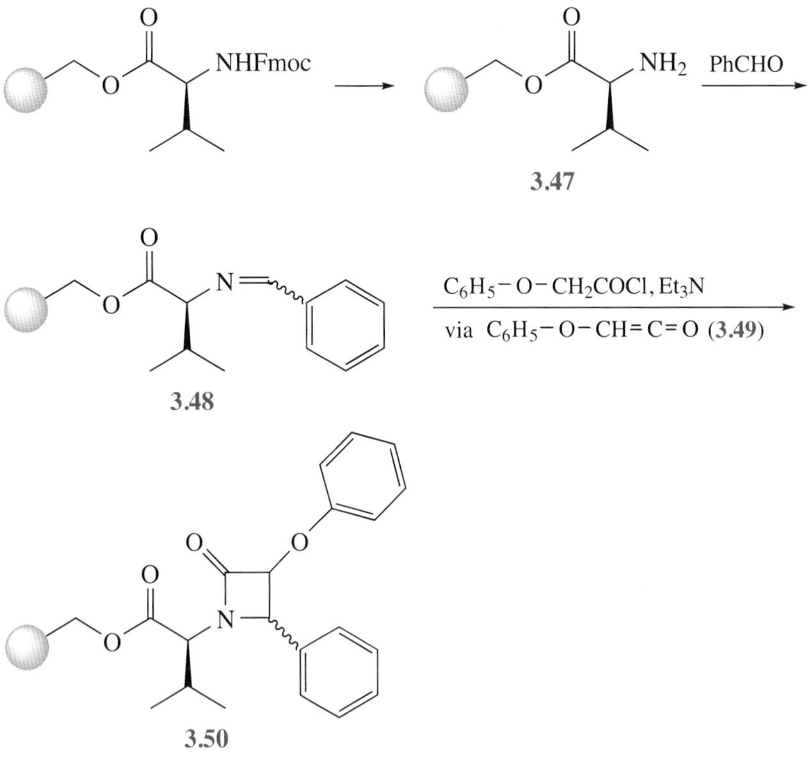

3.47

3.48

$C_6H_5-O-CH_2COCl, Et_3N$

via $C_6H_5-O-CH=C=O$ (3.49)

3.50

Scheme 3.17

Optimisation of reaction conditions

For the scale-up of a solid-phase reaction, it is generally practical to start out by adapting the conditions optimised on the research scale. However, as the scale increases, so do the amounts of reagents used and volumes of solvents. To keep costs of added reagents and reactants reasonable and to make the approach attractive for scale-up, it is imperative to reduce the large amount of reagent equivalents typically employed in solid-phase synthesis. It has been shown that the large excesses commonly used in solid-phase chemistry are not a necessity for scale-up when using high-load resins.

For solid-phase reactions on multigram scales, glass vessels with several necks and ground glass joints, together with an outer glass jacket for heating and cooling are employed as shown in Figure 3.5.

The necks serve as convenient inlet ports for the addition of reagents, inert gases, and for the introduction of a mechanical stirrer paddle. Stirring does need to be controlled so that the mechanical integrity of the polystyrene beads is not affected. For solid-phase reactions employing volumes in excess of 1 dm^3, vessel design includes a removable clamped top to allow periodic sampling of the resin. The equivalent to a traditional work-up in solution-phase chemistry is a wash sequence in solid-phase chemistry. It serves the purpose of washing away excess reagents and reaction by-products from the resin. The content of the washes is generally monitored by HPLC to reduce the amount of wash solvent used. An even more important aspect of a monitored wash is the prevention of contamination of the final product. The compound is then cleaved from the solid support and can be purified using HPLC if necessary.

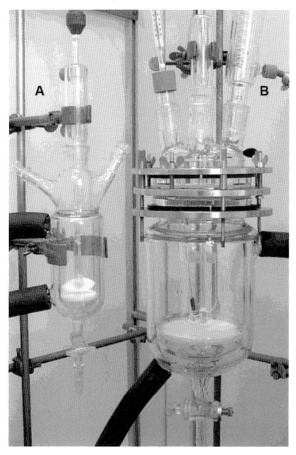

Figure 3.5 Reactors with coarse fritted filter plates: (A) 250 ml flask, equipped with three necks, jacket and mechanical glass stirrer with Teflon® paddle, and (B) 1.5 dm³ flask, equipped with jacket, glass anchor stirrer, and a clamped top with five necks.

■ Now summarise for yourself the benefits of scale-up on the solid phase.

☐ Your list may include the following features that make scale-up on solid phase particularly attractive:

1 The possibility of using established literature or research procedures developed for different supports with only minor modifications can be expected to result in a fast scale-up protocol in chemical development.

2 Resin costs are reduced when a resin can be more highly loaded. More product and less waste are produced with high-load resins.

3 Greatly simplified work-up procedures (washes) allow reducing synthesis time dramatically.

4 Multistep reactions can be expected to be completed more quickly and generally result in crude products with higher purity.

5 High concentrations of reactants and reagents can be employed. This allows the necessary stoichiometries to be lowered without significantly compromising the final product yield and purity.

To give an indication of costs involved, the cost for high-load Merrifield resin to produce product on a 100 g scale via solid-phase reactions can be expected to be of the order of a few hundred pounds sterling (at the time of writing).

In conclusion, solid-phase synthesis was initially developed to allow the high-yielding synthesis of peptides. During the 1990s, developments in molecular biology made it desirable for pharmaceutical companies to be able to prepare large numbers of compounds for biological testing far more rapidly than had previously been possible. This led to an explosion of interest in the solid-phase synthesis of compounds other than peptides, methodology for which is still being developed. The subsequent development of parallel and combinatorial synthesis techniques means that enormous numbers of compounds can now be rapidly prepared and tested. A major advantage of all solid-phase techniques is that they can easily be automated, which both speeds up the synthesis and relieves the chemist of much of the drudgery associated with preparing numerous analogues of a compound by the same route. However, this does not mean that chemists are no longer required, since the synthesis still needs to be designed and tested.

Study note

Before moving on to the next unit, try to write a summary of Section 3 and then compare it with ours. Go to Unit 8 summaries in Unit 8 resources.

1 Introduction

Synthesis occupies a central role in organic chemistry. Its power resides in the ability of a chemist to synthesise precisely any compound. The reasons for wanting to synthesise a particular compound are many and varied. For example, the compound of interest could have been isolated from a plant and its complex structure needs verification. Alternatively, the compound could have interesting biological properties requiring significant quantities to be available – more than is easily or economically extracted from natural sources such as plants or marine sponges. Furthermore, the compound could be a drug analogue and structural variations are required to elucidate its mode of action. Chemists will also attempt a synthesis of a target molecule that has no precedent, for which new conditions, or even new reagents, may have to be developed to achieve the required transformation. For this reason, organic synthesis is continually evolving with the advent of new reagents and conditions that enable reactions to take place faster, more efficiently, under milder conditions, and with greater control in selectivity. Whatever the reason for the synthesis, in tackling a synthetic problem, the chemist will initially begin by inspecting the proposed structure of the target molecule and devising several possible syntheses.

The proposed synthetic routes are primarily based on known organic reactions, though they are likely to involve an emphasis on the chemist's own practical experience. The procedure of selecting possible synthetic routes is aimed towards identifying those simpler organic compounds which are commercially available in reasonable quantities at an acceptable price. Thus, synthetic routes are based on the accumulated knowledge of organic chemistry and the application of a few basic principles. It is the aim of this unit to help you develop an understanding of these principles.

This unit is about learning a skill, namely how to mentally break up a molecule into component pieces that can show how the molecule could be synthesised in the lab from simpler organic compounds. This is the reverse of what we have discussed in the preceding units where we have been developing reactions that *assemble* the target molecules from smaller organic molecules.

1.1   Principles of retrosynthetic analysis

In planning a synthesis, we need to start by analysing the structure of the target molecule and decide which of the bonds in the molecule can be easily synthesised from known reactions; in our planning we 'disconnect' those bonds so that the target molecule is broken up into smaller fragments. For example, when we disconnect one such likely bond in the weedkiller propanil (**1.1**, Scheme 1.1, disconnection shown in red) we form two smaller compounds **1.2** and **1.3**. These smaller compounds are called **synthetic precursors**, and may themselves be broken down further until we arrive at viable starting materials. Any disconnection step is thus the *reverse* of carrying out the reaction, and this process of working backwards, in the opposite direction to which a compound will be made, is called **retrosynthetic**

analysis. You need always to hold in mind that this retrosynthetic process is a 'thought experiment' and not a reaction. Let's consider the propanil example in a little more detail to see what this means.

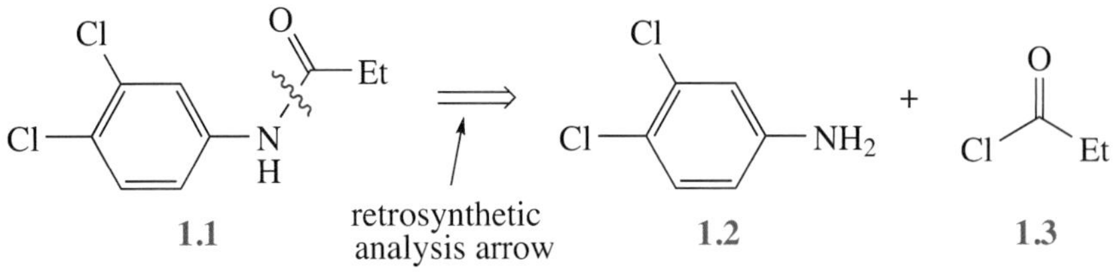

Scheme 1.1

Examination of propanil **1.1** shows the molecule to contain an amide bond. We can disconnect that bond to identify an amine and a carboxylic acid derivative as two synthetic precursors. If you studied the Level 2 module you may recall that the amide functional group can be made from an amine and a carboxylic acid derivative that contains a good leaving group, such as an acyl chloride. Note that we use a particular type of arrow, the retrosynthetic analysis arrow, when writing out disconnections. The use of this arrow means that propanil (**1.1**) can be made from molecules **1.2** and **1.3**. Breaking the molecule down like this is known as a **disconnection** and it is normal to indicate which bond has been disconnected through the use of a 'wiggly' line drawn through the bond being disconnected (shown in red).

■　Try and show a similar disconnection for paracetamol, **1.4**.

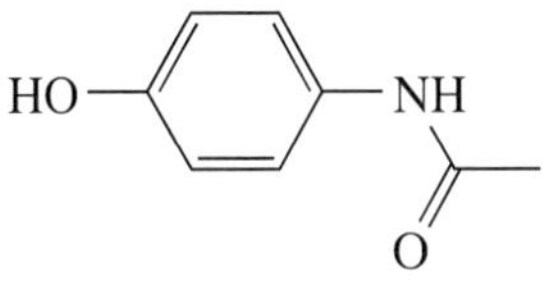

1.4

☐　The disconnection is as follows:

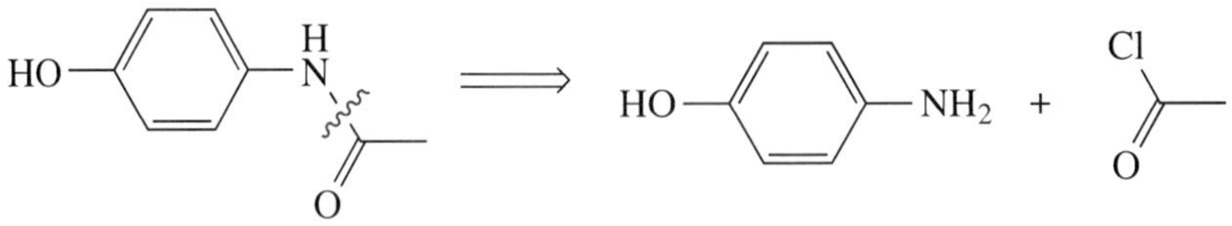

Paracetamol is another molecule that contains an amide bond, and we know that the reaction to produce amides involving an amine and an acyl chloride has a very good chance of succeeding. This identifies another useful skill: *you should disconnect to known reliable reactions*. Look for reactions with which you are familiar, and look to build functional groups about which you know the chemistry.

In the syntheses of propanil and paracetamol we have used a carbon–nitrogen bond-forming reaction to assemble the principal molecular framework. This reaction is just one example of a general type of carbon–heteroatom bond-forming reaction, which we call **C–X bond-forming reactions**. Also into this category go reactions that make esters, ethers, secondary and tertiary amines, thioesters, amides, etc. Reactions that introduce the alcohol functionality, ROH, while technically a carbon–heteroatom bond-forming reaction, are not normally included since they do not extend the molecular framework; this is also true for C–Cl, C–Br, C–SH, C–NH$_2$ and C–NO$_2$.

When analysing the above disconnections, we have proposed ethanoyl chloride (acetyl chloride) in both amide-forming reactions, but ethanoic anhydride (acetic anhydride), or ethanoic acid (acetic acid) with DCC (see the peptide coupling in Unit 8) could also have been used. All of these reagents correspond to an electrophilic acetyl unit, CH$_3$CO$^+$; this unit we refer to as a **synthon**. These synthons have no real existence but are molecular fragments that indicate the polarity of the atoms that will be brought together to form the new bond in the synthesis reaction. So they are fragments that represent how a particular group may be introduced, either as a nucleophile or as an electrophile. They are the theoretical result of the mental exercise of breaking up a molecule into its component pieces, and they express the polarity of known reagents that could be used to carry out the actual synthesis. For example, when envisaging the disconnection of chlorbenside, **1.5**, shown in Scheme 1.2, we can disconnect the bond to give two possible pairs of synthons (**1.6** and **1.7**, and **1.8** and **1.9**). Having written this disconnection, the next thing to do is to try and relate these synthons to reagents. In disconnection A, the sulfur-containing fragment is identified as nucleophilic and so has a '–' associated it. The accompanying carbon-centred fragment is electrophilic and thus has a '+' associated with it. In the other possible disconnection, B, the sulfur centre is electrophilic and the carbon centre nucleophilic, hence the polarity represented by the plus and minus signs is reversed.

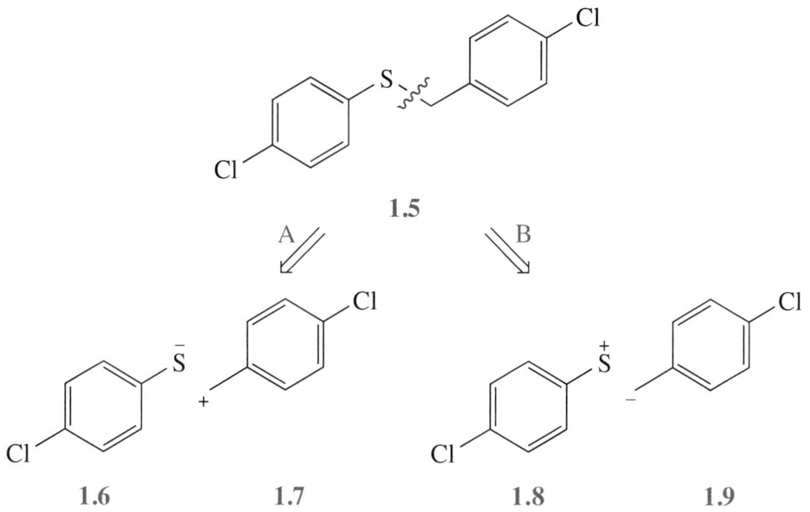

Scheme 1.2

For disconnection A, the nucleophilic synthon **1.6** can be related to thiophenol **1.10**; in an actual reaction the thiophenol would need to be used in the presence of a base to remove the thiophenol proton. The corresponding electrophilic synthon can be related to a derivative containing a good leaving group, such as **1.11** or **1.12**.

synthon

equivalent reagent

1.10

synthon

equivalent reagent

1.11

or

1.12

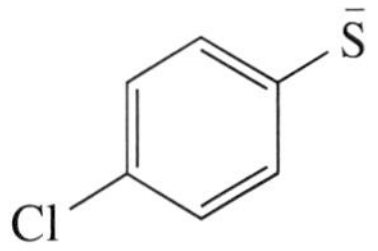

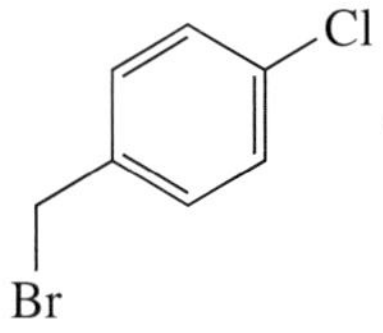

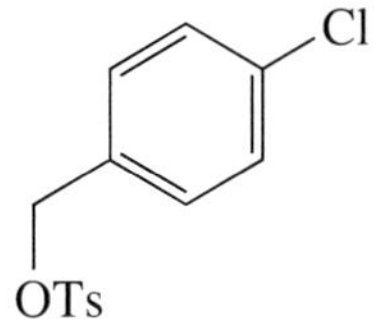

In contrast, disconnection B has no readily available standard equivalent reagents, so would not be considered further.

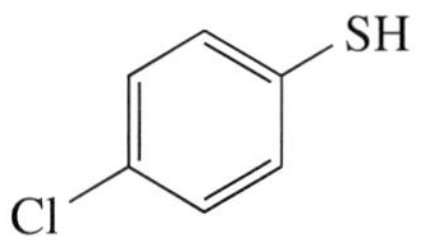

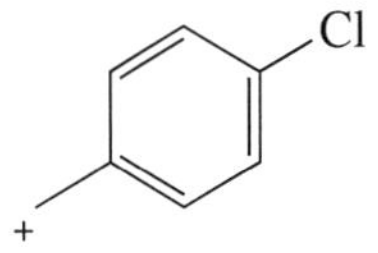

Take a brief look at Data Table 9; this summarises many of the commonly encountered synthons and relates them to their corresponding synthetic equivalents. This table will aid you in your study of the next sections. There is no need to try and memorise it – if you use it regularly in your study of this unit, you will begin to appreciate how to use it for unfamiliar disconnections.

We are now going to explore various types of bond disconnection to see how we can use them to plan the construction of complex molecules. Part of the skill in choosing where to make a bond disconnection comes through recognising key structural features and patterns in the target molecule. The remainder of this unit will help you develop this skill by identifying these features.

Study note

We will start this study by looking at C–X bond disconnections in Section 2.

2 C–X bond disconnections

We start our analysis of target molecules by considering those in which we focus on C–X bonds. These compounds contain bonds between di- and trivalent electronegative heteroatoms like O, N and S. A good guideline for any retrosynthetic analysis of this type of molecule is to disconnect the bond between the heteroatom and the adjacent carbon atom.

$$C-X \quad \begin{array}{l} \Longrightarrow \quad C^+ + X^- \\ \Longrightarrow \quad C^- + X^+ \end{array}$$

2.1 Compounds containing isolated C–X functionality

Generally due to the electronegativity of X, disconnections of this type should be written so as to afford C^+ and X^- as the corresponding centres in the synthons. There are a few exceptions where this is reversed and the carbon centre acts as the nucleophile and X as the electrophile, as in the electrophilic substitution of aromatic systems, but this type of analysis is far less common.

The most common reagents corresponding to X^- nucleophiles are alcohols, thiols, and amines or, indeed, the anions formed upon their deprotonation. The most common C^+ electrophiles are haloalkanes or carboxylic acid derivatives, such as acyl chloride and acid anhydrides.

Let's consider benzyl 3-methylbutyl ether, $PhCH_2OCH_2CH_2CHMe_2$ (**2.1**), which is a component of gardenia perfume. One possible disconnection of the C–O bond (C–X) is shown in Scheme 2.1, which leads to an alcohol **2.2** as the nucleophile and a haloalkane **2.3** as the electrophile.

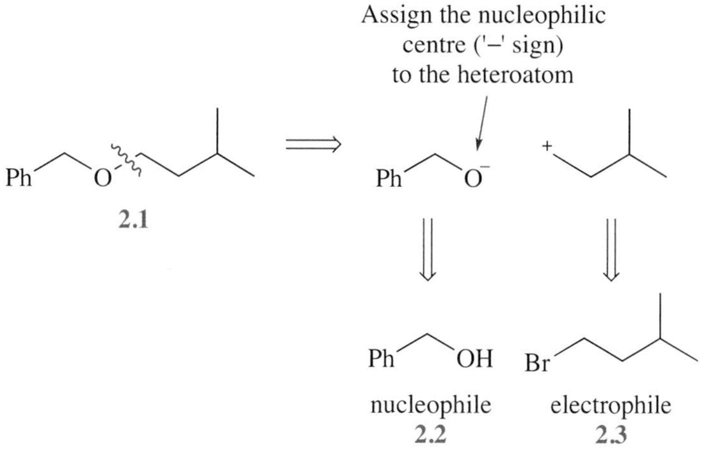

Scheme 2.1

- Show an alternative disconnection for $PhCH_2OCH_2CH_2CHMe_2$.

☐ Disconnecting the other C–O bond of the ether identifies two new synthons **2.4** and **2.5**, which can be related to benzyl bromide and 3-methylbutan-1-ol, respectively.

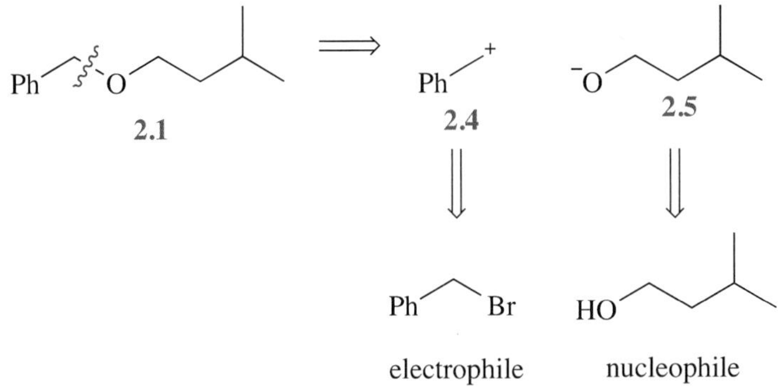

So, as a general rule, we just add H to the nucleophilic synthon to get the reagent, and add a good leaving group, like Br, to get the electrophilic reagent.

Now let's consider another example, $PhCH_2OCOPh$, and apply the same two possible C–O bond disconnections.

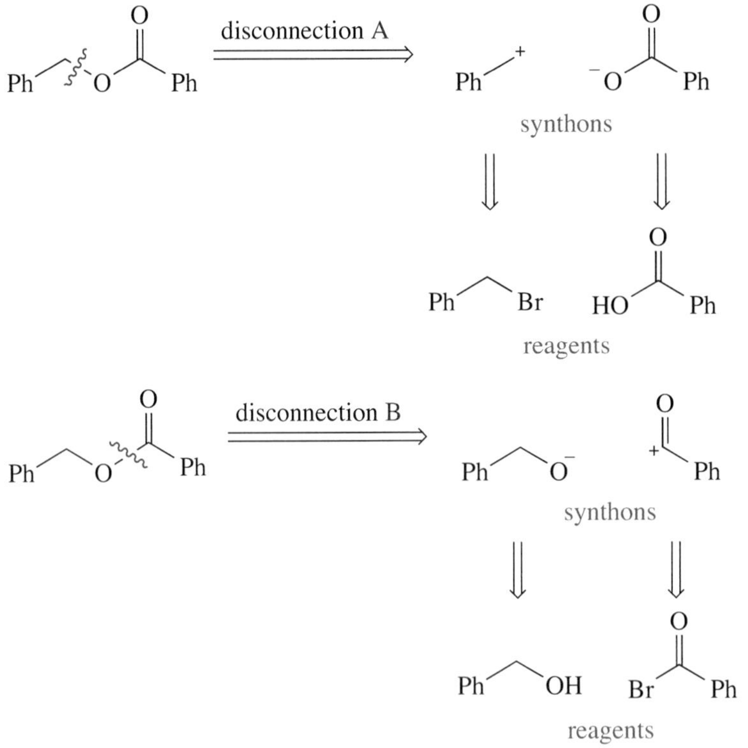

Scheme 2.2

In this case both disconnections are valid. However, as a general rule the latter disconnection would always be recommended first, in part because of the higher reactivity of acyl halides.

Based on the ideas developed above, let's revisit the weedkiller propanil (**1.1**). Disconnection of the two C–N bonds identifies two pairs of synthons.

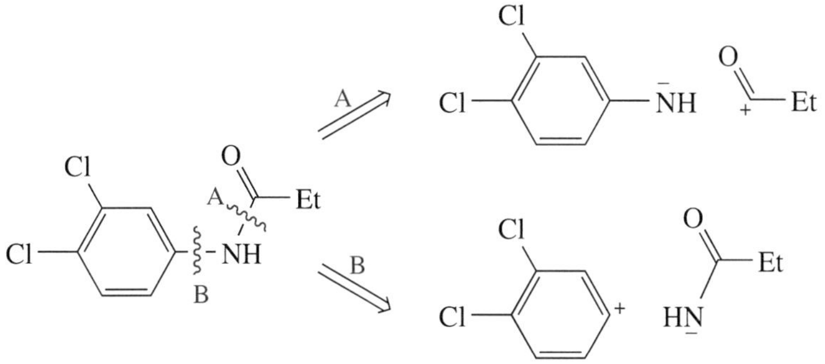

Scheme 2.3

■ Using the principles developed above, try to draw the reagents that correspond to the synthons formed from disconnection A.

☐ The synthons formed are

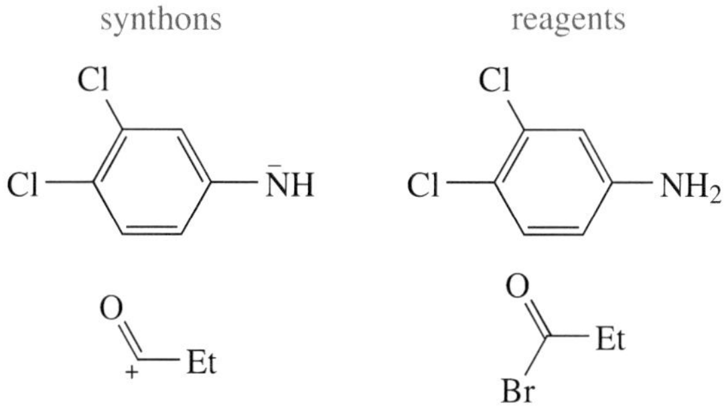

The alternative disconnection, B, reveals another useful lesson in knowing where to disconnect C–X bonds. The nucleophilic synthon, ⁻NHCOEt, corresponds to the readily available reagent EtCONH$_2$, which is easily visualised by simply adding H$^+$ to the synthon. The electrophilic synthon is an aromatic one, which, according to the principle we developed earlier, corresponds to an aromatic halide, for example, Ar–Br. The reaction that is identified here is fundamentally flawed, as it is nucleophilic *attack* on an aromatic substrate, whereas aromatic compounds normally undergo electrophilic *substitution*. Normally there is no nucleophilic substitution at the sp^2 carbon of an aromatic ring. Thus, for path B to succeed synthetically, the normal reactivity of the ring would need to be reversed. This observation allows us to make the following general rule:

Do not disconnect a C–X bond which is directly bound to an aromatic ring.

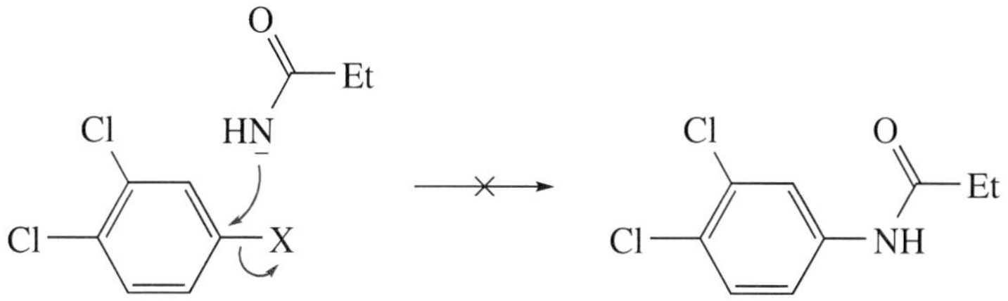

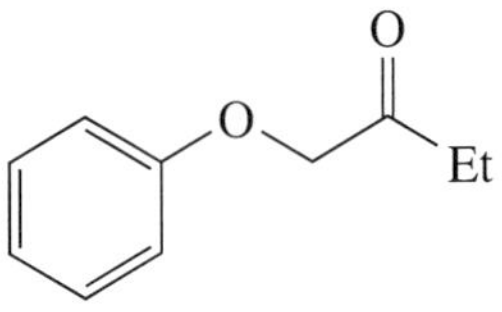

2.6

- On the basis of the above observation, attempt a disconnection for compound **2.6**.

☐ The disconnection is

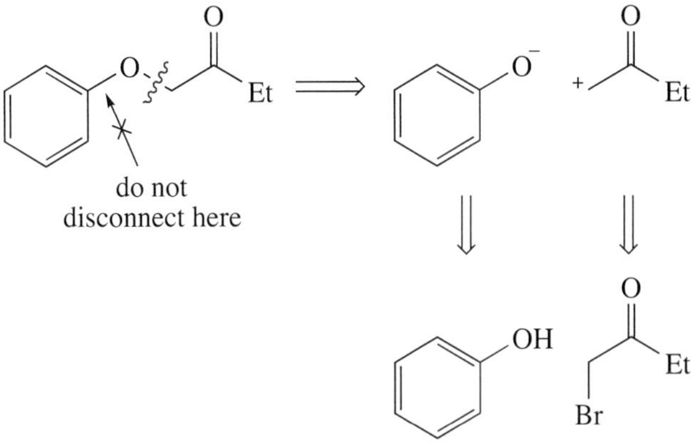

So far we have only considered compounds that contain one C–X bond, but how do we tackle the problem when there are two or more C–X bonds that are crucial to the synthetic strategy? First of all let's start with molecules that have two heteroatoms attached to the same carbon atom.

If you examine the perfume 1,1-dimethoxy-2-phenylethane (**2.7**) you will see it contains two C–O bonds involving the same carbon. We can use our standard approach to disconnect *both* C–O bonds to end up with the following synthons:

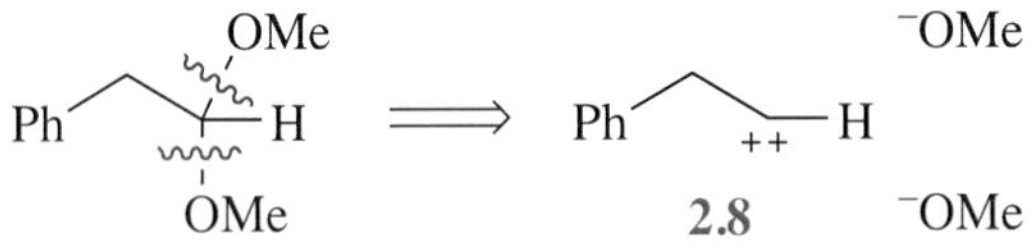

The first point to note here is the use of symmetry; disconnecting the two C–O bonds as shown produces two identical nucleophilic MeO^- synthons and a doubly electrophilic C^{++} synthon **2.8**.

- Use Data Table 9 to identify the reagent corresponding to this electrophilic synthon.

☐ The double electrophilic synthon corresponds to an aldehyde.

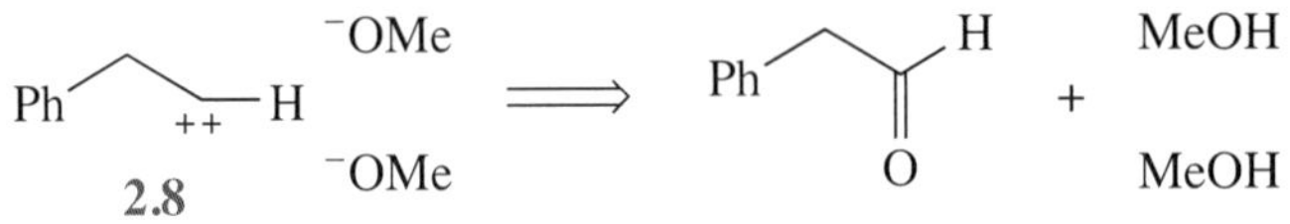

The electrophilic C^{++} synthon is of particular importance since, in general, it corresponds to a C=O functional group, as found in aldehydes or ketones. This is quite reassuring as you may have recognised the functional group in 1,1-dimethoxy-2-phenylethane **2.7** to be an acetal, which, if you have studied the Level 2 module, you will know is formed by reaction between an aldehyde and an alcohol under acidic conditions.

■ Try writing down the disconnections for 2,2-*bis*(ethylthio)propane (**2.9**), which is a key intermediate in the synthesis of the narcotic sulfonal.

□ The disconnection is

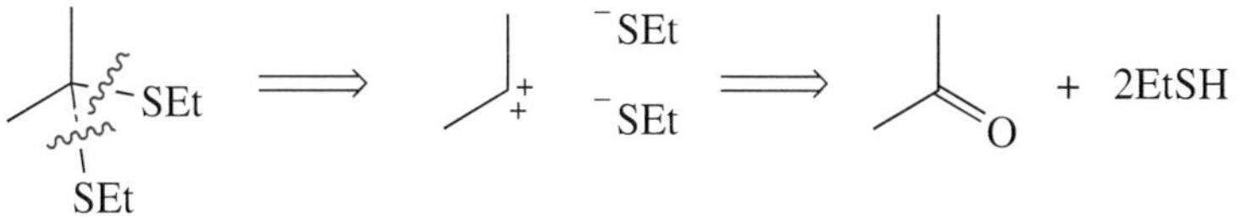

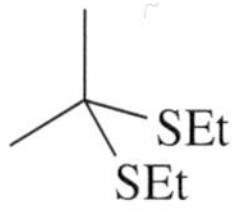

2.9

Again a double disconnection between the C–S bonds leads to a C^{++} synthon and two EtS^- synthons. This is expected as a thioacetal, the functional group in **2.9**, is formed by condensing a thiol with a carbonyl-containing compound, which is what the disconnection has suggested.

2.2   1,2-difunctional heteroatom compounds

Now let's explore the situation where the heteroatoms are in a 1,2 relationship. If we treat compound **2.10** as a standard C–X compound in which the two C–X bonds are unrelated, then two disconnections, A and B, are possible.

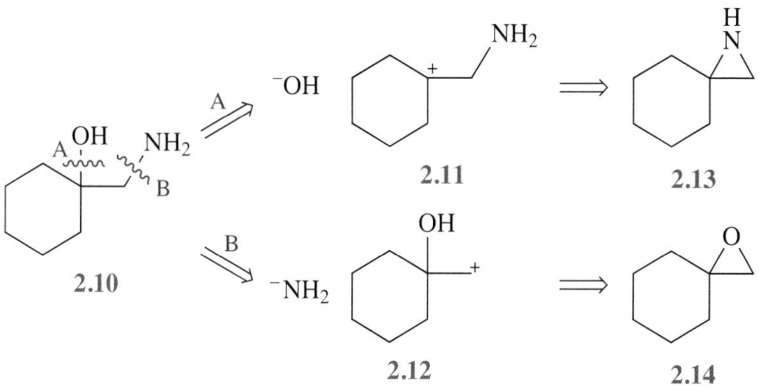

The reagents for the electrophilic synthons **2.11** and **2.12**, are the corresponding 3-membered cyclic aziridine **2.13** and epoxide **2.14**, respectively. The epoxide is a more reactive electrophile than its nitrogen analogue and is the preferred option.

Most 1,2-difunctional compounds can be considered to be derived from synthons such as **2.12** which in turn relate to their corresponding epoxide. For example, retrosynthetic analysis of *bis*(2-chloroethyl)aniline **2.15**, a compound with anticancer properties, is shown in Scheme 2.4. The trick here is to realise that the chlorine atoms could come from the corresponding alcohol via a **functional group interconversion (FGI)**; once this has been identified, the retrosynthetic analysis becomes routine. This disconnection also reinforces the idea of symmetry; two disconnections leading to the same synthon allow for an efficient synthesis. The electrophilic synthon corresponds to an epoxide and the Ar–N= nucleophilic synthon to an amine, in this case aniline.

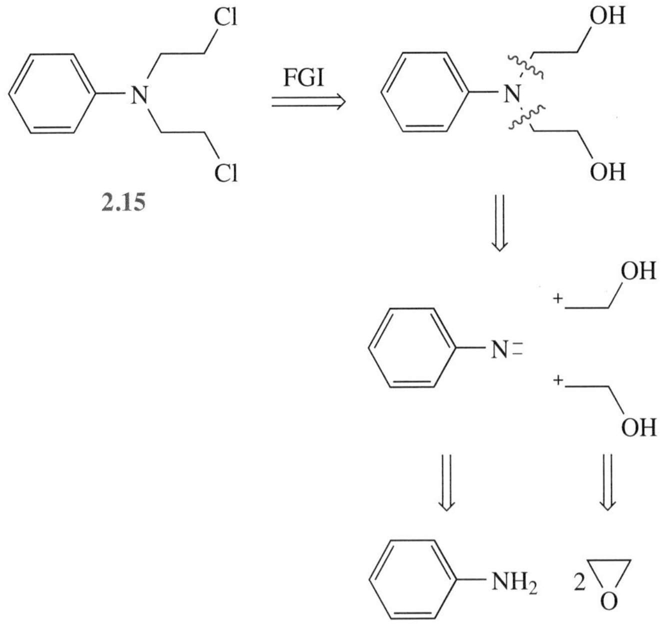

Scheme 2.4

As with all retrosynthetic analyses, it is always a good check to show the forward reaction (Scheme 2.5), as this should help to identify any potential errors. In this case, we would expect the amine to react with the epoxide to give the alcohol **2.16**, which is then reacted with thionyl chloride (SOCl$_2$) to give the desired final product.

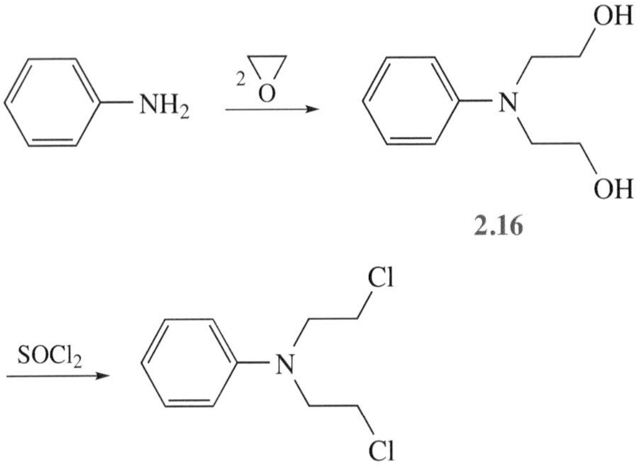

Scheme 2.5

■ The drug propranolol **2.17** illustrates well the points covered so far regarding C–X disconnections. Identify disconnections of the C–X type and specify the reagents to which your predicted synthons correspond.

□ The 1,2-difunctional amino alcohol can be disconnected at the C–N bond. This results in the synthon **2.18** which, in turn, identifies the epoxide

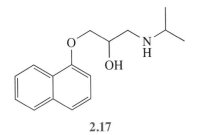

2.17

2.19 as a suitable precursor; the latter can be related to the corresponding alkene **2.20** via an FGI. Disconnection of the C–O bond in **2.20** identifies naphthol (**2.21**) and 3-bromoprop-1-ene (allyl bromide, **2.22**) as potential reagents.

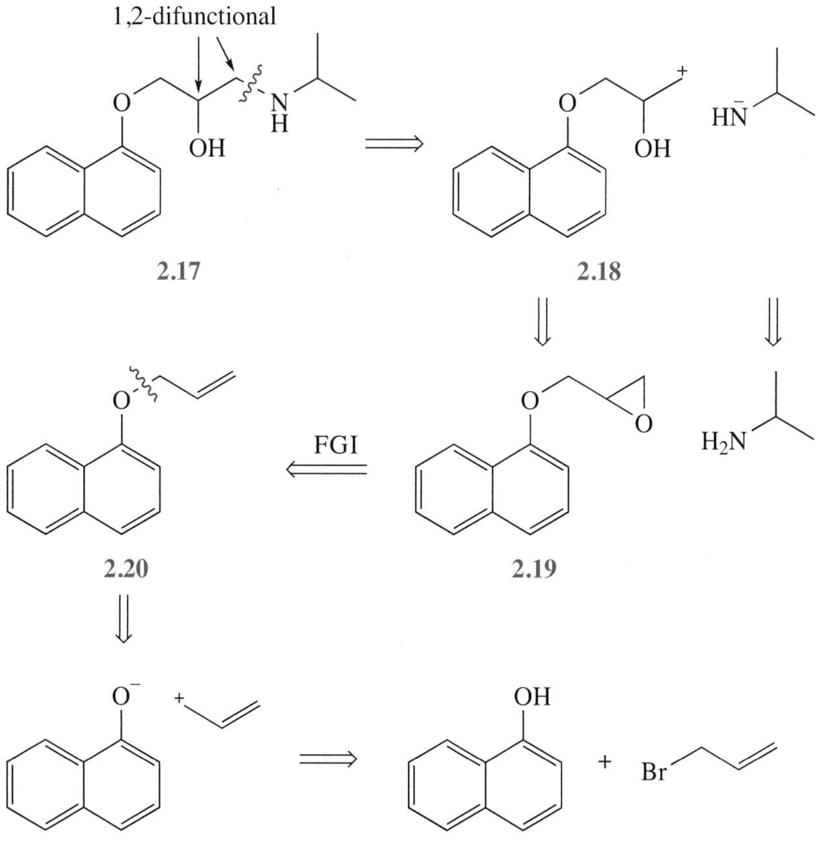

2.17 **2.18** **2.20** **2.19** **2.21** **2.22**

The synthesis corresponding to this analysis is shown in Scheme 2.6.

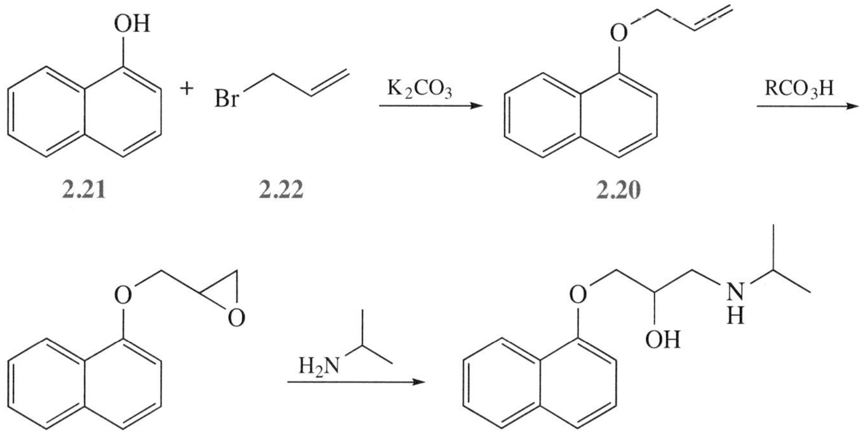

2.21 **2.22** **2.20** **2.19** **2.17**

Scheme 2.6

An alternative approach to 1,2-hydroxyamino (or amino alcohol) compounds, particularly when the amino functionality is a primary one (RNH_2), is based on the relationship between the RCH_2NH_2 group and a nitrile. You will recognise the conversion of nitriles to amino groups as simply a reduction (Unit 6, Data Table 8.2).

$$R-\!\!\!\equiv\!\!N \xrightarrow{\text{LiAlH}_4} R\diagup NH_2$$

This observation therefore allows us to relate 1,2-hydroxyamino compounds to a cyanohydrin (introduced in the Level 2 module), via an FGI instead of an epoxide.

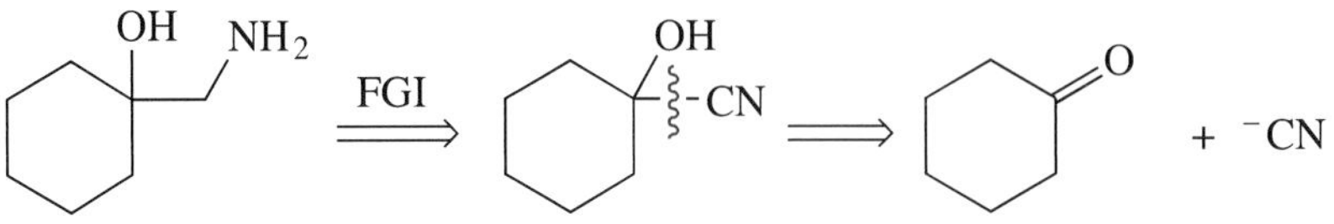

2.10   cyanohydrin

Disconnection of the C–C bond involving the CN group identifies, in this case, a ketone and cyanide ion as the suitable reagents for the synthesis.

Other groups that can also be related to a nitrile in a similar fashion can also be analysed in this manner. So, for example, an α-hydroxyaldehyde can be analysed as follows:

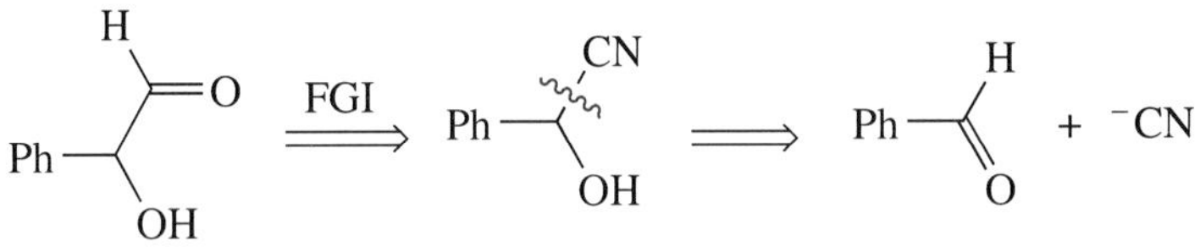

■ Use Data Table 8.2 to identify the reagent necessary to reduce the nitrile functionality to the aldehyde in the target molecule.

☐ DIBAH chemoselectively reduces the nitrile to the aldehyde.

Now let's look at the α-hydroxy acid **2.23**. You should notice the 1,2- relationship between the functional groups. The acid group is another that can be related to a nitrile through FGI, because in the synthesis direction hydrolysis of a nitrile affords the acid functional group:

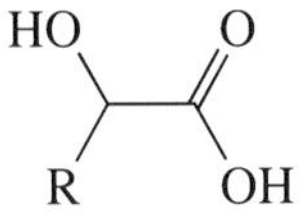

2.23

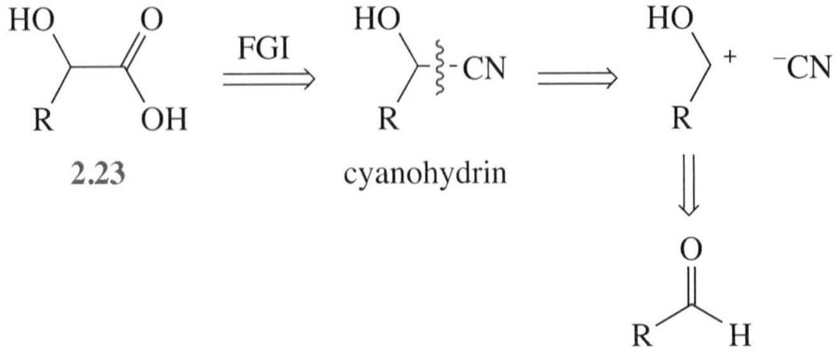

2.23   cyanohydrin

If we now compare this disconnection of the C–C bond in the cyanohydrin with the similar disconnection of the comparable bond in the α-hydroxy acid. We can see that a cyanide is the reagent for the ⁻COOH synthon.

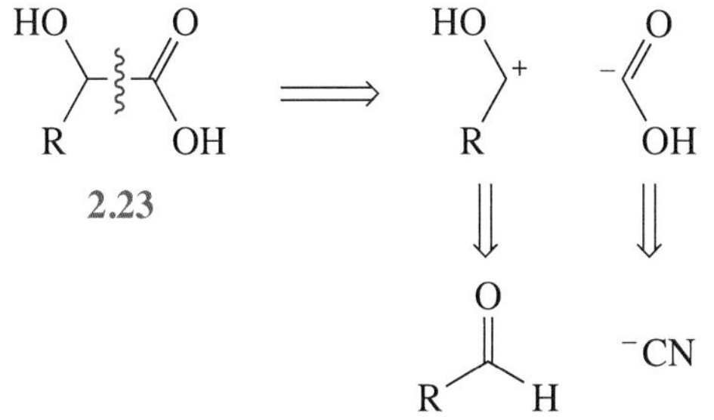

2.23

Note that this synthon has the opposite 'polarity' (here nucleophilic) to that normally associated with a carbonyl carbon atom (usually electrophilic). We shall return to this shortly.

We can see how this works for the synthesis of lactic acid, **2.24**, the retrosynthetic analysis of which is shown in Scheme 2.7.

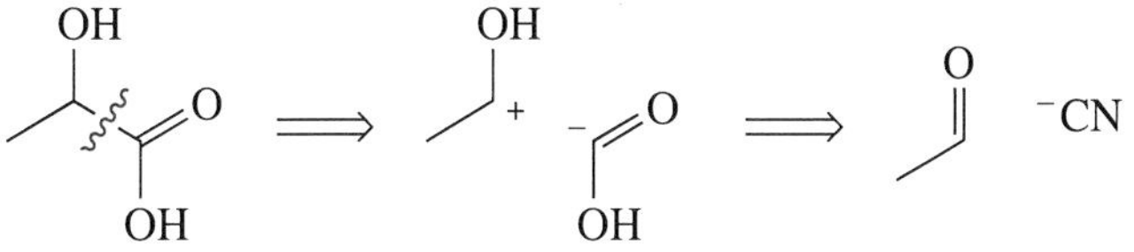

2.24

Scheme 2.7

The synthesis is shown in Scheme 2.8.

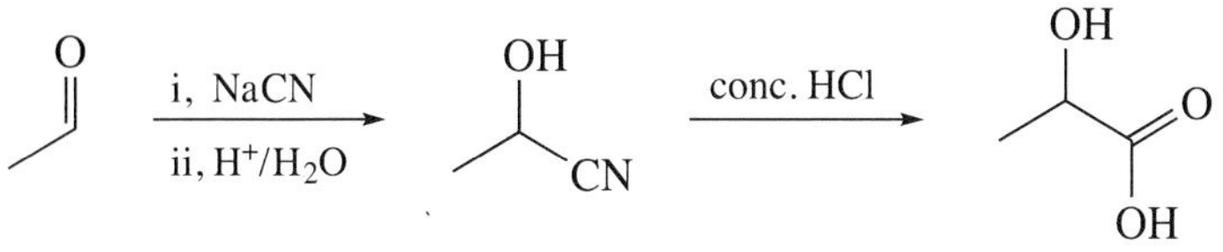

2.24

Scheme 2.8

Applying this type of analysis to α-hydroxyketones is a little more complex as it produces a nucleophilic synthon that we cannot easily relate to a nitrile. For example, disconnection of compound **2.25** identifies an electrophilic synthon corresponding to an aldehyde, **2.26**, and a nucleophilic acyl synthon **2.27**, which is similar to the ⁻COOH synthon, but is unusual as we would normally expect an acyl fragment to be electrophilic, for example, **2.28**.

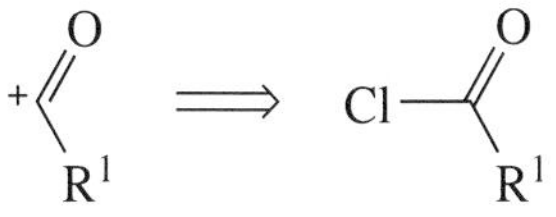

2.28

Such synthons are said to have reverse polarity, and the term 'umpolung', from the German, is used to describe them. Scheme 2.9 contains two examples of reagents that correspond to umpolung of the acyl fragment, including thioacetals (alternatively called dithianes), **2.29**, and the acetylide anion, **2.30**. These synthetic equivalents of a nucleophilic acyl fragment are widely used in organic chemistry.

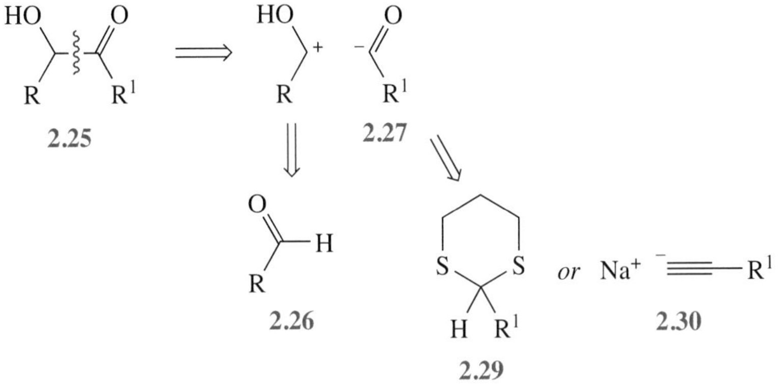

Scheme 2.9

An example of the use of an acetylide is shown in Scheme 2.10:

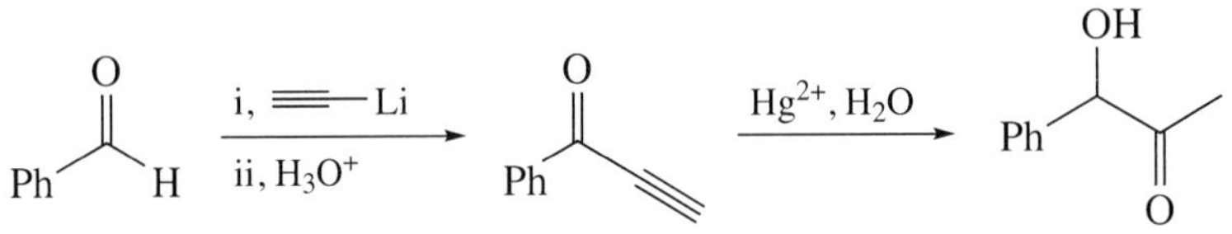

Scheme 2.10

Conversion of the alkyne to a methylketone is accomplished through hydrolysis with mercury(II) salts. Note that this use of an alkynide only produces methyl ketones.

Retrosynthetic analysis of an α-hydroxyketone **2.31**, this time involving a thioacetal is shown in Scheme 2.11. The first stage relates the ketone to a thioacetal through an FGI. Subsequent C–C disconnection leads to a nucleophilic synthon involving the thioacetal and an electrophilic synthon that corresponds to an aldehyde. The nucleophilic synthon can be related to a thioacetal reagent, which in turn can be related back to the corresponding carbonyl compound via a double C–S disconnection as we saw for sulfonal.

The corresponding synthesis of **2.31** is shown in Scheme 2.12.

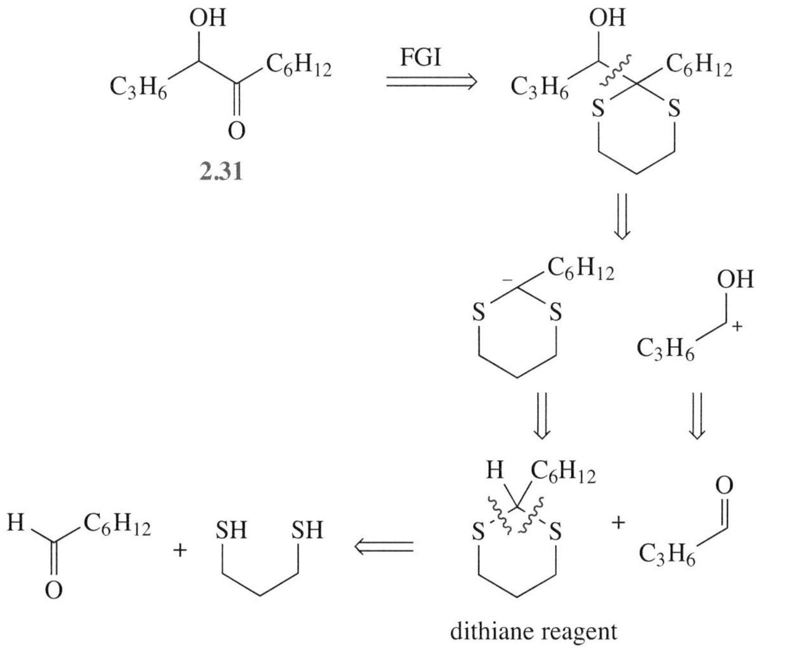

Scheme 2.11

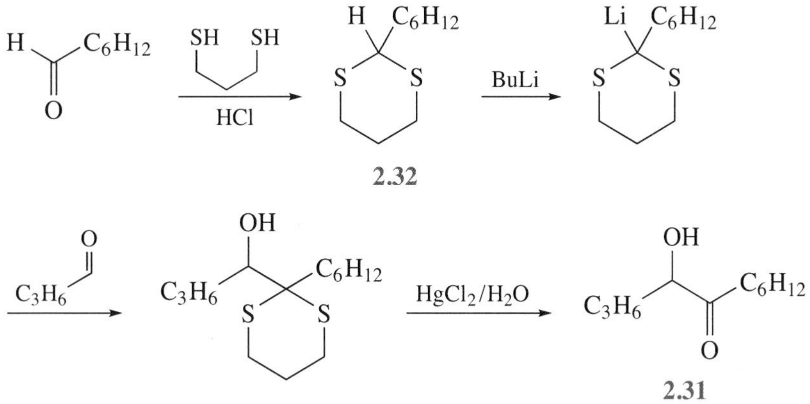

Scheme 2.12

The use of thioacetals is a very powerful synthetic transformation, as this functional group both masks the carbonyl and allows for relatively easy deprotonation of compound **2.32** by use of a base such as BuLi. This is because the C–H bond in the thioacetal is fairly acidic, as the adjacent sulfur atoms stabilise the resulting negative charge. Thioacetals are good carbon-centred nucleophiles and can be used in standard nucleophilic addition and substitution reactions. An example of this can be seen in the synthesis of a precursor, **2.33**, of the aggregation pheromone from the Californian five-spined ips bark beetle.

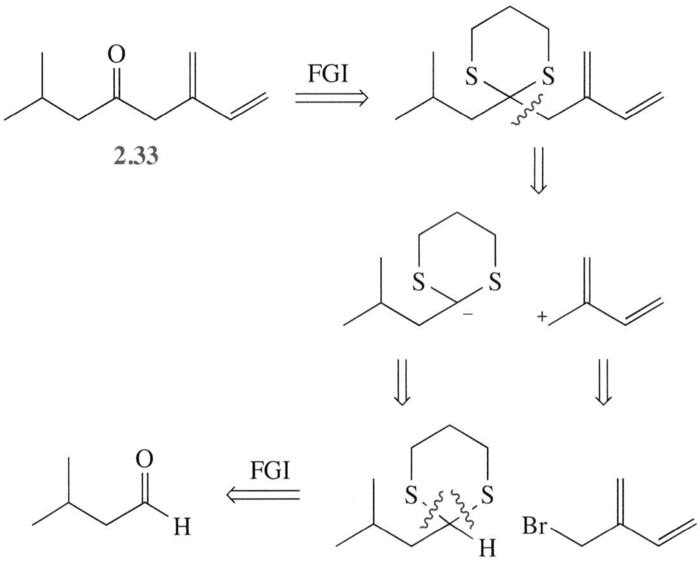

2.33

The forward synthesis is shown below.

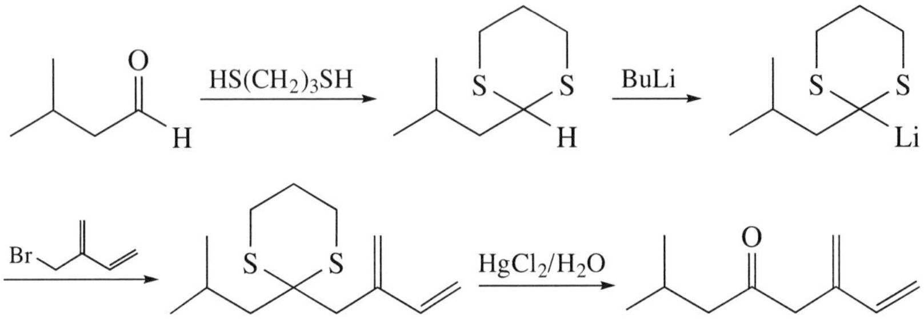

2.33

2.3 More remote C–X disconnections

We can build upon the principles discussed already to devise retrosynthetic analysis for heteroatoms linked in 1,3-fashion. Take a look at compound **2.34**: where might you want to disconnect this molecule?

Your first idea might be to try a C–S disconnection, since disconnecting next to a heteroatom will usually result in good nucleophilic synthons. This would be a logical disconnection as it would lead to 2-bromopropane as the electrophilic reagent and a thiol, **2.35**, as the nucleophilic reagent.

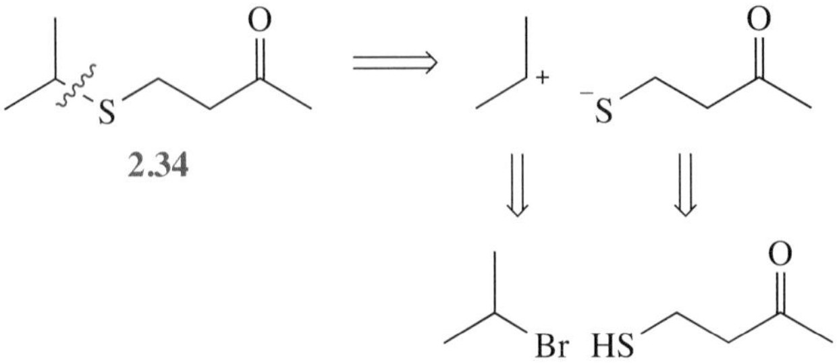

2.34

2.35

■ Find another disconnection for **2.34**. Draw the synthons resulting from this disconnection and then refer to Data Table 9.2 to find the synthetic equivalent for this disconnection.

☐ The alternative disconnection is

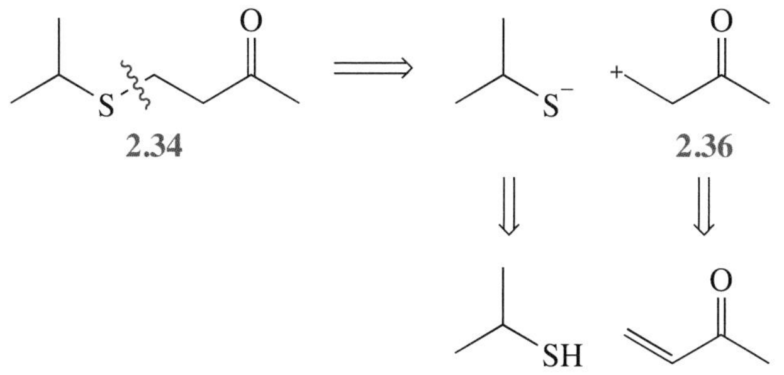

2.34   **2.36**

You should hopefully have found that the synthon **2.36** corresponds to an α,β-unsaturated ketone. This type of synthon is only invoked when the corresponding alkene is conjugated to an electron-withdrawing group. The synthesis reaction is termed a Michael addition, which you will have encountered in Unit 7. This reaction works well with O, N and S nucleophiles, and you will see later that it is also a very powerful reaction when deployed with carbon nucleophiles.

■ Now try to disconnect tertiary amine **2.37** using a synthon that corresponds to an α,β-unsaturated ketone.

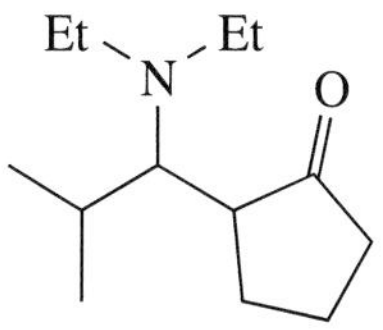

☐ The disconnection is

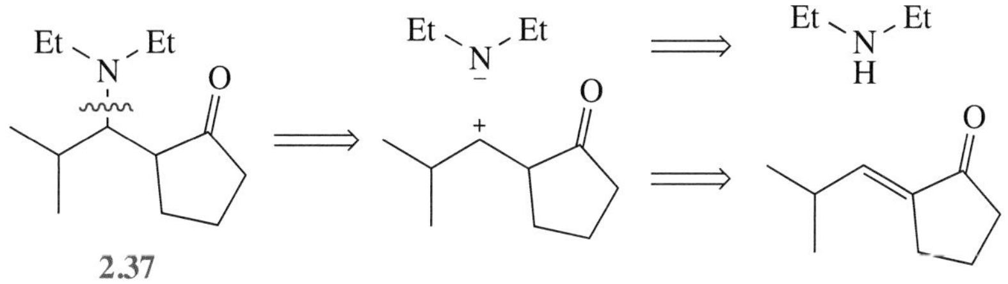

2.37   **2.37**

3 C–C bond disconnections

3.1 Disconnections involving aromatic rings

Having discussed C–X disconnections, which are relatively easy to spot, we are now going to focus on C–C disconnections, which are of course the most important in organic chemistry as they enable us to extend the carbon scaffold of a molecule. One of the easiest structural features to identify, involving C–C bonds is an aromatic ring. The aromatic ring, as mentioned earlier, generally undergoes electrophilic substitution, so the disconnection should have the aromatic component acting as the nucleophile. There are two ways in which the aromatic ring can act as a nucleophile:

i either as the parent, neutral aromatic compound, ArH, which usually necessitates the presence of a Lewis acid catalyst, or

ii as a Grignard, or similar organometallic reagent (ArMgX) which is generated from a haloaromatic compound.

■ First of all let's consider 4-methoxyphenylethanone (**3.1**) which is a component of hawthorn blossom extract. Disconnect this target molecule to suggest suitable reagents.

□ The disconnection is as follows:

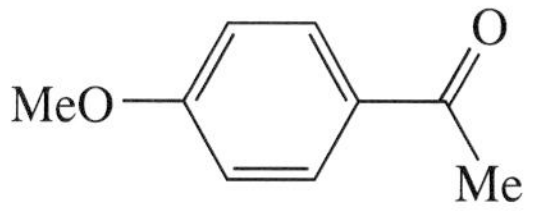

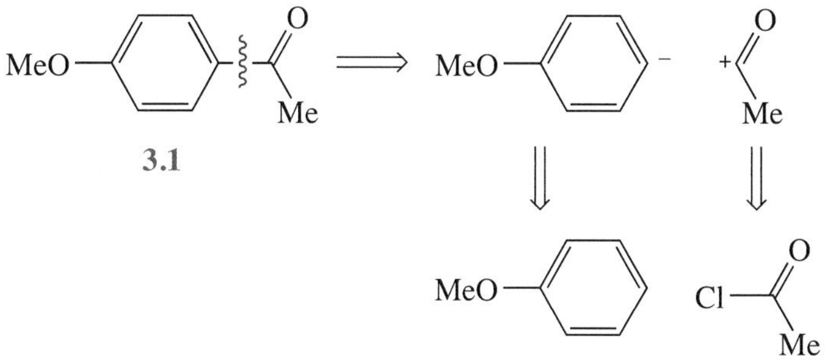

Disconnecting the C–C bond adjacent to the aromatic ring such that the carbon centre in the aromatic ring is the nucleophilic synthon suggests methoxybenzene and ethanoyl chloride as suitable reagents. The synthesis reaction would therefore be a standard Friedel–Craft acylation and would need AlCl$_3$ as a Lewis acid catalyst. One point to note here is that the target molecule has a carbonyl group adjacent to the aromatic ring and the Friedel–Craft acylation is the method of choice for this functionality. You should therefore look out for this structural feature when dealing with simple aromatic compounds. If a carbonyl group is adjacent to the aromatic ring, disconnect between the carbonyl group and the aromatic ring.

How do you think you would go about forming compound **3.2**? This aromatic compound contains no heteroatom functionality, but the basic disconnection principles still hold and should point towards a nucleophilic aromatic ring.

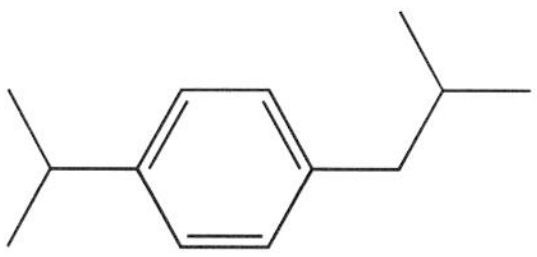

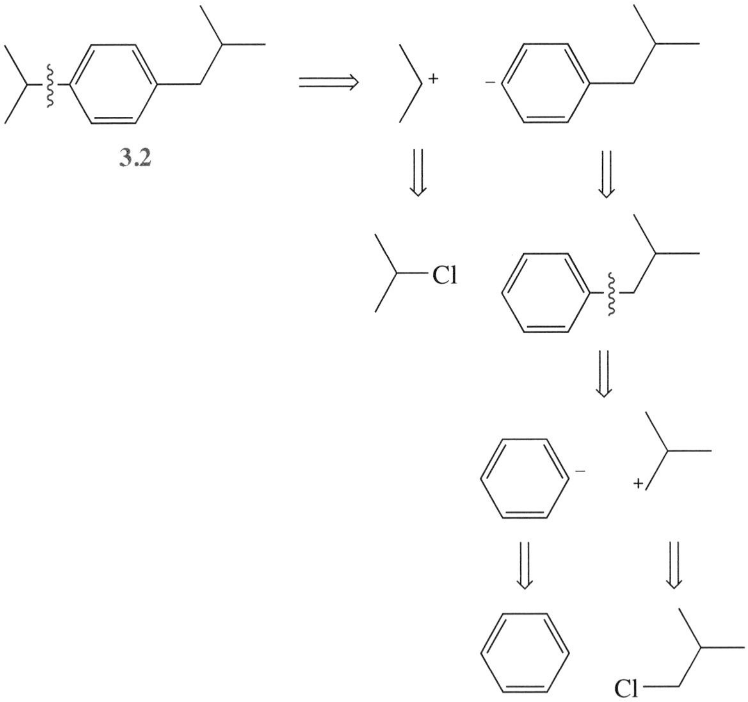

3.2

The first disconnection points towards a Friedel–Craft alkylation, which offers the chemist another way to form carbon–carbon bonds involving an aromatic ring. Another point to note about this disconnection is the regiochemistry of the substitution reaction that has been identified, which would need to occur 1,4- with respect to the substituent already on the ring. This would indeed happen in this case due to the electron-donating effects of the alkyl substituent which is 2,4- directing, with the 4- position being almost exclusively substituted due to the increased steric bulk around position 2. The second disconnection points to another Friedel–Craft alkylation, this time between benzene and 1-chloro-2-methylpropane. This reaction looks fine in principle, but brings to light a problem associated with Friedel–Craft alkylations when they are actually carried out. Under Friedel–Craft's conditions, 1-chloro-2-methylpropane produces a primary carbocation that rearranges to a more stable tertiary carbocation before substitution occurs; thus, the wrong alkyl group would be introduced onto the aromatic ring.

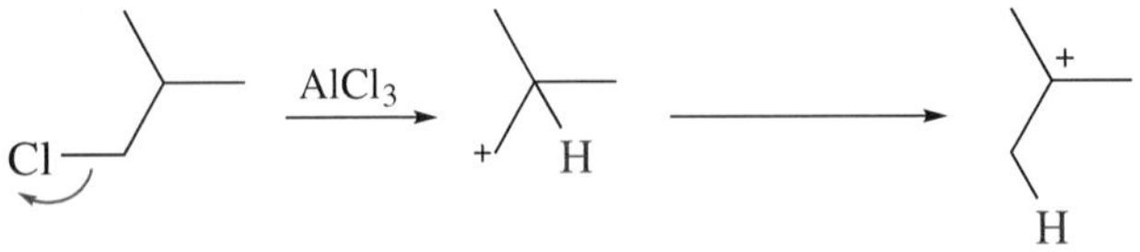

Furthermore, the monoalkylated benzene ring that would be produced is more reactive than benzene itself, so a second alkylation with the same reagent could occur.

These common problems (carbocation rearrangement and ring activation) associated with Friedel–Craft alkylations are not seen with Friedel–Craft acylations – because the acyl cation doesn't rearrange, and the acyl substituted aromatic ring is less reactive than the parent aromatic ring – so this latter reaction is used in preference. The trick, though, is to recognise that the ketone afforded by Friedel–Craft acylation must be converted into the desired alkane.

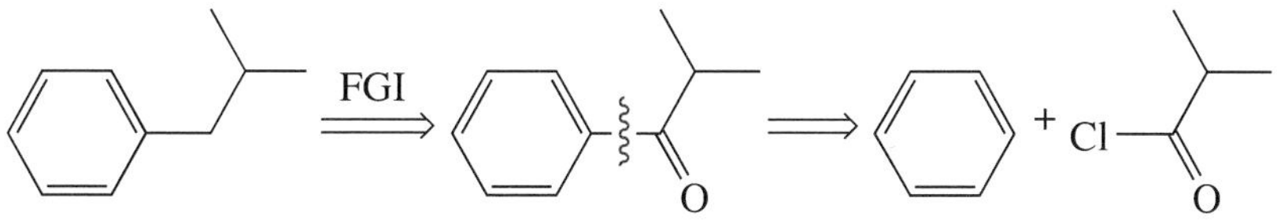

The synthesis, including the reduction step to the required alkane, is shown in Scheme 3.1.

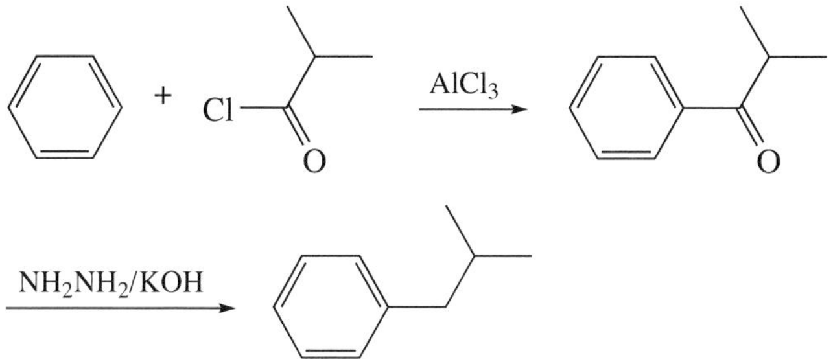

Scheme 3.1

3.2 Alcohols and carbonyl compounds

We start our analysis of other types of C–C bond by considering those which have a functional group attached to one of the carbon atoms. Our major concern here will deal with alcohol- and carbonyl-containing compounds, since these two functional groups can be converted into nearly all other functional groups by appropriate FGIs.

■ Write down the synthons generated by disconnection of one of the C–C bonds to the carbon atom involved in the functional group for both alcohol and carbonyl compounds:

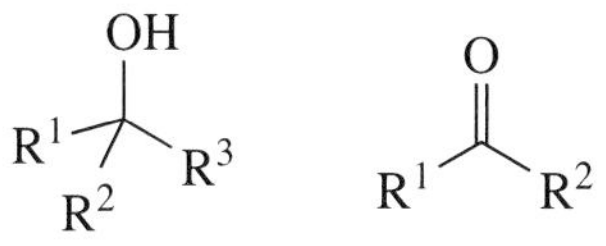

☐ The synthons are:

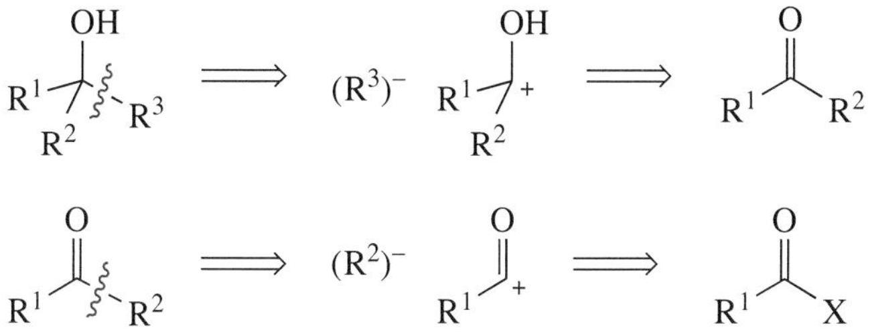

The first disconnection identifies reaction of an aldehyde or ketone with a nucleophilic carbon reagent, of which Grignard reagents RMgX (X = halide)

are the best known example for alkyl nucleophiles. A good example of this reaction is the synthesis of **3.3** which is required for synthesis of a pheromone secreted by the queen honey bee. The compound is easily synthesised in high yields by treating cycloheptanone with MeMgBr.

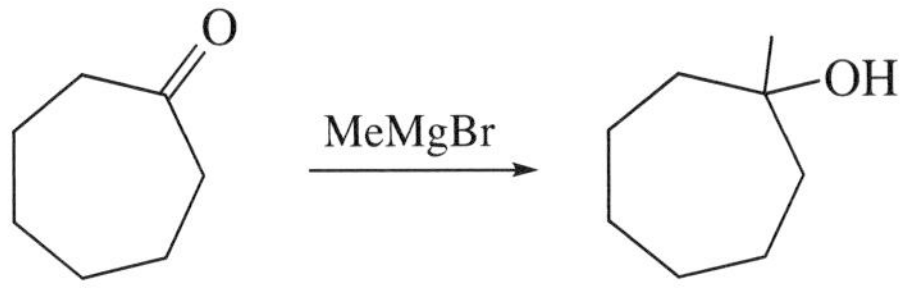

3.3

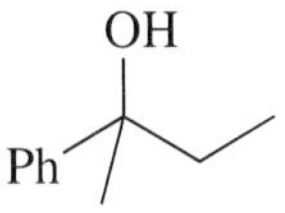

▪ Examine the molecule **3.4** and identify a synthesis starting from benzene alone.

□ One possible disconnection is shown below:

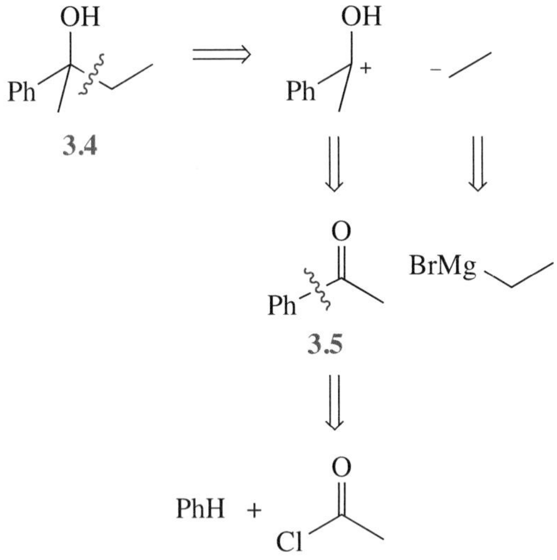

3.4

OH

Ph

3.4

This retrosynthetic analysis takes advantage of a Friedel–Craft acylation. The important marker here was **3.5**, which contains a ketone adjacent to the benzene ring.

Another potential method for preparing **3.4** is to directly use the aromatic compound as the Grignard reagent.

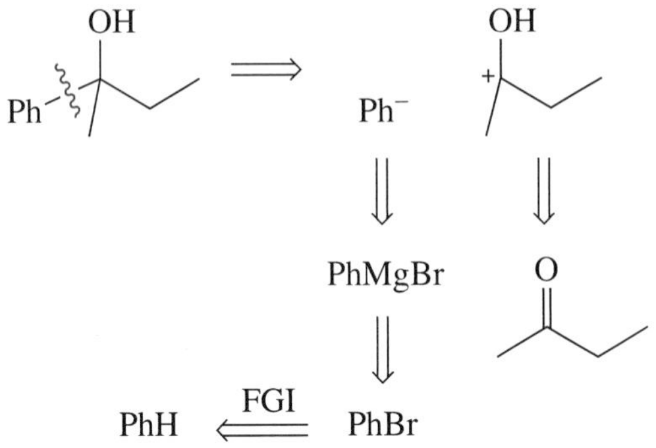

For the synthesis, this would require conversion of benzene into bromobenzene (using Br_2 with $FeBr_3$), which could then be easily transformed to the required Grignard reagent and added to butanone. This offers an alternative pathway for deploying nucleophilic carbon reagents based on benzene that do not require Friedel–Craft chemistry.

The earlier analysis of carbonyl compounds identified reaction of a nucleophilic carbon reagent with a carboxylic acid derivative. In practice, this reaction is a little more complicated, because the final product, rather than being a ketone, is often an alcohol. Why? The reason behind this observation comes from the ketone itself being susceptible to nucleophilic attack. This is summarised for reaction of an ester in Scheme 3.2. In this case, the ketone formed from the first nucleophilic attack is *more* reactive than the starting ester!

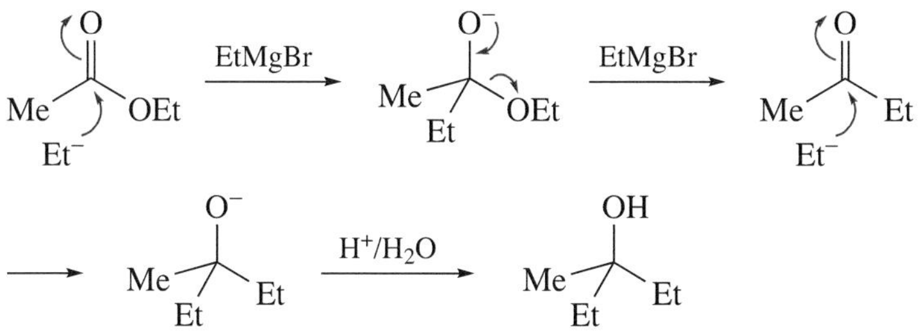

Scheme 3.2

We can use this observation to our advantage if the product is a tertiary alcohol with two identical substituents; this can be synthesised from an ester using two equivalents of the appropriate Grignard reagent. A generic retrosynthetic analysis highlighting this observation is shown in Scheme 3.3. Note how the two disconnections next to the alcohol group lead to a doubly electrophilic synthon.

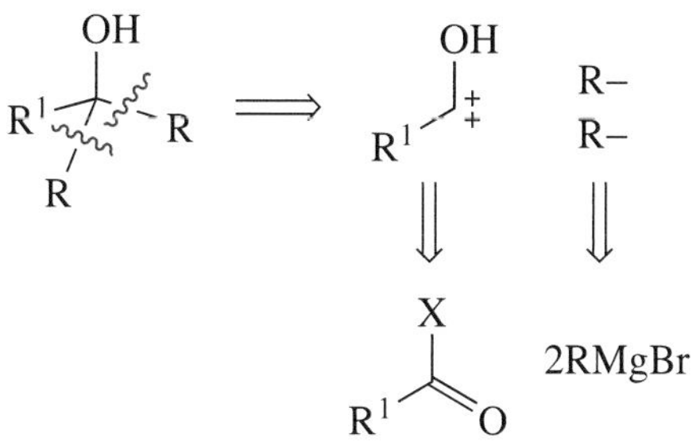

Scheme 3.3

This approach is highlighted well in the synthesis of the tranquiliser phenaglycodol, **3.6**.

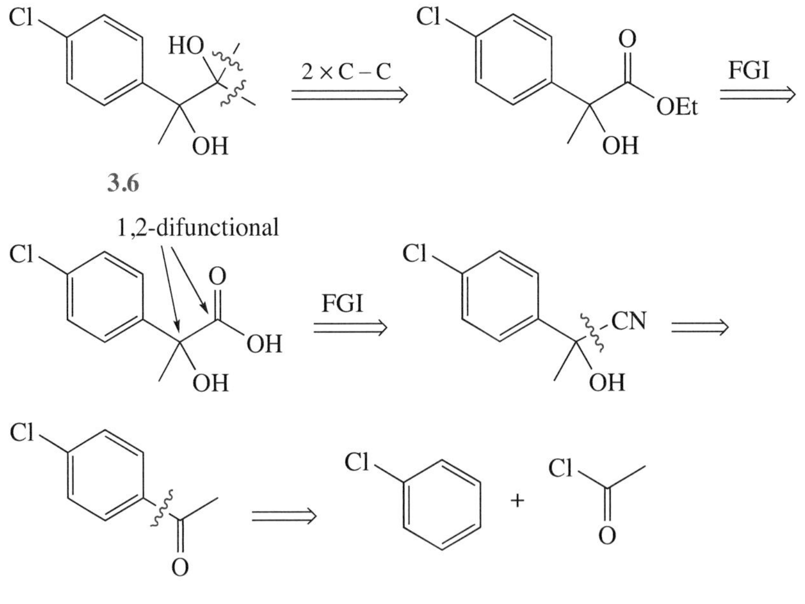

3.6

1,2-difunctional

Phenylglycodol contains a tertiary alcohol substituted with two methyl groups. Its immediate precursor is identified as an ester that could react with excess MeMgBr. The ester itself can be related to the corresponding acid, which turns out to be α- to another alcohol; we identified this functionality earlier (Section 2) as being related to a nitrile through an FGI (hydrolysis). This nitrile in turn comes from the addition of cyanide to a methyl ketone which can be synthesised via a Friedel–Craft acylation. The synthesis is shown in Scheme 3.4.

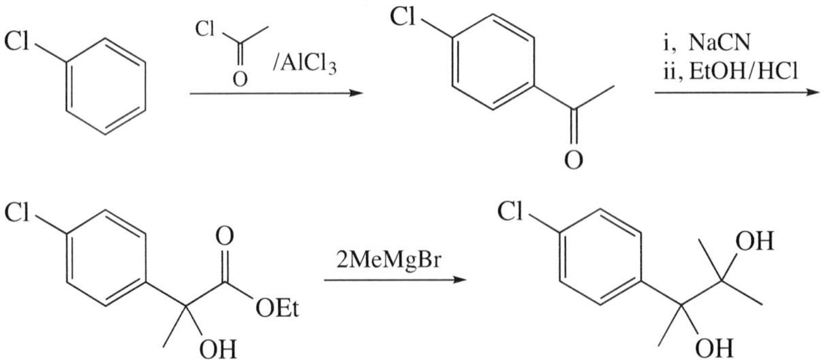

Scheme 3.4

A summary of C–C disconnections that correspond to Grignard reagents is shown in Table 3.1.

Table 3.1 reveals an interesting approach to obtaining ketones through use of Grignard reagents. We have previously seen that Grignard reagents usually add twice to esters, which means that stopping at the ketone stage is very unreliable; the reaction will result in the tertiary alcohol instead. However, access to the ketone can be accomplished if the Grignard reagent is used in conjunction with a nitrile or an aldehyde. With a nitrile, direct reaction affords a ketone (after acidic work-up). With an aldehyde, reaction forms a secondary alcohol, which requires oxidation to the desired ketone.

Table 3.1 C–C disconnections of alcohols and ketones that identify Grignard reagents.

1

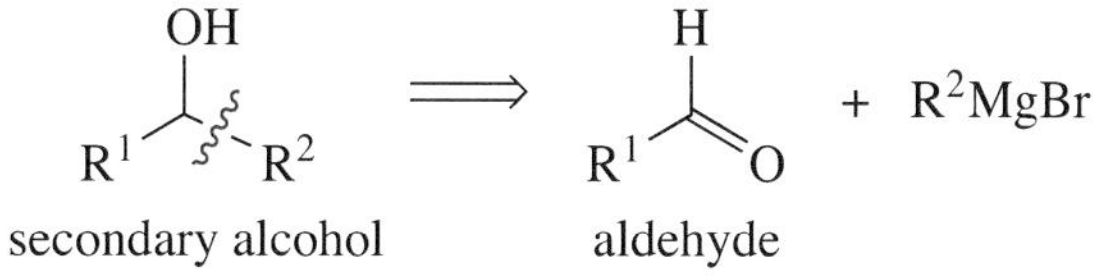

secondary alcohol $\Longrightarrow$ aldehyde $+ R^2MgBr$

2

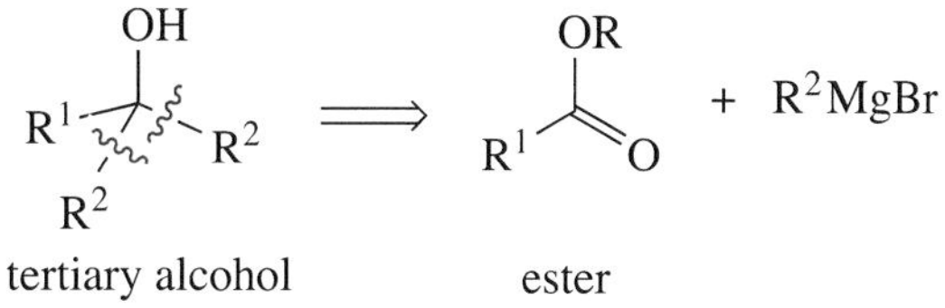

tertiary alcohol $\Longrightarrow$ ester $+ R^2MgBr$

3

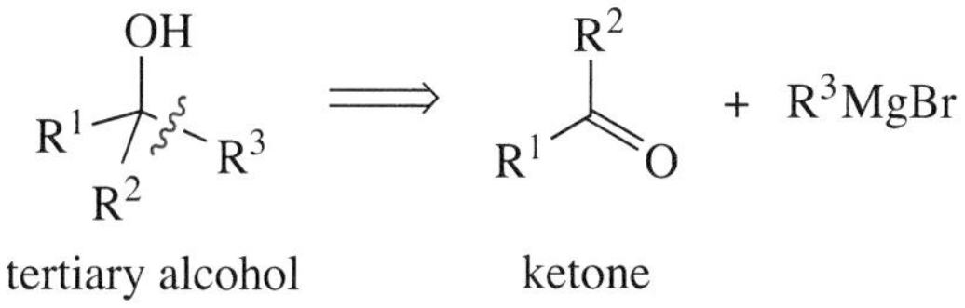

tertiary alcohol $\Longrightarrow$ ketone $+ R^3MgBr$

4

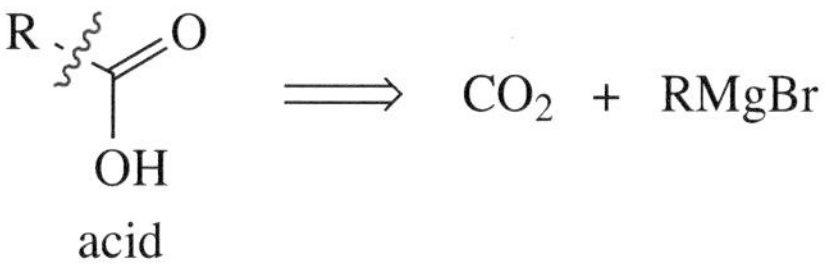

acid $\Longrightarrow$ CO_2 + RMgBr

5

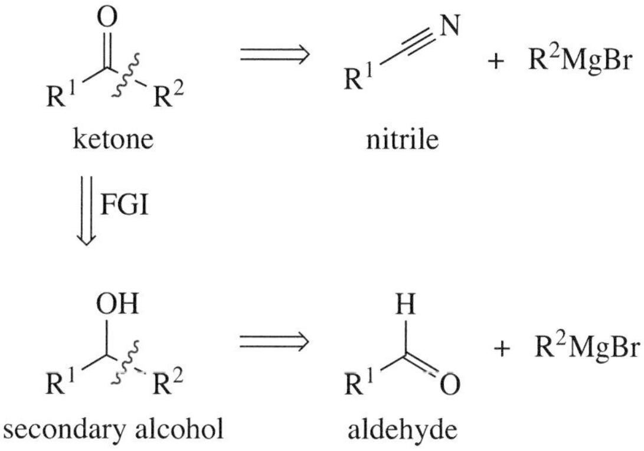

ketone $\Longrightarrow$ nitrile $+ R^2MgBr$

‖ FGI

secondary alcohol $\Longrightarrow$ aldehyde $+ R^2MgBr$

6

ketone $\underset{FGI}{\Longrightarrow}$ secondary alcohol $\Longrightarrow$ aldehyde $+ R^2MgBr$

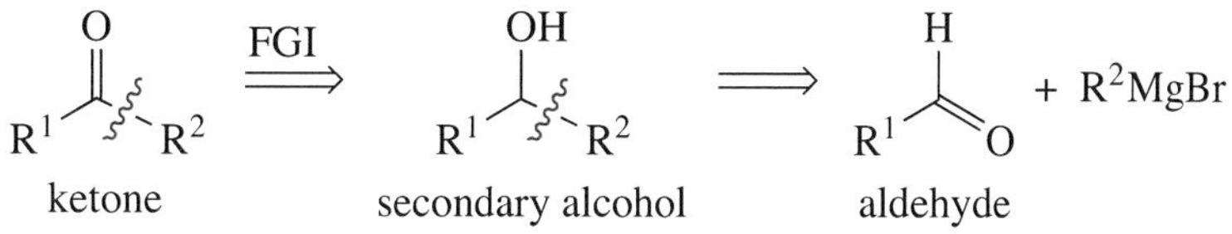

So far, our discussion of C–C disconnections has considered only C–C bonds that are directly linked to functional groups, and these are obvious places to choose to disconnect a molecule into synthons.

However, disconnection of more remote bonds may also be of synthetic utility. If we consider alcohol **3.7**, we can see that it's a tertiary alcohol but all the substituents on the tertiary carbon centre are different; this therefore rules out using the approach of a Grignard reagent with an ester. However, if we undertake a disconnection beta to the alcohol, this identifies a nucleophilic synthon (Ph⁻), for which an organometallic reagent (Data Table 9.2) can be used, and an electrophilic synthon **3.8**, which, by referring to the Data Table, you should hopefully see corresponds to the epoxide, **3.9**.

3.7 **3.8** Ph⁻ ⟹ PhMgBr

3.9

You should be aware that the epoxide can be attacked at either carbon, but as this reaction is under nucleophilic control it will almost certainly open at the least hindered position to give the desired product (Unit 6).

■ Use retrosynthetic analysis to plan a synthesis of **3.10**.

☐ Normal C–X disconnection of the amide bond identifies the amine reagent piperidine and a carboxylic acid. A C–C disconnection next to the carboxylic acid group then identifies the Grignard reagent **3.11** and CO_2 as the reagents for the forward reaction.

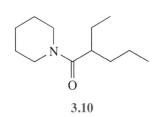

3.10

3.10 ⟹ piperdine + HO

FGI

Br ⟸ BrMg

3.11

+ CO_2

The forward reaction, starting from 3-bromohexane is shown in Scheme 3.5.

Br i, Mg / ii, CO_2 HO NH / DCC **3.10**

Scheme 3.5

At this stage it is also worth mentioning the regioselectivity associated with Grignard reagents when they are reacted with α,β-unsaturated carbonyl compounds. Grignard reagents and organocuprates have different regioselectivities; Grignard reagents prefer 1,2-addition while the organocuprates show exclusive 1,4-addition (as shown in the right-hand part of Scheme 3.6). Examination of Scheme 3.6 shows that both molecules **3.12** and **3.13** can be disconnected to reveal the same precursor, **3.14**. So it is crucial that the appropriate organometallic reagent is chosen for the CH_3^- synthon in order that the desired product is achieved.

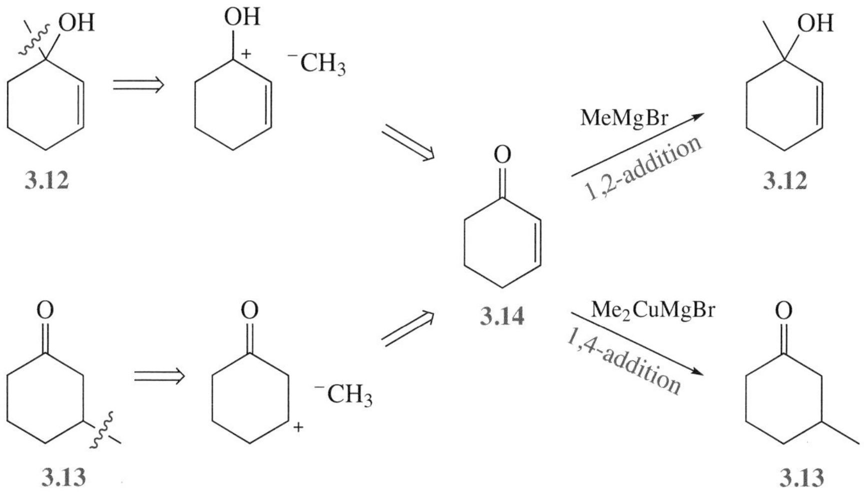

Scheme 3.6

3.3   C–C bond disconnections using non-Grignard reagents

Acetylide anions are good carbon-centred nucleophiles capable of opening epoxide groups. In addition to epoxide ring opening, they will also undergo additional reactions with carbonyls, and they will displace halides via standard S_N2 type reactions. They therefore offer the chemist a method of introducing triple bonds, as well as double bonds (via an FGI), into the molecular structure. Let's take a look at molecule **3.15**. We can envisage disconnecting one side of the triple bond to yield synthons **3.16** and **3.17,** which have acetylene and 1-bromopropane as their synthetic equivalents.

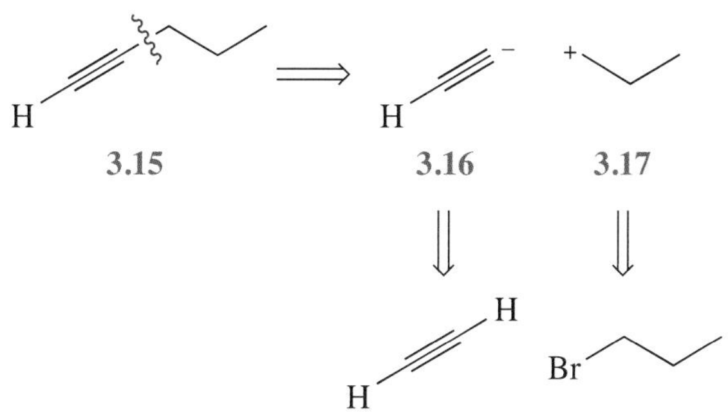

The synthesis is shown in Scheme 3.7. This reaction is only possible due to the acidic nature of the terminal C–H bond, which allows the use of $NaNH_2$ to remove the proton to form the acetylide anion.

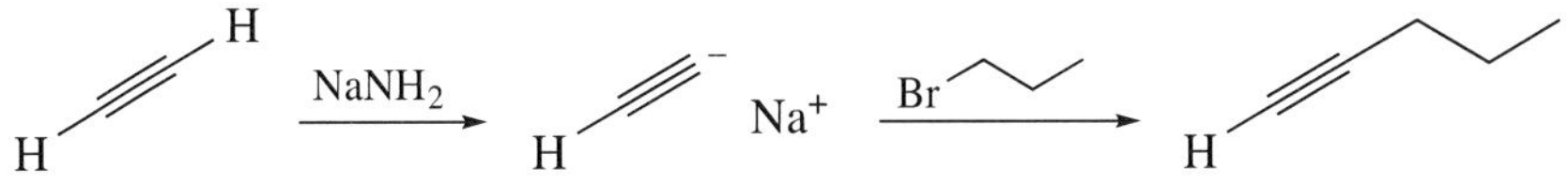

3.15

Scheme 3.7

Scheme 3.8 summarises the disconnections that highlight the key uses of acetylene as a reagent. Whether it is participating in a 1,2-addition reaction, the opening of an epoxide or an S_N2 reaction, it is always used as a nucleophilic reagent. Consequently, such a fragment within a molecule is always disconnected to afford a nucleophilic synthon.

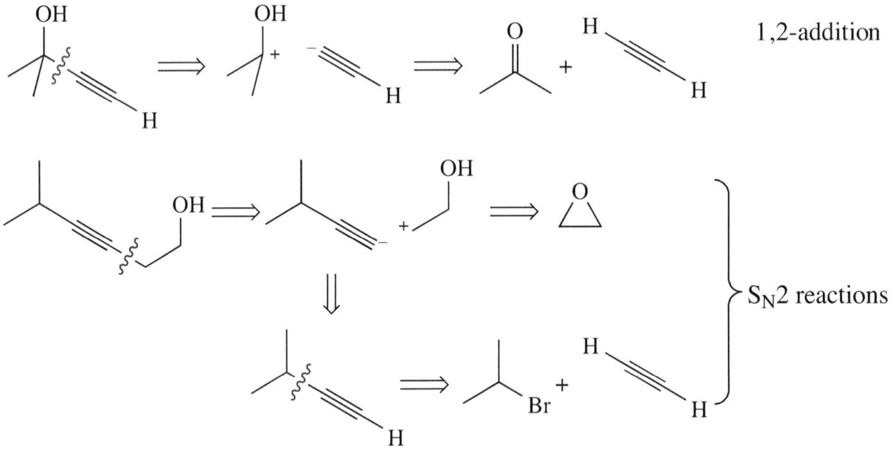

Scheme 3.8

Alkynes have another major use as synthetic intermediates as they are easily transformed into E or Z double bonds through reduction (Unit 6). This offers us a convenient FGI to consider when dealing with isolated carbon–carbon double bonds; these E and Z double bonds can be considered as being derived from alkynes.

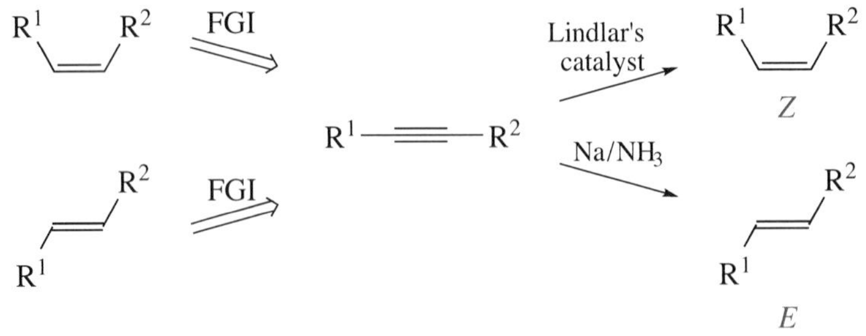

A good example of this is shown in the retrosynthetic analysis of leaf alcohol (**3.18**), a component found in violet oil that has the characteristic smell of green leaves and grass (Scheme 3.9). In the analysis, an FGI relates the Z-double bond to an alkyne that facilitates a C–C disconnection next to the alkyne functional group.

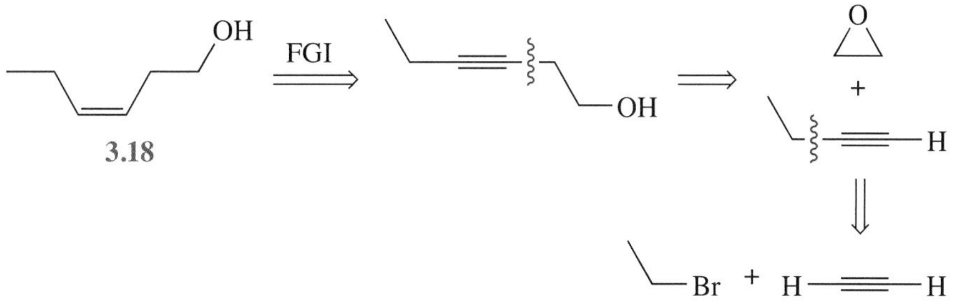

Scheme 3.9

- Using the principles based on disconnecting an alkyne, construct a synthetic route for compound **3.19**. You might find it useful to disconnect one of the C–O bonds first.

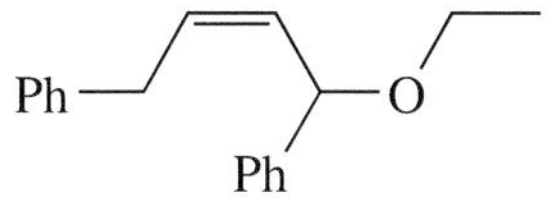

3.19

- The synthetic route is:

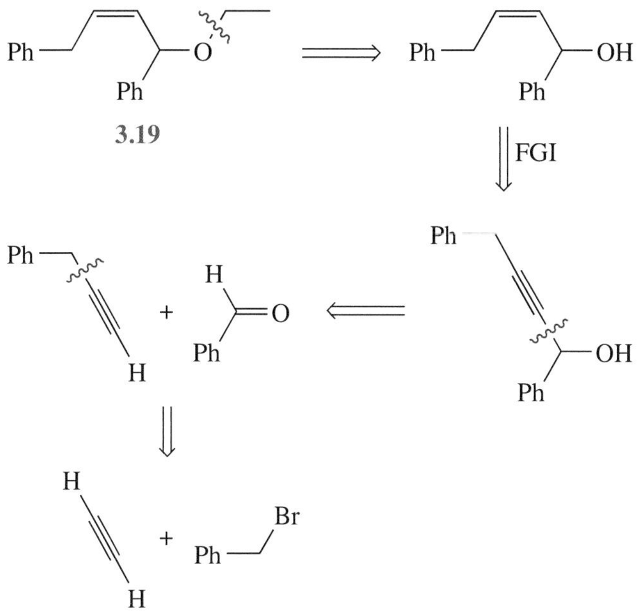

The synthesis (Scheme 3.10) starts with acetylene. The FGI identified in the retrosynthetic analyses is accomplished in the third step of the synthesis.

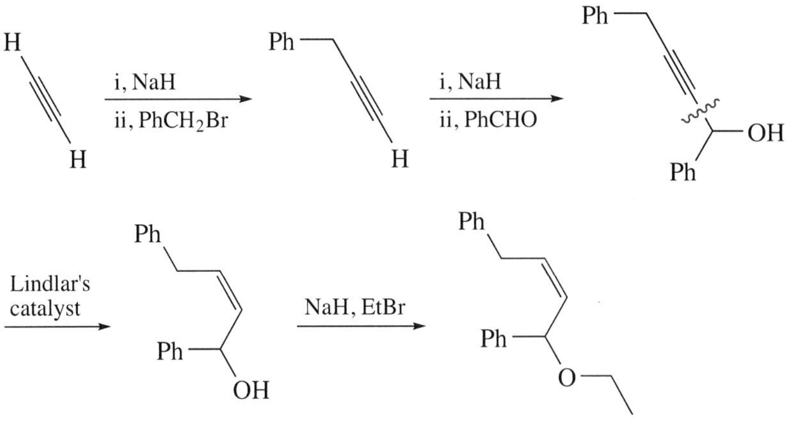

Scheme 3.10

3.3.1 Other methods for alkene formation: Wittig reactions

Alongside the use of alkynes as masked *E* and *Z* alkenes, it is worth noting the use of stabilised and unstabilised phosphorous ylides, which are, respectively, capable of creating *E* and *Z* alkenes through reaction with aldehydes and ketones (Unit 7). You may remember that *Z* alkenes can be derived from **unstabilised** phosphorous ylides (via the Wittig reaction); the disconnection of a generic *Z* alkene is shown in Scheme 3.11. This disconnection also shows the ylide to be derived from an alkyl halide; the Wittig reaction thus offers the chemist a way of connecting together two carbon fragments, via an aldehyde and an alkyl bromide.

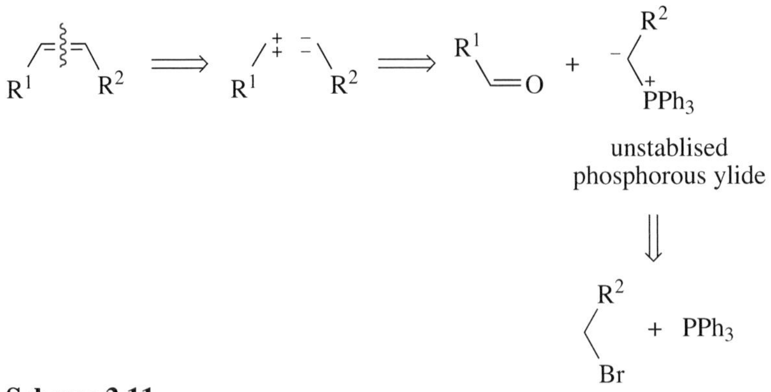

unstablised
phosphorous ylide

Scheme 3.11

This type of disconnection is exemplified within the synthesis of an insect attractant (**3.20**) from the female sugar beet moth. The reaction offers an alternative to the use of alkynes for the synthesis of isolated double bonds; however, it is limited to isolated double bonds with *Z* stereochemistry only.

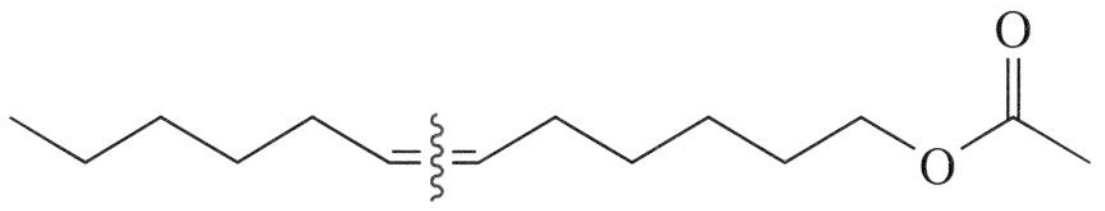

3.20 *Z*-alkene

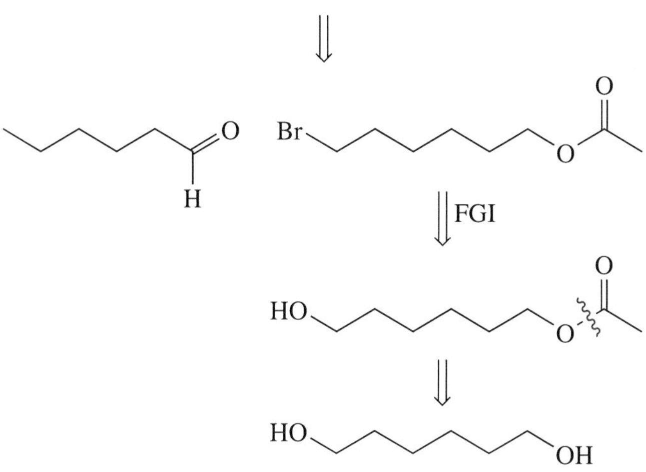

FGI

What about *E* double bonds? From Unit 7 you may have noticed that *E* double bonds are made via **stabilised** phosphorous ylides and these result in **conjugated** alkenes. The standard disconnection corresponds to the Horner–Wadsworth–Emmons (HWE) reaction, and is shown in Scheme 3.12.

The Horner–Wadsworth–Emmons reaction is sometimes known simply as the Wadsworth–Emmons reaction.

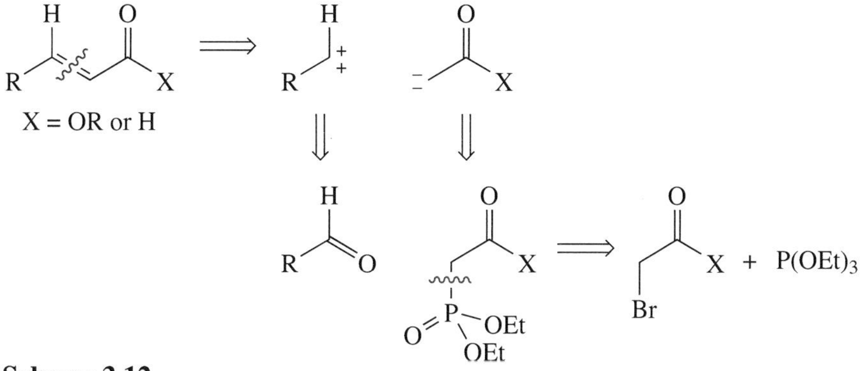

Scheme 3.12

The C–C disconnection shows the electrophilic synthon to correspond, once again, to an aldehyde. However, the nucleophilic synthon is derived from a phosphonate which itself is ultimately derived from an α-halo ester or α-halo carbonyl compound. This means we are able to form an *E* alkene between an aldehyde and α-halo carbonyl derivative by first converting the latter into the corresponding phosphorane. An example of this is shown in the retrosynthetic analysis of *E*-9-oxodec-2-enoic acid, **3.21**, a pheromone of the queen honey bee. Here, the phosphorane is derived from ethyl bromoacetate.

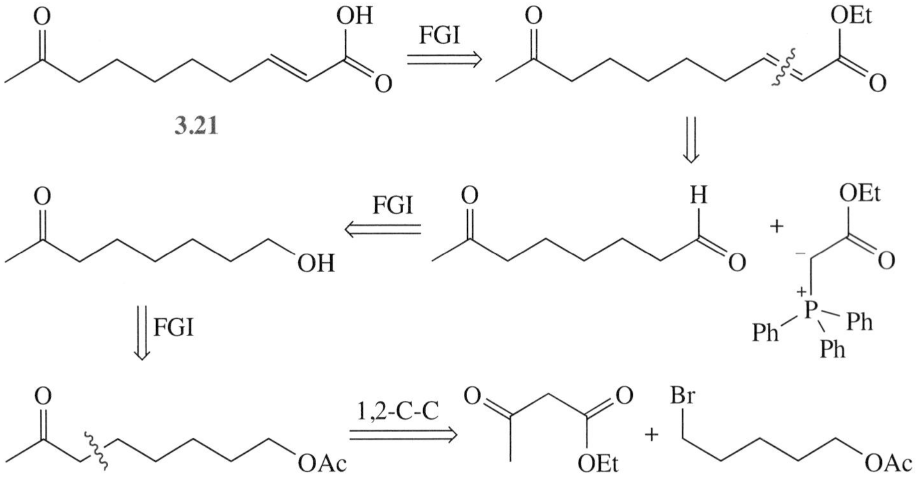

3.21

The synthesis is shown in Scheme 3.13. The key observations here are the chemoselectivity and stereoselectivity of the stabilised phosphorane procedure. The reaction is chemoselective and occurs only with the aldehyde, not the ketone; this would be expected, due to the increased reactivity of an aldehyde over a ketone (Unit 7). The reaction is stereoselective in that stabilised phosphoranes preferentially give rise to E alkenes.

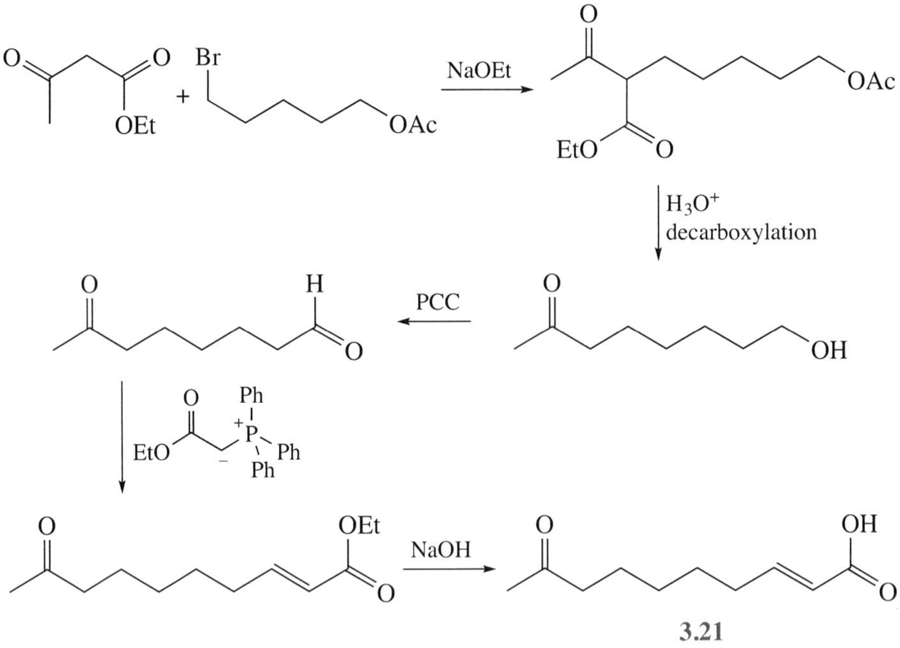

Scheme 3.13

The use of both stabilised and unstabilised phosphorous ylides, and their resulting alkene stereochemistry, has been used in the synthesis of bombykol, **3.22**, the sex attractant pheromone of the female silk moth, *Bombyx mori*.

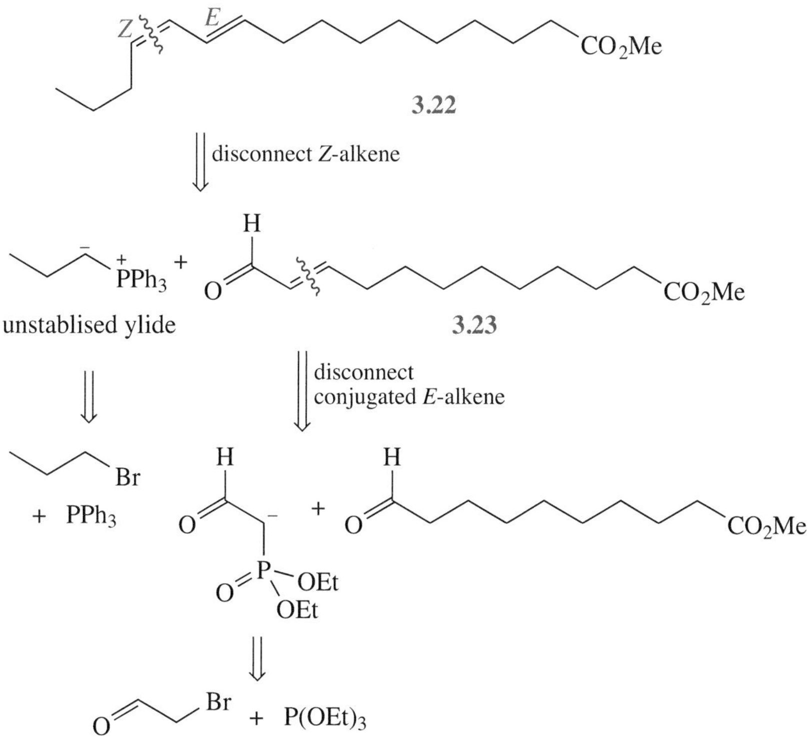

3.22

disconnect *Z*-alkene

unstablised ylide   **3.23**

disconnect
conjugated *E*-alkene

+ PPh₃

+ P(OEt)₃

The key point in this retrosynthetic analysis is the disconnection order. By disconnecting the *Z* alkene first we can identify conjugated aldehyde, **3.23**, which contains an *E* double bond. Disconnection of this *E* alkene identifies the use of a HWE reaction which, by incorporating an aldehyde functionality into the reagent, introduces the necessary second aldehyde functionality required in intermediate **3.23**. This group is subsequently coupled with an unstabilised ylide to afford the *Z* alkene in the target bombykol.

■   Propose a retrosynthetic analysis molecule **3.24** that uses a phosphorous ylide as a key step within the synthesis. Start by assessing the alkene bond stereochemistry.

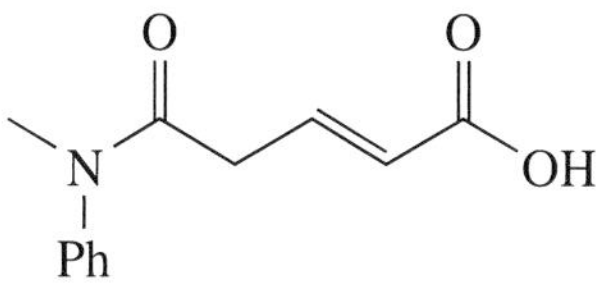

3.24

☐   The retrosynthetic analysis is:

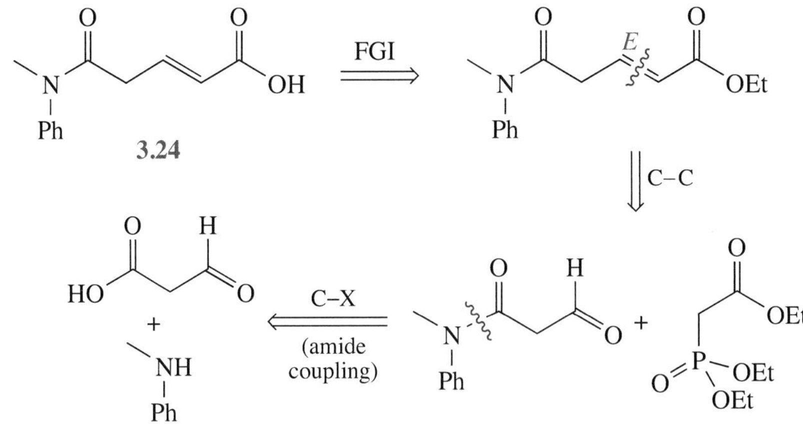

3.24

3.4   1,2 C–C disconnections adjacent to carbonyl groups

Disconnection of the 1,2-bond next to a carbonyl can yield two pairs of synthons (Scheme 3.14). You may be able to spot potential problems thrown up by disconnection A. First, the nucleophilic synthon has a Grignard reagent as its synthetic equivalent, and any synthesis would require this to react with an α-halocarbonyl as the electrophilic counterpart. However, the carbonyl of the α-halocarbonyl is also electrophilic and will compete for the nucleophile. Second, Grignard reagents do not couple with C–X (C–Br) bonds in this way.

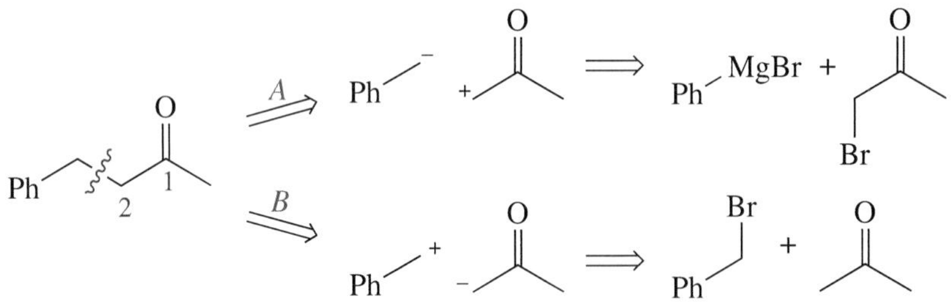

3.25

Scheme 3.14

The pair of synthons highlighted by disconnection B relate to standard synthetic equivalents: a benzyl halide and a nucleophilic enolic carbon alpha to the carbonyl group, which we know from Unit 6 is particularly easy to generate. However, you should be aware from the discussion of the aldol reaction in Unit 7 that acetone itself would not be a good choice as the reagent, as it would self-condense. To overcome this problem we need to use alternative synthetic equivalents for the nucleophilic synthon **3.25**, two of which are shown in Scheme 3.15.

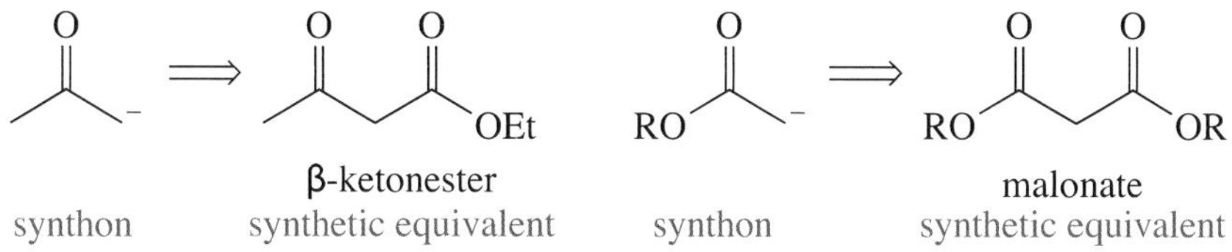

β-ketonester
synthon   synthetic equivalent   synthon   synthetic equivalent

malonate

Scheme 3.15

β-ketocarbonyl derivatives (**3.26**) are particularly useful reagents, as we have seen in Unit 7 where we discussed the reactions of malonate esters ($R^1 = R^2 = $ O-alkyl) and ethyl acetoacetate ($R^1 = CH_3$, $R^2 = $ O-alkyl).

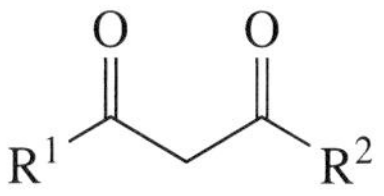

3.26

The first point to appreciate about β-keto derivatives is that there is an acidic central proton that is easily removed by a weak base to produce a potent nucleophile, as illustrated by the β-keto ester ethyl acetoacetate **3.27** in Scheme 3.16.

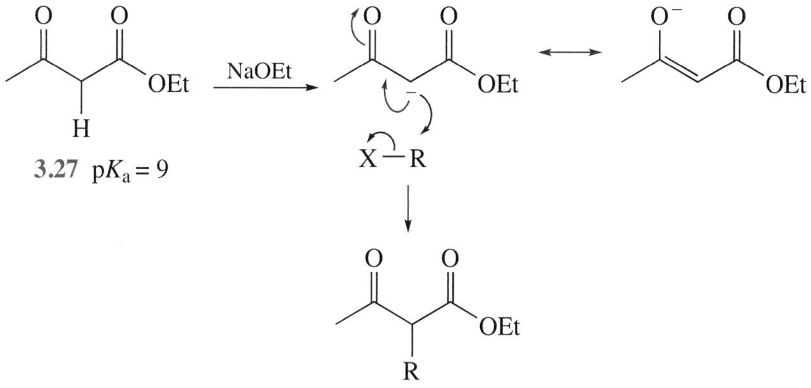

3.27 $pK_a = 9$

3.28

Scheme 3.16

The second noteworthy point is a practical one: the base used should match the alkoxy part of the ester (here EtO⁻). The third point to appreciate about this enolate equivalent is how it is related to the synthon **3.25**. Hydrolysis of the ester is **3.28** and will lead to a carboxylic acid, which, upon heating, decarboxylates to afford the ketone (Scheme 3.17). This strategy therefore allows you to remove any carboxylic acid derivative positioned beta to any carbonyl group, leaving just the carbonyl group in the molecule.

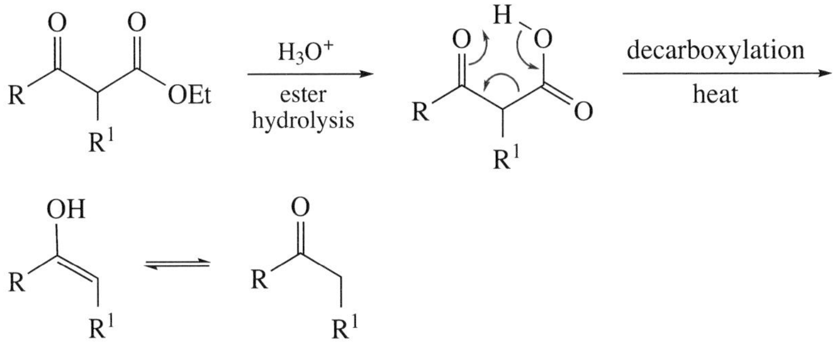

Scheme 3.17

A good example of this strategy is shown in the retrosynthetic analysis of farnesol (**3.29**) which identifies a synthesis starting from geraniol, **3.30** (Scheme 3.18). You might recognise the HWE with the stabilised phosphorous ylide (Unit 7) to yield the *E*-double bond.

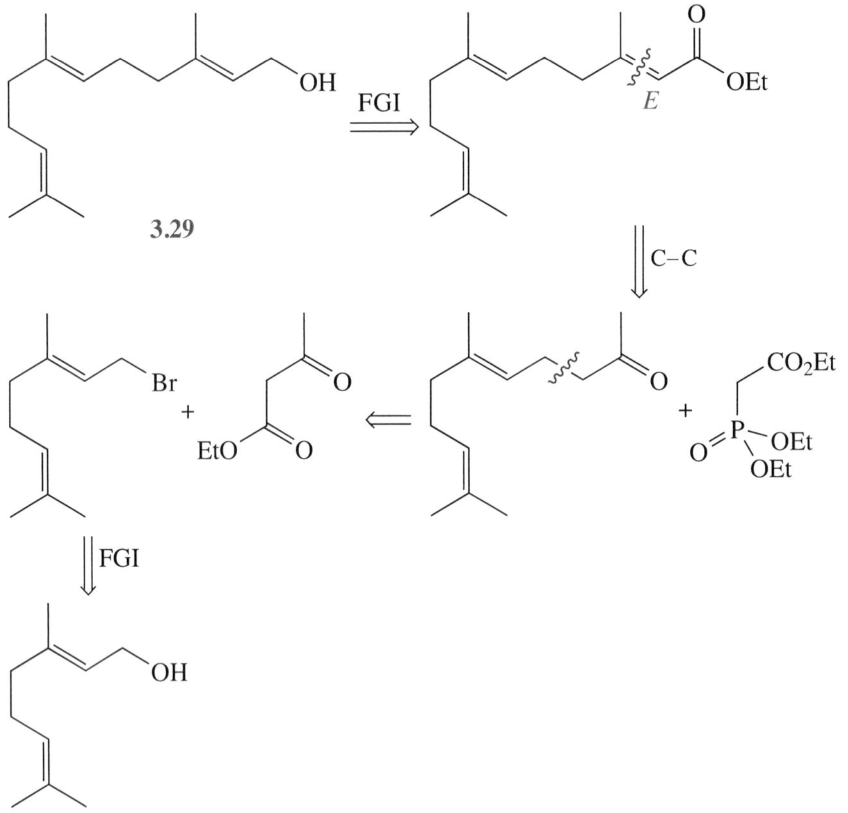

Scheme 3.18

The synthesis can be accomplished as follows:

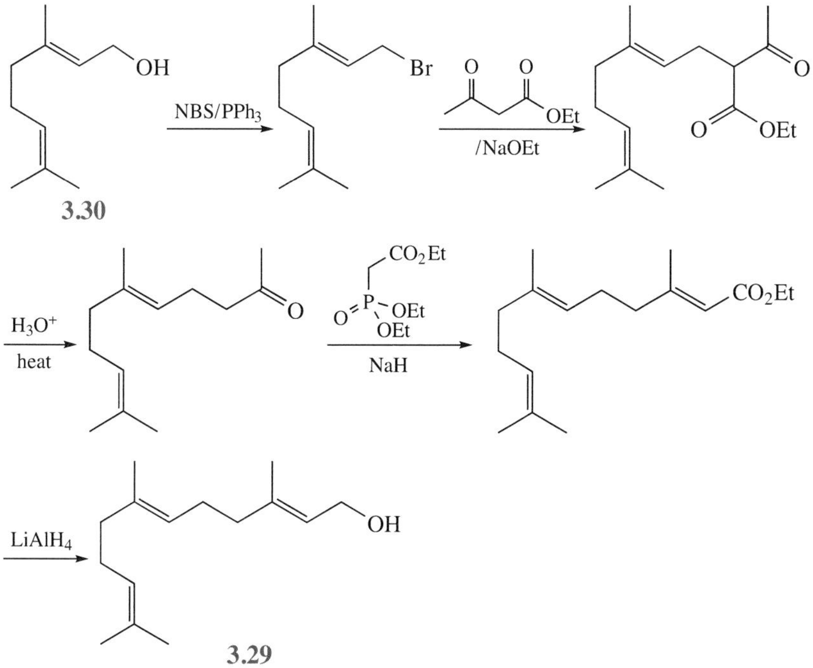

3.30

3.29

■ Devise a retrosynthetic analysis for molecule **3.31**, using enolate chemistry similar to that employed in the farnesol synthesis.

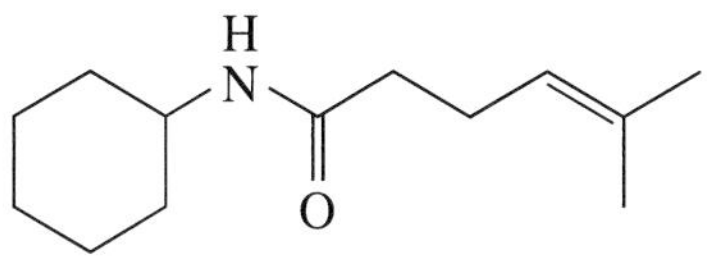

3.31

□ The retrosynthetic analysis is:

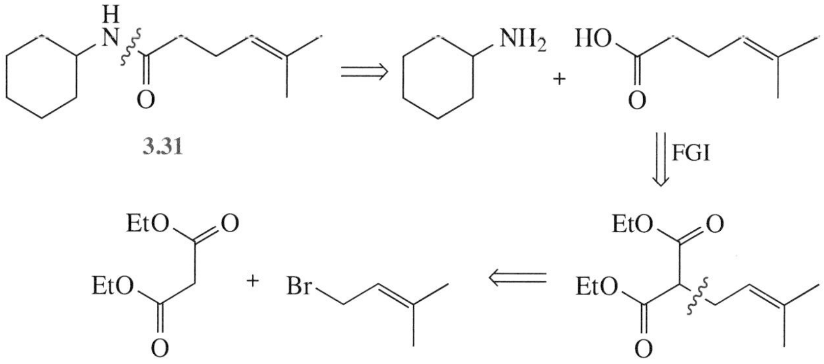

3.31

■ Propose a synthesis of **3.31**, identifying the required reagents:

□ The proposed synthesis is

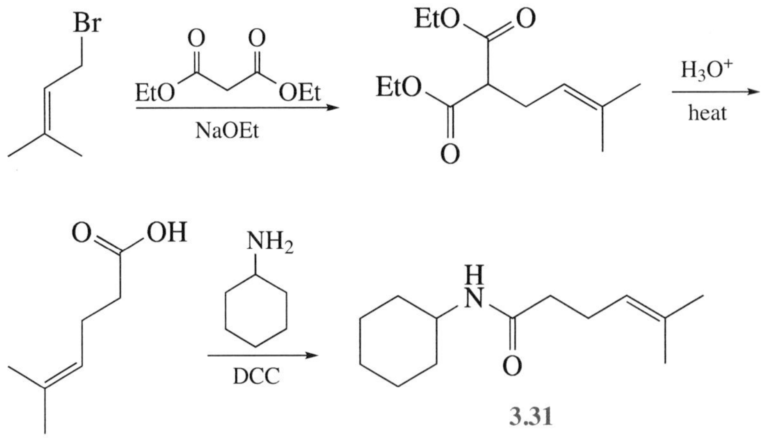

3.31

3.5   Compounds containing inter-related functional groups

In Unit 7 you were introduced to several key reactions of the carbonyl group, namely the aldol condensation, the Claisen condensation and the Michael addition. These three reactions are incredibly useful at building the carbon skeleton within a molecular structure. This next section deals with both the aldol and Claisen condensation by looking for the types of scaffold they produce. The **aldol** reaction produces **α,β-unsaturated carbonyls** or **α-hydroxy carbonyls** with the functional groups in a **1,3- relationship**, while the **Claisen** produces **1,3-dicarbonyls**. It is also useful to add to these **1,5-dicarbonyls** which are a result of **Michael additions** involving activated enolates (we have already seen this type of chemistry with 1,3-C–X disconnections). The key points of these strategies are summarised in Scheme 3.19.

The following examples highlight key points in Scheme 3.19.

The first, shown in Scheme 3.20, involves a cyclic α,β-unsaturated ketone – so we would think 'aldol' and disconnect the C=C bond to reveal **3.32**. This latter compound is another dicarbonyl compound, one with a 1,5- relationship between the functional groups, so we would think 'Michael' and disconnect to ethyl acetoacetate and methyl vinyl ketone.

Aldol reaction

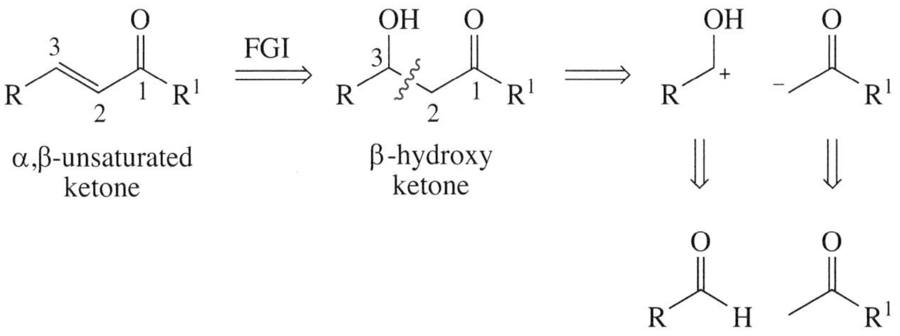
FGI
α,β-unsaturated ketone
β-hydroxy ketone

Claisen reaction

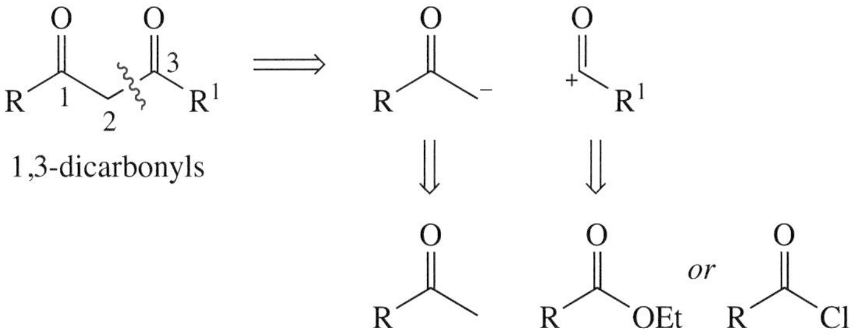
1,3-dicarbonyls
or

Michael addition

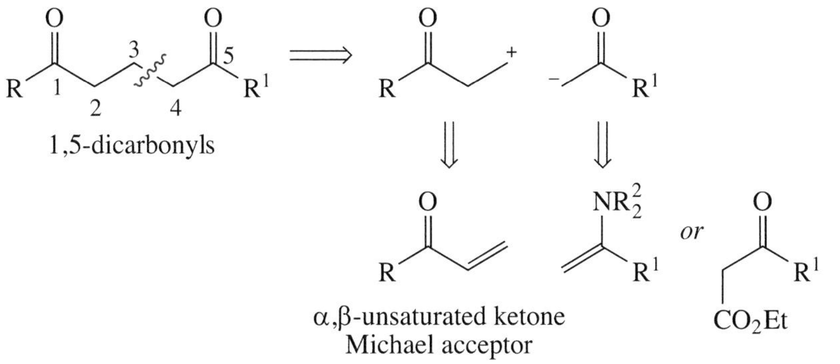
1,5-dicarbonyls
or
α,β-unsaturated ketone
Michael acceptor

Scheme 3.19

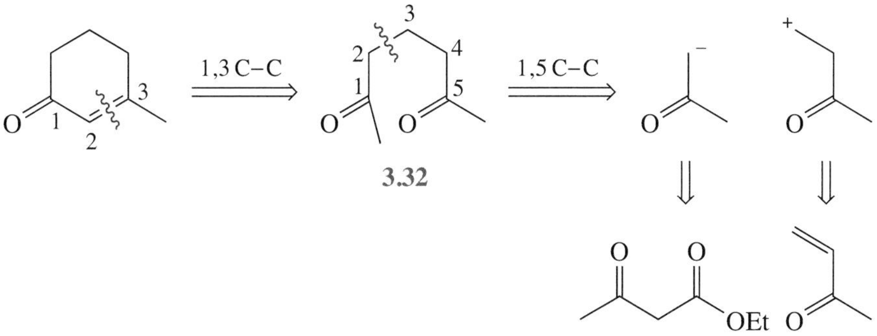
1,3 C–C
1,5 C–C
3.32

Scheme 3.20

The synthesis is shown in Scheme 3.21. Note that molecule **3.32** is symmetrical, so there is no special requirement to control which ketone methyl group enolises (for example, by adding an activating group such as an ester) to react with the other carbonyl for the final aldol step (Unit 7).

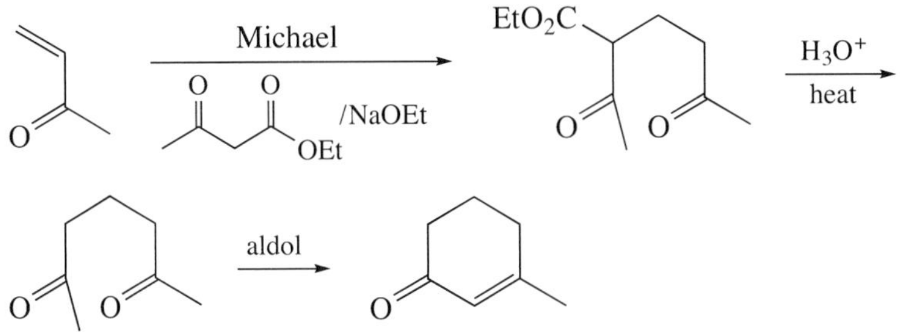

3.32

Scheme 3.21

Scheme 3.22 shows a molecule that has a 1,5- relationship of two carbonyl groups suggesting a disconnection corresponding to a Michael addition reaction. A standard 1,5- C–C disconnection reveals the Michael acceptor **3.33** and ethyl acetoacetate. Subsequent analysis of **3.33**, using a 1,3- disconnection related to aldol chemistry, reveals 4-chlorobenzaldehyde and again ethyl acetoacetate as the starting materials.

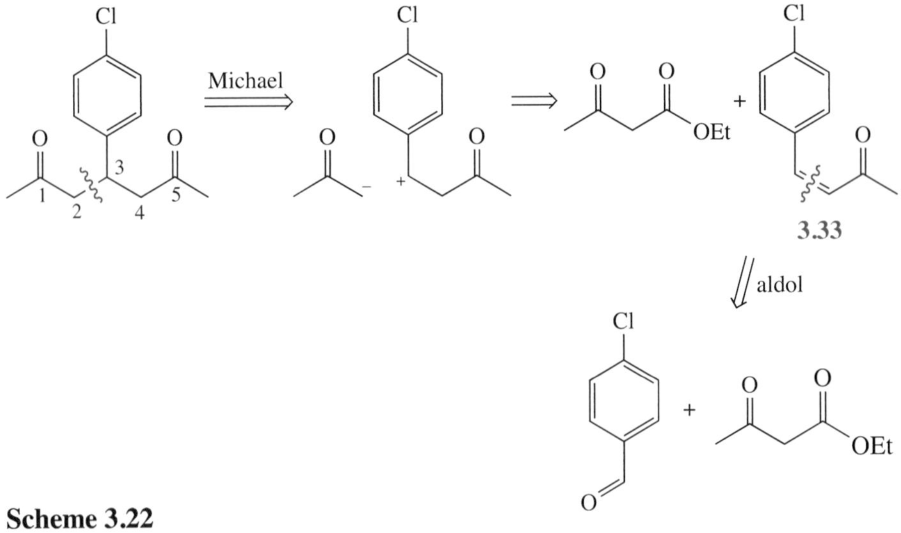

3.33

Scheme 3.22

The synthesis is shown in Scheme 3.23.

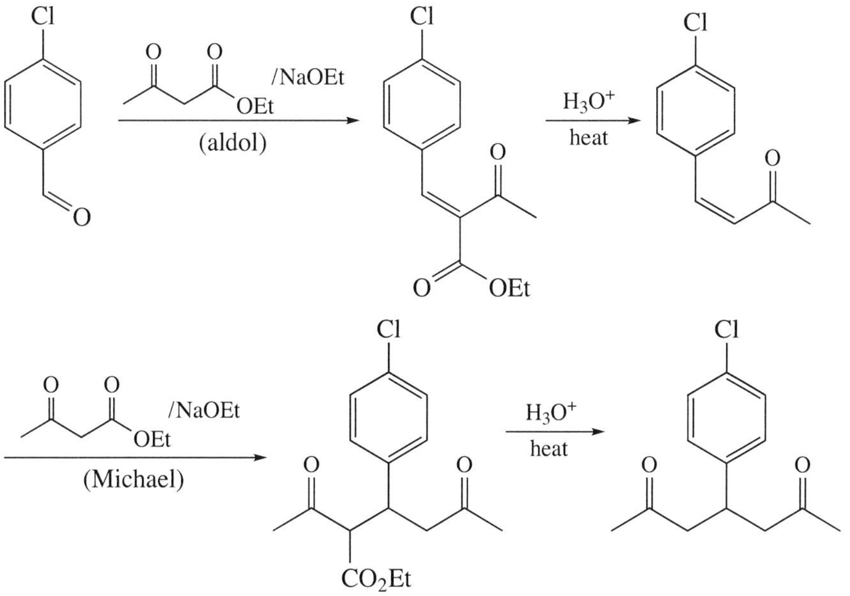

Scheme 3.23

The next restrosynthetic analysis invokes the use of an aldol reaction, and involves the use of diethyl malonate (**3.34**) as a synthetic equivalent.

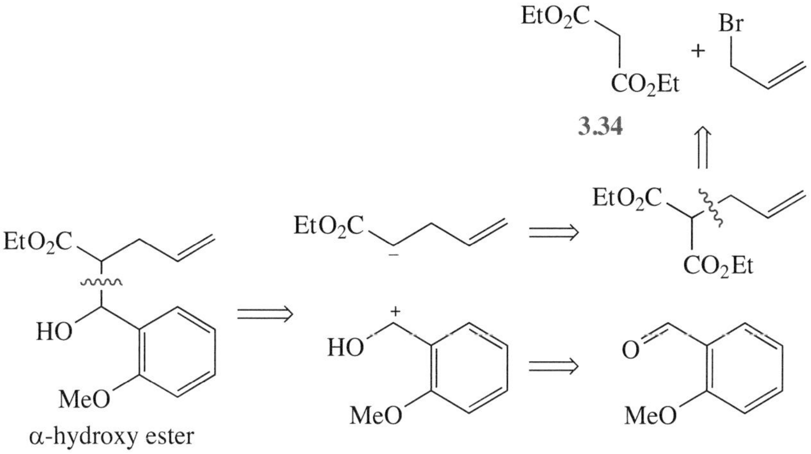

The additional activation is required as enolates of esters are difficult to form and unwanted side reactions can occur. However, use of malonate as a synthetic equivalent allows the corresponding aldol reaction to occur much more readily. The two ester groups are in a beta relationship to each other, which means decarboxylation is possible using heat, as identified in the synthesis in Scheme 3.24.

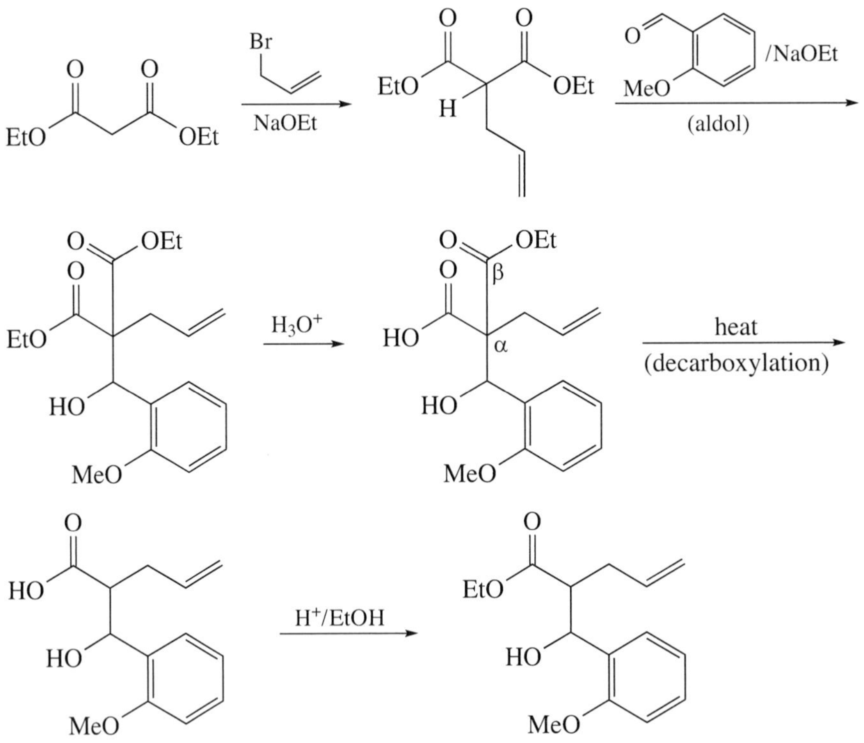

Scheme 3.24

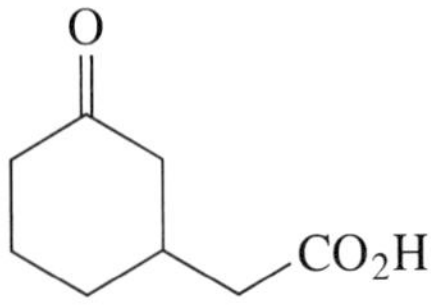

■ Propose a retrosynthetic analysis and corresponding synthesis for molecule **3.35**.

□ The retrosynthetic analysis is:

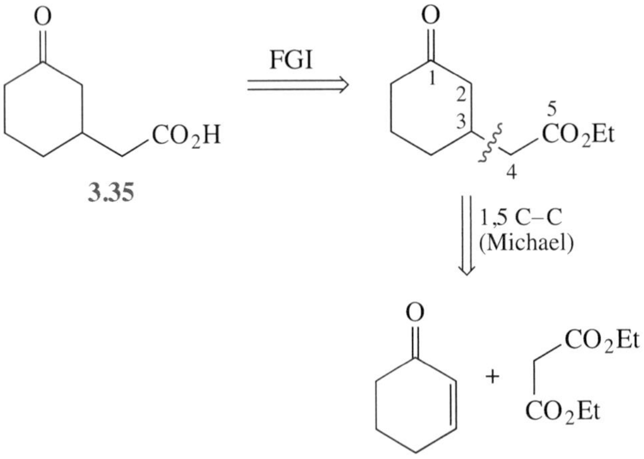

The corresponding forward reaction is

3.35

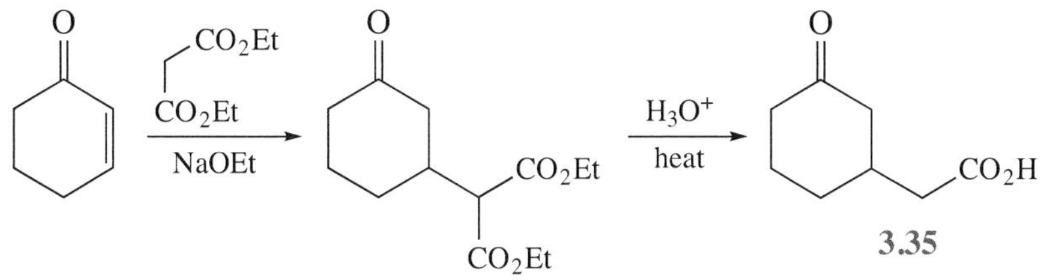

■ Propose a retrosynthetic analysis and corresponding synthesis for molecule **3.36**.

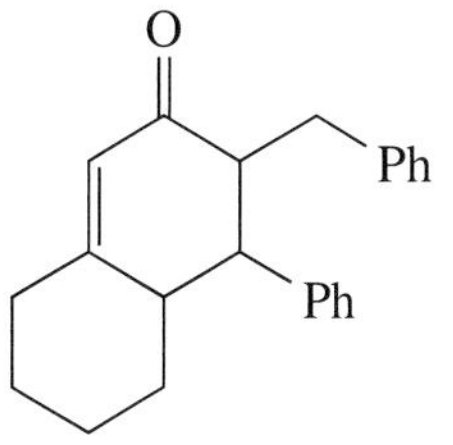

3.36

□ The retrosynthetic analysis is:

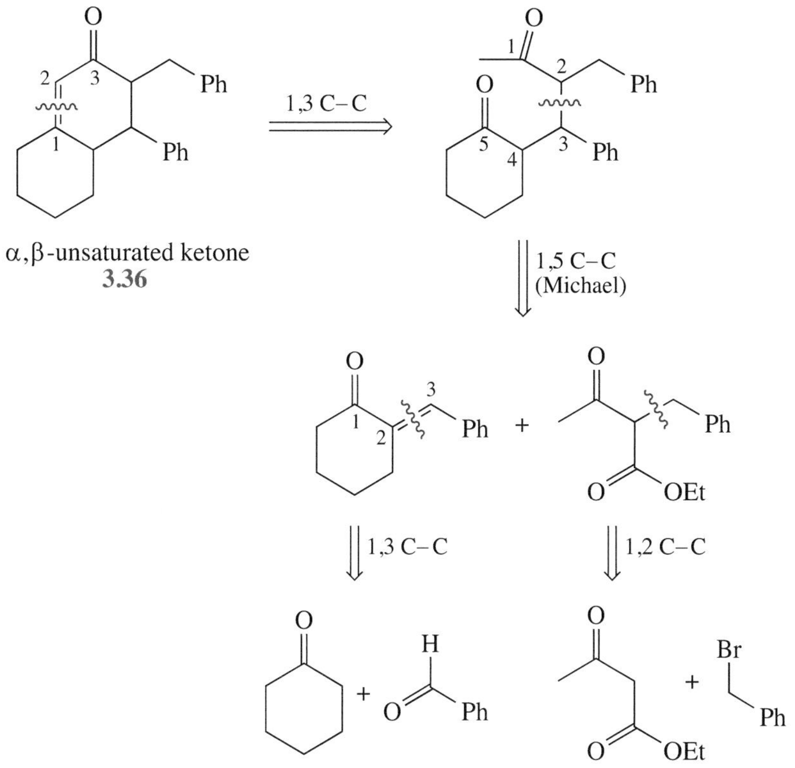

α,β-unsaturated ketone
3.36
1,3 C–C
1,5 C–C
(Michael)
1,3 C–C
1,2 C–C

The corresponding forward reaction is

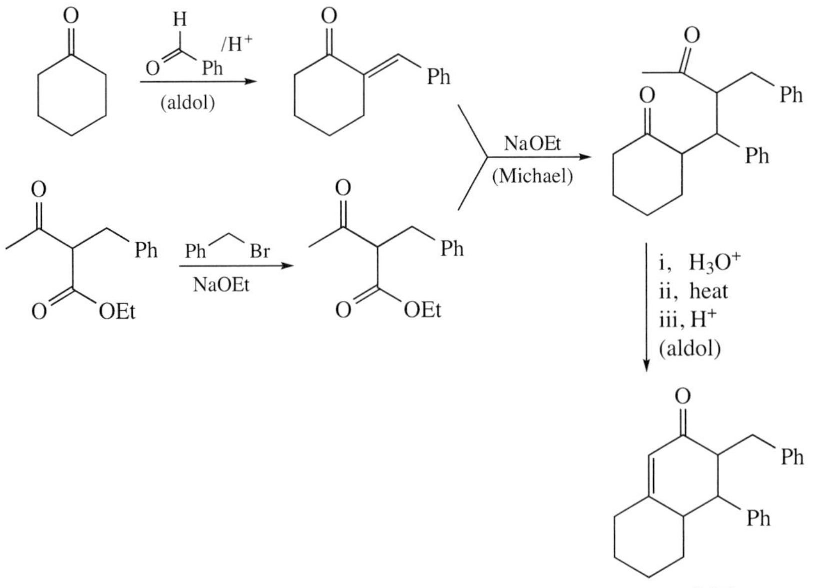

3.36

■ Propose a retrosynthetic analysis and corresponding synthesis for molecule **3.37**.

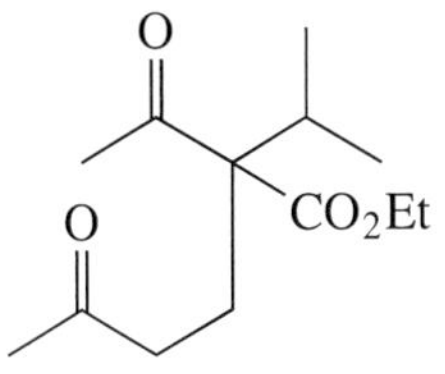

3.37

□ The retrosynthetic analysis is

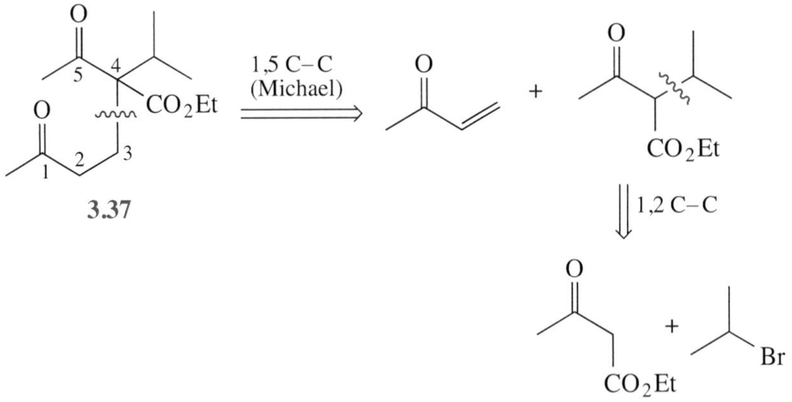

3.37

The corresponding forward reaction is

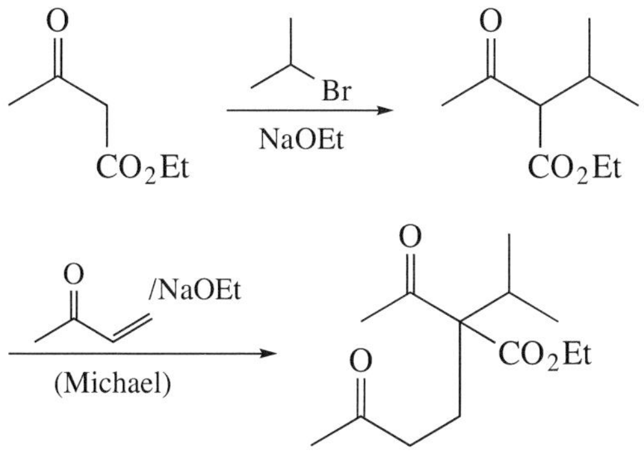

3.37

3.6 1,6 C–C disconnections

How do we go about building up molecules with dicarbonyl groups in a
1,6- relationship? Such a molecule is octa-2,7-dione (**3.38**). We can see that a
standard disconnection in the middle may identify a suitable electrophilic
synthon (**3.39**) that corresponds to the reagent **3.40**, but the nucleophilic
synthon raises a problem: the carbonyl within it is electrophilic, which is
likely to lead any corresponding reagent to undergo unwanted, but
competitive, self-condensation.

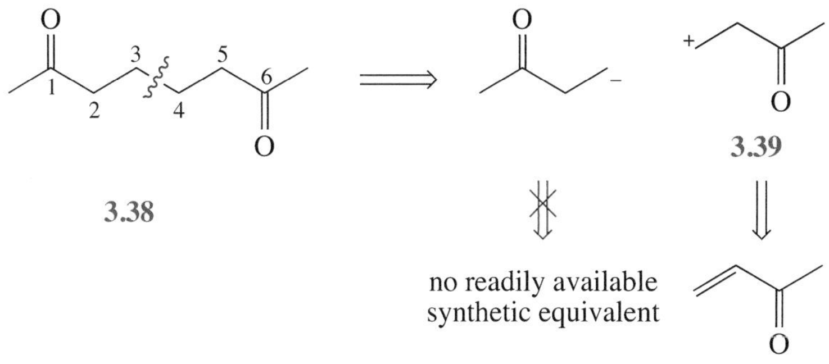

3.38

no readily available
synthetic equivalent

3.39

3.40

However, we can overcome this problem by using an alternative strategy, one
that involves a functional group interconversion rather than a disconnection.
Ozone is well known to oxidise alkenes to dicarbonyl compounds
(Scheme 3.25) and this reaction can therefore be used to produce 1,6-
dicarbonyl groups when applied to cyclic alkenes.

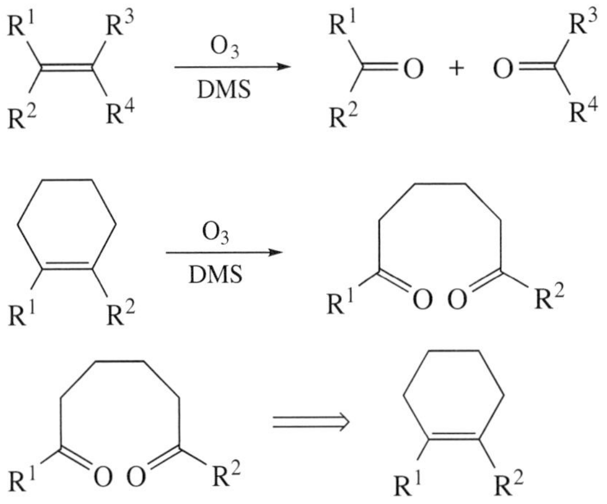

Scheme 3.25

This approach can be used for compound **3.41**. The first disconnection is a standard 1,3- C–C disconnection corresponding to the aldol reaction. This leads to the 1,6-dicarbonyl compound **3.42** which can be obtained, via ozonolysis, from **3.43**.

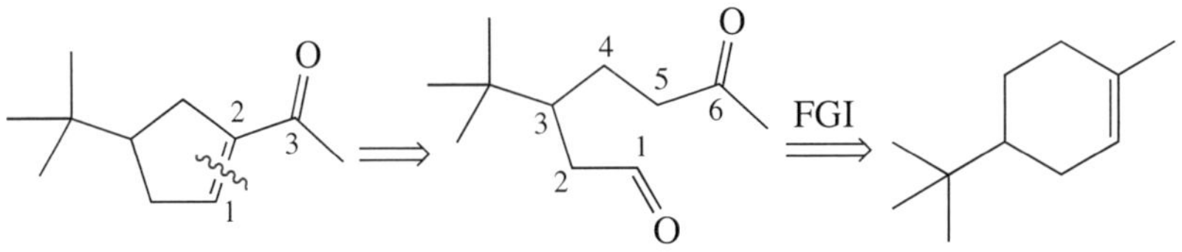

| 3.41 | 3.42 | 3.43 |

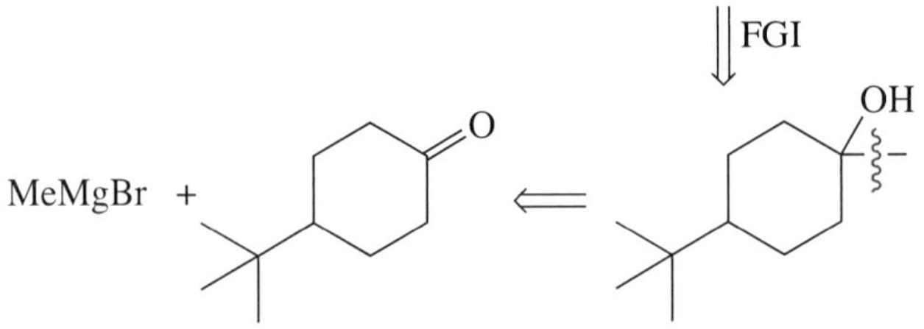

Study note

This concludes our discussion of C–C disconnections. Section 4 sets out some guidelines to help you develop your skills in retrosynthetic analysis.

The corresponding synthesis is shown in Scheme 3.26.

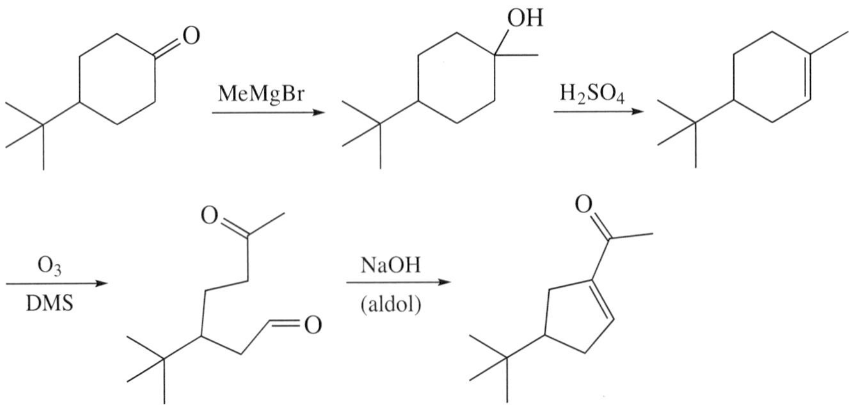

Scheme 3.26

4   Some important guidelines

We are now in a position to draw up a series of rules regarding retrosynthetic analysis that should apply to most compounds.

1   Identify the functional groups and disconnect those containing C–X bonds (esters, amides, ethers) within the framework.

2   When more than one disconnection is possible, disconnect towards the middle of the molecule to make the synthesis convergent as possible.

3   Look to convert functional groups to those based upon oxygen, for example, C–OH and C=O, as all other functional groups can be derived from these.

4   Identify the relationships between functional groups, for example, are they 1,3-dicarbonyls?

5   Look for symmetry in a disconnection or disconnect at a branch point.

6   If you have to disconnect a C–C bond in an unfunctionalised molecule, add in functionality that can be removed at a later stage, for example, double or triple bonds.

7   Examine all other possible disconnections to provide alternative synthesis. There is almost always more than one way to disconnect a molecule.

8   **Always draw the forward reaction; use this to look for potential errors and problems.**

9   **Never** disconnect a synthon; only disconnect molecules.

This is by no means an exhaustive list and is only an aide to developing the key skills covered in this unit. In the course of examining both C–X and C–C disconnections we have identified a range of different synthons. You should take a look at Data Table 9, which summarises these major synthons and relates them to their synthetic equivalents. It can't be emphasised enough that retrosynthetic analysis is a skill developed by practice and experience.

> **Study note**
>
> Now that you have reached the end on this unit, try to write a summary of Unit 9 and then compare it with ours. Go to Unit 9 summaries in Unit 9 resources.

References

McMurry, J. (2008) *Organic Chemistry*, 7th edn, Brooks/Cole, Belmont, USA.

Pereira de Jesus-Tran, K., Cote, P.-L., Cantin, L., Blanchet, J., Labrie, F. and Breton, R. (2006) 'Comparison of crystal structures of human androgen receptor ligand-binding domain complexed with various agonists reveals molecular determinants responsible for binding affinity', *Protein Science*, vol. 15, pp. 987–99.

Wlodawer, A., Savage, H. and Dodson, G. (1989) 'Structure of insulin: results of joint neutron and X-ray refinement', *Acta Crystallography*, Section B, vol. 45, pp. 99–107.

Acknowledgements

Grateful acknowledgement is made to the following sources for permission to reproduce material in this book.

Cover

Adapted from pdb 1nnb, Bossart-Whitaker, P., Carson, M., Babu, Y.S., Smith, C.D., Laver, W.G., Air, G.M. (1993) 'Three-dimensional structure of influenza A N9 neuraminidase and its complex with the inhibitor 2-deoxy 2,3-dehydro-N-acetyl neuraminic acid', *Journal of Molecular Biology*, 232: 1069–83.

Unit 8 Section 3

Figures 3.2 and 3.3: Courtesy of Activotec (www.activotec.com); Figure 3.5: Meisenbach, M., Allmendinger, T. and Mak, C. (2003) 'Scale-up of the synthesis of a pyrimidine derivative directly on solid support', *Organic Process Research and Development*, vol. 7(4), 2003. The American Chemical Society;

Some figures in this publication were created using data from The Protein databank http://www.rscb.org.

Every effort has been made to contact copyright holders. If any have been inadvertently overlooked the publishers will be pleased to make the necessary arrangements at the first opportunity.

Module team

Module Team Chair and Academic Editors

James Bruce (Chair)
Jim Iley
Peter Taylor

Module Team Authors

James Bruce
Peter Taylor
Yao-Zhong Xu

Curriculum Manager

Yvonne Ashmore

External Assessor

Dr Nick Greeves (University of Liverpool)

Consultants

Simon Ainge (King Henry VIII School, Coventry)
David Gamblin (St Paul's School, London)
Christopher Perry (University of Wolverhampton)
Clare Sansom (Birkbeck College, University of London)

Production Team

Rob Barnes
Greg Black
Martin Chiverton
Roger Courthold
Michael Francis
Sarah Gammon
Rebecca Graham
Rafael Hidalgo
Vivien Hoare
Chris Hough
Jason Jarratt
Martin Keeling
Corinne Owen
Will Rawes

Other Contributors

The S346 Module Team gratefully acknowledge the following S344, S377 and S304 Module Team members and Associate Lecturer for their contributions to S346 and for the use of their original materials:
Alan Bassindale, Jim Iley, Roger Hill, Jane Loughlin, Kevin McCullough (Heriot-Watt University), David Roberts, Peter Taylor